THE CHARLTON
/TANDARD CATALOGUE OF
HAGEN-RENAKER
/ECOND EDITION

By
Gayle Roller

Publisher
W. K. Cross

The Charlton Press
Toronto, Ontario ● Birmingham, Michigan

Canadian Cataloguing in Publication Data

The National Library of Canada has catalogued this publication as follows:

The Charlton standard catalogue of Hagen-Renaker

2nd ed.-
Biennial.
ISSN 1481-806X
ISBN 0-88968-197-X (2nd edition)

1. Porcelain, american—California—Periodicals.
2. Hagen-Renaker, Inc.—Catalogs.   3. Art pottery, American—
California—Catalogs. 4. Porcelain animals—California—
Catalogs.

NK4210.H27A4   738.8'2'0294794   C99-900174-4

EDITORIAL

Editor	Jean Dale
Assistant Editor	Angelika Rocos
Graphic Technician	Davina Rowan
Graphic Technician	Alan Ho

ACKNOWLEDGEMENTS

The Charlton Press wished to thank those who have assisted with the second edition of *The Charlton Standard Catalogue of Hagen-Renaker*. This book would not have been possible without the kind co-operation of many people.

Special Thanks

Special thanks go to Martha Armstrong, Jo Ellen Arnold, Joan Berkwitz, Carolyn Boydston, Donna Conners, Sharon Damkaer, Denise Deen, Bonnie Sumser Elber, Nancy Falzone, Renee Giles, Karen Grimm, James Lawson, Sheryl Leisure, Jenny Palmer, Tracy Phillips, Dawn Sinkovich, Cheri Stewart, Heather Wells and William Wiemhoff.

A very special thanks goes to the people who made Hagen-Renaker happen: Nell Bortells, Maureen Love Calvert, Bill Nicely, Helen Perrin Farnlund, Jim and Freya Renaker, John and Maxine Renaker, and Susan Nikas.

A SPECIAL NOTE TO COLLECTORS

We welcome and appreciate any comments or suggestions in regard to the Charlton Standard Catalogue of Hagen-Renaker. If any errors or omissions come to your attention, please write to us, or is you would like to participate in pricing or supply previously unavailable data or information, please contact Jean Dale at (416) 488-1418, or e-mail us at chpress@charltonpress.com.

A note from the author

Of the original *The Hagen-Renaker Handbook* (1989), Tracy Phillips said, "It's been through heat, snow, rain and mud. It's been tossed in canvas bags, car trunks, and office desk drawers. It's entertained me through countless boring meetings. It's helped me locate untold numbers of treasures, and trained several others to do the same." I hope that this book will prove just as useful in helping collectors locate even more of those elusive Hagen-Renaker models.

**Printed in Canada
in the Province of Ontario**

The Charlton Press

**Editorial Office
2040 Yonge Street, Suite 208
Toronto, Ontario. M4S 1Z9
Telephone: (416) 488-1418 Fax: (416) 488-4656
Telephone: (800) 442-6042 Fax: (800) 442-1542
Web Site: www.charltonpress.com**

LIVING TREES

Living Trees are planters produced from the mid-1960s to the early 1970s that contained real moss and ivy. Hagen-Renaker sold these planters ready-to-go. They came in a variety of shapes, sizes and finishes (bisque and gloss). Values are unavailable as they are seldom seen for sale, probably due to the poor rate of survival.

Also produced for a very limited time were 'bonsai pots'. These were produced for the Hagen-Renaker nursery and were usually planted with juniper. The most distinctive pots were 'woodgrain' under a burnt orange glaze. This woodgraining technique was achieved by pouring the slip slowly into the mould and giving each layer a little time to harden. Surface irregularity similar to rings in the trunk of a tree resulted. Dark brown bisque 'traditional' bonsai pots were also produced. These pots were unmarked and meant to be 'training' pots for other nurseries.

GLOSS ASHTRAYS AND PLANTERS

Ashtrays and planters were produced in a gloss finish, c.1959 to 1961. A red-orange gloss ashtray, measuring 6 ¼" in diameter and 2 ¼" deep, was produced with 'Hagen-Renaker, Inc./California' around the top of the ashtray.

TABLE OF CONTENTS

HAGEN RENAKER ARCHIVES

Over the years Hagen-Renaker produced trial or prototype figures. Moulds were made, pieces cast and decorated, but for one reason or another, these pieces were never released.

Perhaps the pieces failed the 'kitchen-window test,' or they did not get any orders at the gift shows, or failed at prime test markets such as Disneyland or Knott's Berry Farm.

All trial or prototype figures are very rare and naturally are not priced due to their scarcity.

INTRODUCTION
By Gayle Roller

HISTORY

"The transistor radio saved Hagen-Renaker." According to Jim Renaker, son of the founders of the ceramics company, this technological advance inadvertently contributed to the company's survival.

Hagen-Renaker was one of hundreds of small potteries flourishing in California in the early 1950s. Ironically, Hagen-Renaker was often undersold by cheaper imported copies of its own designs that were frequently available on the market just six weeks after it had introduced the originals. When transistor radios started to become popular and the Japanese diverted resources from the production of ceramics to the production of transistor radios, this eased the strain on Hagen-Renaker. Nevertheless, the company would not have survived if the family had not believed in its pottery and in its magical designs. There definitely was more to the story.

John and Maxine Renaker

The story began with John and Maxine Renaker in Culver City, California, in 1944. The popularity of ceramics in California and the influence of John's mother, Moss Renaker, an artist working in a pottery, persuaded John to explore ceramics production more fully as a livelihood. His first step was to build a kiln in his garage to begin production and experimentation. Then, in 1945, he went to work for Walkers Pottery in Monrovia, while his family remained in Culver City and made bisque figures for a jobber. Other people also took

John and Maxine Renaker, 1988

a hand in shaping the future: Maxine's father, Ole Hagen, had purchased a lot on West Chestnut Street in Monrovia and erected a building, as Maxine has recorded, "to help his only daughter realize a dream." To honour him, the Renakers thought it was only fitting that his last name should stand first in the name of their new company. On the day after Easter in 1946, the family moved to the building, and John left Walkers Pottery to work full time at Hagen-Renaker. Moss recommended Helen Perrin (later Helen Perrin Farnlund), a very talented artist, to John and Maxine, and she joined the staff of the company, which was still in its infancy. In those early days, Hagen-Renaker was producing miscellaneous art ware and the brown-edged dinner ware.

The next major development occurred in 1947 when Maxine, who was showing a touring group of Brownies how to model clay, created a thumb-sized duck with an "insouciant attitude," as John describes it. He was much captivated by the piece and, in effect, it inaugurated the Miniatures line. Baby ducks soon followed and customers started sending in postcards for reorders. Helen volunteered to try her hand at miniatures and modelled a hippo. In 1948, at the January gift show, Hagen-Renaker products were displayed on a card table in a corner of the Walker showroom, and eighty percent of the sales were for miniatures. The decision was made to drop all other products and lines to concentrate on the miniatures, much to the dismay of the sales force, and despite warnings of impending failure. It proved to be a prophetic vision: more than fifty years later, the Miniatures line has outlasted all other lines and is still selling strongly.

In 1949, Bill Mintzer, Joe Griffith, Bill Nicely, Nell Bortells and many others were added to the line-up of talent. About sixty people were on the payroll. To accommodate increased production, Hagen-Renaker rented nearby small buildings that were zoned for industry. Then, in 1950, the company acquired Thomas Pottery and established Walker-Renaker Pottery to make porcelain bisque figures. The most famous and successful piece from Walker-Renaker is "Holy Cow," a cow figurine designed by Helen and decorated with a halo and flowers by Moss. At one time, a crew of eighty produced this and related pieces.

Hagen-Renaker continued to expand and, by 1951, the company occupied eleven buildings in Monrovia and employed more than two hundred people. In 1952, the Designer's Workshop line was started and was run by Bill and Nell. Prior to 1951, Tom Masterson came to work as a designer and, just after he was hired, Maynard Freeman of the future Freeman-McFarlin Pottery applied for the same job. To keep pace with the growth, Hagen-Renaker maintained a steady hunt for new models and new ideas from 1953 to 1960. Nell had seen the sketches of Maureen Love (now Maureen Love Calvert), a decorator, and suggested that she try sculpting. Otto Annala, Suzy Singer, Don Winton, Will Climes and Martha Armstrong (now Martha

Armstrong-Hand) also came to the plant to make their contributions.

The Disney franchise was acquired in 1955, and Hagen-Renaker experimented with a line of dolls (Dominique dolls), enamel jewelry and bought the line of pixies designed by Millesan Drews. Millesan then designed Keiki figures (Hawaiian children) for Hagen-Renaker. The company also purchased Arcadia Ceramics in partnership with John Bennett to produce a line of novelty salt and pepper shakers. With so much going on, there was a need to consolidate production under one roof and, in 1956, a new building was erected for this purpose.

Easter silliness at the pottery, c.1955

The Little Horribles were introduced in 1958 and were immediately successful. At the peak of their popularity, Bill was able to produce 1,200 *Purple People Eater* models a day. When Bauer Pottery went out of business, Hagen-Renaker hired its mould makers, designers and casting-shop foreman. The next innovations were the launch of two lines of wall plaques and the use of the enamelling technique for the new Black Bisque line.

Wall plaque, *Perch* (F-5,)
using the enamelling technique

Despite this vigour, Japanese competition had eroded sales badly by the late 1950s and, in 1960, Hagen-Renaker closed down operations for nearly a year, sold the big plant and moved back to one of the early buildings. These statements cannot convey the financial and

emotional upheaval that was experienced both by the family and by the employees, who were told that Hagen-Renaker was closing even as they received their usual cheques. The coda for this tragedy was the car accident in which Bill Mintzer and Joe Griffith were killed while moving pottery from one building to another.

In the face of such a setback and unfavourable circumstances, the dream of a pottery was kept alive by Bill, Jim, Maxine, and Phil Leitsch, Hagen-Renaker's California salesman. In 1962, Hagen-Renaker built a new pottery plant in San Dimas, and sales began to climb once more.

Over the next ten to fifteen years, the Miniatures line flourished, but the Designer's Workshop line was trimmed and then discontinued in fall 1972, to be revived briefly in 1975.

Susan Nikas, John and Maxine's daughter, became secretary-treasurer of Hagen-Renaker in 1974, and Bill retired in 1978 but still works as a technical consultant. In 1981, Hagen-Renaker acquired the Freeman-McFarlin pottery in San Marcos. This newer, larger facility, under Jim's direction, allowed the production of larger pieces. Both new and exciting and original, time-honoured Designer's Workshop moulds were released. In 1986, finances forced the decision to close the San Marcos pottery.

The Miniatures line, which has been the lifeblood of Hagen-Renaker for more than fifty years, is still going strong: two million pieces were produced in 1997. The Specialties line, a sort of miniature Designer's Workshop line, was launched in fall 1990 and accounts for about ten percent of total production.

Amazingly, three of the original designers — Maureen, Nell and Helen — are still designing for Hagen-Renaker. However, others have had a hand in design at various times. Susan, now company president, remains dedicated to maintaining the Hagen-Renaker tradition of quality design in miniatures, and one of her new designers, Robert McGuinness, has an especially fine touch with both human and animal figures. Susan says that she remains amazed at some of the design risks that Hagen-Renaker took in the early days, such as the

Susan Nikas in her office

skinny legs, tongue and tail on the 'Ranger' dog. These days, under Susan's direction, Hagen-Renaker is experimenting more and more with pieces that are joined together (for instance, the Specialties butterflies and flowers), lustre finishes, and attached bases.

Longevity and dedication is not limited to designers: several employees have clocked in over thirty years each. Don Meyer began as a mould maker in Monrovia and worked at the company until three years ago, while his wife, Blanche, retired from Hagen-Renaker at the age of sixty-five. Linda Morales is currently assistant production manager and has been with the company for thirty years; her mother, Nellie Carrion, was personnel manager for three decades. Production manager Mary Lou Salas is a relative newcomer, with twenty-five years of service. Another veteran, Lucia Payne, was office manager from the 1950s until she retired in her seventies.

One way or another, working with clay has been in the blood of generations of the Renaker family. Moss, who was an artist and knew the workings of a pottery, was the one who suggested to John that he start up his own pottery. The next generation, John and Maxine's four children, was basically raised at the pottery. As mentioned above, Susan is currently company president. Two more children, Jim and Mary, founded their own potteries. Jim worked at Hagen-Renaker until he left to run his own pottery, Ceramica Regalmex, for twenty years. He and his wife, Freya, produced terra-cotta (low-fired) pots and art figures, including the Chia Pet, the design for which was based on a revival of 1920s Mexican folk art. Ceramica Regalmex still exists in Mexico. Jim then headed up the San Marcos pottery in the 1980s. Mary and her husband, Eric Brazel, started Beachstone in Leucadia, California, in the 1980s to manufacture beads, pins and animal figurines. John and Maxine's fourth child, David, was active at Hagen-Renaker in the late 1950s, creating the illustrations used on the order forms and dreaming up ideas for the Little Horribles line. Jim and Freya's son Eric ran Loza Electrica, a pottery based in Mexico, creating animal figures and licensed cartoon characters, among other items. Don Terlinden, who is married to Susan's daughter Ekaterine, has drawn illustrations for the order forms since the 1980s.

Hagen-Renaker has inspired dedication in legions of collectors because its design magic sparks a recognition that speaks to the heart. From happy dragons to regal Siamese cats to the sleek perfection of the Thoroughbred 'Silky Sullivan,' Hagen-Renaker has captured a unique appreciation of the animals of the earth and crafted their images from the very stuff of the earth. I hope that this book will do justice to the wonderful ceramic production of Hagen-Renaker and the people behind it.

DESIGNERS

The heart of Hagen-Renaker is the designers, while the lungs and brain are the mould makers, cleaners and decorators who bring the pieces to life.

John and Maxine Renaker

John and Maxine were the first designers. John proved to be an excellent judge of the appeal, pose and character of a figurine, and Susan still uses him as a critic. Many pieces have been tried by the "kitchen-window" method to see if they were interesting even while washing dishes. John's figurine designs were limited to the calico cat and patchwork dog, but he also created the forms used for the dinnerware. Maxine designed the original miniatures and, in later years, occasionally created a variety of other pieces (miniature pandas and lionesses, among others).

Helen Perrin Farnlund

Helen had attended Scripps College and then Art Center School in Los Angeles. Besides drawing and painting skills, she had some commercial design experience and expected to be a portrait painter. She went to Carmel and studied with Armin Hauser and Finn Froelich, sculptors of much work throughout the United States. Helen was originally hired as a decorator but later designed the hippo, the precursor of several hundred miniature designs. She says that her first pieces were inspired by some of her young daughter's picture books. Helen was also Art Supervisor for Duarte Schools and later, with her husband, created a program to teach the basics of music to people of all ages using percussion instruments. Helen says that she was originally upset that her designs lost so much in mass production but is now glad that she was given the opportunity to have a part in something that brought pleasure to so many people.

Nell Bortells

Nell is a Monrovia native who studied at Chouinard. She came to work as a decorator for Hagen-Renaker, intending to earn some money toward her schooling. One day, bored with decorating, she made a little mouse out of clay. John walked by and asked who had made the mouse, and Nell said that she had. He picked it up and came back with twenty-five dollars. She made a little cheese for the mouse and was rewarded with ten dollars. Nell was quite impressed with this money, at a time when decorators were paid as little as a dollar and a half an hour. In 1952, she and Bill Nicely were asked to manage the Designer's Workshop. In 1955, she had an opportunity to go to Europe to study fine art and had made arrangements to take advantage of what was probably the chance of a lifetime when John took her out for breakfast, told her that he had the Disney contract and asked her to stay. She did, and she still managed to get to Europe some years later. In 1958, a unique kind of inspiration struck Nell, and the Little Horribles line was born. When Hagen-Renaker ran into financial problems, Nell retired and found employment with the phone company. She has enjoyed making her art (figurines and works in pen and ink and oil) and has occasionally made designs for Hagen-Renaker, most recently the ant and the Specialties dancing frogs. Nell enjoys the movement

x

of ballet and the drama of Wagnerian opera, and this is reflected in the figurine shown below:

An original decorated, fired-clay Wagnerian diva.

Maureen Love Calvert

Maureen trained at the California School of Fine Arts in San Francisco. She had done commissioned portraits of horses in pastel before she joined Hagen-Renaker in June 1951 to work in the decorating department. Nell saw her sketches and suggested that she do a sculpture. Maureen especially likes stoneware with a highly textured surface, and she sculpts models of local birds in her own studio. Hagen-Renaker carried her work as Maureen Love Originals for several years.

Sketch of *OK Ya Te Hay*

Tom Masterson

Tom came to work for Hagen-Renaker as a designer around 1951. His work blossomed incredibly, showing masterly development from the early horses to the artistry of the Pedigree Great Dane. After his career at

Tom, Maureen and Helen, admiring Maureen's work

Hagen-Renaker, he designed realistic human bodies for the instruction of medical students and crash test dummies which had bones that replicated human bone fractures in car accidents. He was also interested in music. His widow, Bess, said that "he was interested in everything and never sat still." He is now deceased.

Martha, working on the View-Master *Bambi*™ scene, 1956.

Martha Armstrong-Hand

Martha states that Hagen-Renaker has been dear to her heart since John and Maxine were not only the best employers she had, but also her friends, and they remain so to this day. They met in 1955 when she was working on Disney's *Bambi* for View-Master.

Martha worked for Hagen-Renaker from 1956 to 1958. From 1963 to 1975, she worked as an in-house designer for Mattel. Her designs there included *Kiddles* and *The Sunshine Family*. (Please see Karen Bischoff's article, "A Legend Among Her Peers: Martha Armstrong-Hand," in the January/February 1989 issue of *Dolls: The Collectors Magazine* for more details about Martha's fascinating life.) She is now a master doll maker and was recently invited to do design work at the Hummel pottery in Germany.

Other Designers

Other designers included Don Winton, Bill Climes and Millesan Drews, who were all potters in their own right. Don and his brother, Ross, founded Twin Winton pottery in 1936, and Bill was part of Will-George, a pottery that he founded with his brother, George, in 1934. Millesan was making her pixies in Hollywood around 1948 (as determined from a dated pixie). Otto Annale, Jane Manske and Armae Conacher also designed pieces for Hagen-Renaker. More recently, Nance Brown, Edith Carrion, Shi Yi Chen, Robert McGuinness and Kristina Lucas have contributed pieces to the company's production.

PRODUCTION, STEP BY STEP

1. An artist designs a figurine shape in modelling clay.
2. If the first draft is approved, a mould is made for the design.
3. From that model, a wax replica is made so that the artist can refine details.
4. From the wax model, another mould is made that, if satisfactory, becomes what is called the waste mould.
5. A metal model is made from the waste mould to make a block-and-case, which is the master mould for production moulds. It is made out of epoxy. Plaster production moulds (negatives) are made from the epoxy master mould and sent to the slip-casting department.
6. Slip, which is clay suspended in water to a consistency of heavy cream, is poured into the plastic moulds. Clay casting is an ancient technique practiced since the discovery of gypsum, which is used to make plaster of Paris. It takes advantage of the fact that dry plaster will absorb water from clay and thus harden the fluid slip poured into a plaster cavity. The hardened clay forms a shell and the remaining slip is poured out.

The casting area

7. The slip is allowed to dry and harden further. Then the mould is separated and the figurine, not dry but leather-hard, is removed. At this stage, the pottery is called greenware. The piece is placed on a tray to dry or on a shallow, damp plaster tray to prevent drying. In the latter case, the casting hole is sealed with damp clay (patched) or damp clay parts are added (stuck up).
8. The piece is thoroughly dried before being finished to take advantage of the maximum strength of the unfired clay. The parting lines (created in the castings by the joining of the separate sections) are scraped, sponged or sanded off. During handling, an average of one out of every five pieces is broken and thrown away. Even the most skillful finishers break a high proportion of pieces (for example, the antlered deer).
9. The finished ware is taken to the spray department. Sprayers use pencil-type spray guns to shade the ware.
10. From the sprayers, the ware is passed to hand decorators who add spots, eyes, and so on.

A Specialties cow being decorated

11. After the piece is decorated, it is waxed to a refractory kiln tray and sent to a kiln. The first firing changes the greenware to bisque. The kiln takes sixteen hours to go from room temperature to approximately 1,800 degrees fahrenheit and back to room temperature. This is a lower heat than the final temperature, as care must be taken not to reduce the absorptive quality of the bisque from vitrification.

Rocking Horse ready for bisque firing

12. After the bisque firing, the ware is sent to the glazing department. The glazers apply melted beeswax to the bottom of each figure before dipping it into the glaze slip. The slip is a suspension of fitted and ground glasses in water. The bisque body absorbs the water and a coating of hardened glass adheres to the figure. The glass melts during the final firing, giving the figure its translucent shiny coat. If there were glaze on the bottom of the figure, the figure would be welded to the kiln tray.

Glaze being applied to miniatures

13. If the piece is decorated with a gold or lustre overglaze, it is fired a third time at a lower temperature.

A tray with Specialties giraffe without its spots

The decal being applied to the giraffe, which will then be low-fired

The frame of the kiln can be rolled back to allow more efficient loading and unloading

The packaging department

TECHNIQUES

Every pottery company has a signature look, which is the result of the combination of techniques that are employed. The colours that we see on Hagen-Renakers can be a mixture of several techniques. Slip, the liquid clay that is poured into the mould, can be tinted to impart an overall colour to the piece. Underglazes, which are a mixture of clay and tints, can be sprayed over the piece for shading. Heavier applications of underglazes can create opaque areas over a small or large area. Glaze, a glass coating that is fired on, can be tinted. Areas of glaze or underglaze can be scratched through to reveal the colour underneath. On top of the glaze, colour decals, metallic colours, or iridescent colours can be applied by a low-firing. If the piece is not destined to receive a glaze, it can be bisque-fired and painted with stains or cold paints, which are similar to acrylic paints. Hagen-Renaker has been extremely innovative in its approach to ceramics. Always looking for a better or different way to produce art ware, particularly under the leadership of John Renaker, the company has never relied solely on the tried and true.

An example of a piece using the more unusual techniques is the Designer's Workshop dragon, which

Designer's Workshop Dragon (28)

was made with tinted slip and sprayed with underglazes for the shaded areas on its head and body. Solid underglazes were painted on its eyes and blue eyebrows, which were then scratched through or sgraffitoed. It was then bisque-fired. Clear glaze was applied and fired. Iridescent colours were painted on its wings and back fin, gold was painted on its scales and, finally, it was low-fired to set the iridescent colours and gold.

A totally different look was achieved in the Black Bisque line. White, untinted slip was cast and then sprayed black with matte underglaze. The sgraffito technique was used to draw lines down to the white, and then jewel colours were applied to specific areas and

Black Bisque Bull (13)

fired. The result is a porous, very matte black and white piece with shimmering areas of bumpy turquoise or green colour.

Stoneware has been tried twice: first, in the A-500 Stoneware line, and second, in the 1989 Stoneware line. Stoneware clay fires at a much higher temperature than

Stoneware/Specialties Pintail Duck on Pond (2005)

earthenware clay does, making it stronger and giving it a hand-built feel. The A-500 pieces were tumbled with abrasives to give them a silky surface. Sgraffito was used extensively in the 1989 Stoneware ducks to give very precise edges of wing and feather colour.

The majority of Hagen-Renaker pieces feature a combination of slip tinting and underglazes for their colour effect. Because the intrinsic body is coloured and not just painted on, the fine sculpting details of legs and faces are not obscured by paint. This is part of the Hagen-Renaker magic.

In the factory, the slip is tinted to one of the many time-tested recipes that are kept in large drums for use by the slip casters. Often, many animals are produced at a time and use the same slip colour, which makes a great deal of sense from the factory's standpoint. Basic tans, browns, greens, greys, yellows and, of course, plain white fulfil most needs. To give the individual types of animals their own distinctive colours, the underglaze paints are then sprayed on or brushed over the slip colour. An amazing variety of colours can result. Tan with a very light shading of brown can make a palomino horse; more shading of brown can make a Pekinese dog; a heavy shading of brown, with only the belly left bare, can make a dachshund. Thus, when we look at an individual piece's colours, we look first at the slip colour. This can usually be found on the belly or under the tail of the piece. Because the slip is coloured, it also shows in the dry-footed areas. These are the areas that are wiped clean of glaze — and are therefore not shiny — so that the glaze does not stick to the shelf when the piece is fired. The areas of exposed slip will be lighter than the glazed areas are; if you wish, you can wet the areas of exposed slip and they will darken for a moment. The colour is richer when covered with the glaze.

Many layers of underglaze paints can be applied to the piece before it is glazed. Each one changes the overall look of the piece. For example, a brown 'Honora' has a tan slip that is shaded with brown and then has white painted on the legs. The knees, hocks, hooves, tail, mane and face are then shaded with black. The eyes and braids are painted last. A Pedigree collie may have the same colours and look like a tricolour collie.

When the Korean Conflict was in progress (1950 and 1951), certain metallics were not available for use in ceramics and Hagen-Renaker had to devise new formulas to compensate.

VARIATIONS

Variations occur throughout a production run. Slip colours may be a bit darker or lighter, owing to the amounts of the ingredients used, or the individual batches of colour and underglaze may change.

Variations may occur in decoration: an individual decorator might make more or less effort to shade a given piece. Cost may determine the use of colours: a colour may be dropped if another colour could substitute. For instance, the hooves of San Dimas chestnut horses are painted with a concentrated spray of the shading colour instead of black, saving another series of steps and thus keeping costs down. This is particularly important to keep in mind when looking at the 1960s colours, which were chosen at a time of low profits, when every penny counted.

Variations may also occur during demoulding and drying, when thin areas such as legs and tails can change their shape somewhat. These areas are quite pliable when freshly demoulded (leather-hard), and it is up to the factory worker to reshape the part into its expected look. Drying can cause warpage owing to weight on the part; thicker areas dry more slowly than thin pieces do. In addition, some of the detail may be rubbed off while a piece is being handled or while the seams are being cleaned.

Sometimes Hagen-Renaker took the time to plug the pour hole in the belly of the piece and punch a smaller hole for air. In the San Dimas era, when economy was a deciding factor, pour holes on larger pieces often remained unplugged, as plugging a pour hole is tedious and time-consuming. In the quality-conscious San Marcos era, pour holes were again plugged.

Small changes were occasionally made in individual moulds, sometimes to make the model easier to produce (for example, *Cutting Horse and Rider* was made in one piece instead of two pieces) and sometimes to lessen breakage (for example, the tail of the Siamese cat *Ah Choo* was modified). Sometimes the mould was modified because the master mould had somehow been destroyed, as was apparently the case with the standing Arabian *Abdullah*. Although Hagen-Renaker has never been afraid to take innovative chances with its designs and has produced very complex and fragile pieces, certainly the longer-running pieces lasted because they were economical to mould, fire, ship and display. No company lasts long without keeping an eye on the bottom line.

In the late 1950s, ceramic materials were so inexpensive and labour was so abundant that creative alterations abounded. Many, many more designs were tried than actually entered into full production. A piece might reach the stage of being shown to various retailers by a sales representative. Pre-sales indicated an interest that the factory might decide to pursue. Pieces might be test-marketed: for instance, the Keikis were apparently test-marketed at Knotts Berry Farm in Buena Park, California. Following trends, such as with the Little Horribles *Purple People Eater*, was a tricky business: although Hagen-Renaker stopped production of the *Purple People Eater* the very day that the song dropped off the charts, the company was still left with hundreds of these models.

LINES AND ERAS

Collectors delight in classifying their pieces, and each collectable tends to fall naturally into a pattern. The wide scope of Hagen-Renaker's products and designs makes it difficult for novices to place individual pieces within the context of the company's overall progression. Generally, collectors have divided the pieces into their specific lines and eras. The **lines** consist of like products, such as Disney pieces, pixies, and Specialties. This book is divided into sections on each line. In brief, these are the major lines:

Miniatures: This line comprises all species of animals (including dogs), and the size of the models ranges from one-quarter inch to four inches.

Designer's Workshop: This line comprises figurines of cats, horses, cattle and birds (but no dogs)ranging in size from two inches to thirteen inches.

Pedigree Dogs: These figurines depict dogs of various breeds and range in size from one-half inch to twelve inches.

Disney: This line comprises licensed Disney figurines only.

Little Horribles: This is a line of human caricatures and goofy creatures.

Specialties: This is a recent line of detailed figurines ranging in size from one inch to five inches.

The **era** in which a piece was produced is sometimes evident from the time at which the line was produced. In other words, if the pixies came out only in the 1950s, they fall into that era. Only in the long-lasting lines do we question the era of an individual piece for the purposes of identification. The Designer's Workshop, Pedigree dog and Miniatures lines are the three that really spanned one era or more.

Collectors refer to the eras by the Hagen-Renaker pottery's location. Early in Hagen-Renaker's history, the company was located in **Monrovia**, California, a small industrial town near Pasadena, where the company had several individual locations. In 1960, the large property holdings in Monrovia were sold and the company moved back to an earlier, less expensive building and then eventually closed. In the late 1950s, John had become interested in the greenhouse-nursery business and had purchased nursery properties, and so, when it was decided to start up the pottery again, it was in a building in San Dimas, a pre-existing nursery site. The factory is still located there. All the Miniatures and Specialties models made since the mid-1960s are usually referred to as **San Dimas. San Marcos** refers to the former Freeman-McFarlin pottery, located in San Marcos, California, that was purchased in the early 1980s and sold in 1986. A few Designer's Workshop pieces were reissued from San Marcos along with continued Freeman-McFarlin pieces and brand-new designs. Some miniatures were apparently made there also.

When a collector wishes to date a piece and evaluate which era it falls into, it is important to check the individual listing on the piece first. For the Designer's Workshop pieces (with a few exceptions) and the Pedigree dogs, the general rule is that, if it was made before 1962, it is a Monrovia piece; if it was made only between about 1963 and 1975, it is a San Dimas piece; and, if it was made only in the 1980s, it is a San Marcos piece. Some confusion may exist as to the exact date in the 1960s when Monrovia pieces changed into San Dimas pieces; prior to this book, it was always assumed that 1966 was the significant year of change because a San Dimas address appeared on the order forms from then on. However, since the move from Monrovia to San Dimas was apparently made earlier, re-evaluation of this perception may be in order. It may be that the changes

that collectors have always associated with the Monrovia and San Dimas looks took place gradually over the period between 1963 and 1966. For the Miniatures line, the eras are either Monrovia or San Dimas. Again, the feel changes, with much less hand detailing in the middle and late San Dimas period.

If a piece's individual listing indicates more than one of these eras, then the collector must take into account the look of the piece and pay cautious attention to stickers, if present, and whatever additional information may lead to a conclusion. Other collectors can help, and only familiarity will allow a collector to classify every piece. There are no hard-and-fast rules for identification.

Learning to classify Hagen-Renakers takes time and attention. There is no substitute for first-hand knowledge. It is well worth the effort to see these beautiful pieces first-hand and let them work their magic on you. Once you hold 'Rajah,' the Designer's Workshop adult elephant, in your hands and admire its sculpted skin texture or study the graceful lines of 'Zara,' the six-inch Arabian mare, you may be hooked.

IDENTIFICATION

When looking for identifying marks on a Hagen-Renaker, there are several possibilities to consider. The most common identifying mark is a paper sticker, card or studio card. Less common is a mark in the clay, either hand-written on the piece or incorporated into the mould. There may be hand-painted or ink-stamped marks.

It is important to remember that, during Hagen-Renaker's long history, the company was producing pottery primarily to make a profit and was not even aware that, sometime in the future, collectors would try to reconstruct its actions. Identifying marks were made when and if it seemed to be a good idea, either to protect the company from copyright infringement or to remind the retailer or customer of the factory of origin.

Stickers

Looking at it from Hagen-Renaker's point of view, stickers that were made up and paid for were to be used, regardless of whether the piece that they were intended for was in production or whether they were the most current stickers. Pottery sells at the wholesale level for very little money, and stickers are expensive to design and print; Hagen-Renaker's choice of gold foil for many of its stickers added to the cost. As a result, dating a piece or even identifying the mould based on the sticker is a questionable practice. In addition, a very few cases have surfaced in which Hagen-Renaker stickers were found on non–Hagen-Renaker pieces. For example, Hagen-Renaker distributed the Roselane pottery line as a favour to the new widow of Roselane's owner, and Hagen-Renaker stickers were placed on some of the pieces even though they had not been made by Hagen-Renaker. Moreover, one case of a collector who bought a horse model ('Abu-Farwa') based on the model's sticker serves a warning to all of us: the horse was a Japanese copy. The sticker may have fallen off and been put back on the wrong horse, or the original 'Abu-Farwa' in the collection may have been broken. Stickers fall off sometimes; they can also be removed with little trouble. Collectors have been known to buy a broken piece and remove the sticker to put it on a mint piece. It goes without saying that this practice is unacceptable. Stickers, or any paper product of definition, should enhance but not define a piece. In conjunction with other factors, stickers are often a good indication of the era in which a piece was produced.

Oval (twenty-eight or thirteen millimetres in size), square (fourteen millimetres), round (thirteen millimetres), rectangular (three-eighths millimetre by three-quarters millimetre), football-shaped (twenty-five millimetres) and medal-shaped (a rectangle twenty-five millimetres in length with a half-circle connected to the bottom line) stickers have been used.

The **oval** stickers are the large or small "California" stickers: "Hagen-Renaker/California" is lettered in gold on a black background with a gold "California" in the middle. A tiny black star presumably shows were San Dimas is. This sticker was first used in 1967. The same sticker with a dark brown background may have been used from 1980 to 1984. A large black oval imprinted with "Hagen-Renaker/D.W./Made in U.S.A." was applied to the San Marcos pieces from 1984 to 1986. Smaller ovals were also used.

The square stickers, used for the price, are gold with black lettering, for example, "Hagen-Renaker/ $4.00/California."

The **round** stickers are gold with black lettering that may spell "Hagen-Renaker, copyright" or "H-R, Inc." This "Hagen-Renaker, U.S.A." sticker was on a doeskin 'Fez.'

Much smaller round stickers are applied to the miniatures. Round silver and blue stickers were used at San Marcos, apparently only in 1986. They had a blue centre imprinted with "HR/Designers Workshop" and a silver outer ring imprinted in blue with "Hagen-Renaker, Incorporated, of California."

The **rectangular** sticker is blue with silver lettering, for example, "An original design/Hagen-Renaker/ Monrovia, California." The Brahma bull bears one of these stickers.

The **football-shaped** stickers are black and gold: "Hagen-Renaker" is printed in gold on black and the name is printed in black on gold. These stickers may have been used from 1959 to 1963.

The **medal-shaped** stickers may be black and gold, or green and gold. They may state the name and the year

or breed, the year, or the name or breed without the year. The year seems to have been printed until 1958.

These are a selection of stickers removed from 1974 Designer's Workshop horses: 'Zilla' and 'Lippet' black and gold medal-shaped stickers, a green and gold medal-shaped sticker for 'Roughneck,' three small black and gold "California" stickers, two large black and gold "California" stickers, and one thirteen-millimetre round "Hagen-Renaker, copyright" sticker.

A very good collection of stickers is seen in the pages of this book, especially in the Pedigree dogs section, and a comprehensive catalogue will not be attempted. Many thanks to Jo Ellen Arnold for providing pictures of some very nice Monrovia dogs with their original stickers.

Other Marks

A very few pieces had marks made in the mould or etched into the clay. These pieces would include but not be limited to plates, bowls and other housewares and a few early animals. For example, the early large Masterson horses had "© HR" inscribed into their inner leg. The 'King Cortez' from San Marcos had "HR

(copyright)" carved into the mould. One nine-inch *Zara* from San Marcos has HR © DW etched into the clay on her belly. Often decorators would incise their initials into a hoof or a base. Marks in the clay are nice when present but lack of a mark does not mean the piece is copy.

Early pieces had hand-painted marks under the glaze. See the Early Hagen-Renaker section for examples. Early miniatures sometimes had an ink-stamped "Hagen-Renaker ©" or some variation on their dry-footed portion. Sometimes only a portion of the stamp shows. Later miniatures and San Marcos pieces often had "HR" (in fancy script), with or without a small "©" and with or without "made in USA." Again, if the piece is marked in this way, it is a definitive indication of origin, but the lack of a mark does not mean that the piece is a copy.

Commonly, the miniatures that are produced in San Dimas come glued to a square of heavy paper printed with a few lines: "©/HAGEN-RENAKER. INC./MADE IN SAN DIMAS, CA.-USA/(To remove, soak in water). " Some of these lines may be missing, and a price may appear in an upper corner. The retailer has the option of ordering pieces with or without the attached display cards and of having the display cards come with or without the price. The company is now faced with attaching bar codes to the cards for the use of electronic checkouts. If these cards are attached to the piece, and especially if they show a date, it is a good indicator of age. However, collectors should be aware that the date was changed only every few years, and so the date does not reflect the exact year in which the piece was made.

Hagen-Renaker has tried a variety of display techniques. A Plexiglas spinner was available for a time, and clear hanging display holders were also marketed. At one time, the Designer's Workshop racehorses came with a racing ticket attached. Little Horribles came in a clear plastic box with an accompanying studio card. 'Butch,' the large cocker spaniel, had a studio card describing the illustrator and the history of the piece. In San Marcos, the large 'Nataf' horse came with a studio card. The San Marcos grizzly bear has been seen with a Freeman studio card and a large black and gold oval Hagen-Renaker sticker on the card. The studio card identified the manufacturer and enhanced the sale at the retail level. The card was easy to remove and the customer often did so.

SALES AND SALES REPRESENTATIVES

It is very important to note that Hagen-Renaker issued spring and fall order forms to coincide with spring and fall gift shows. That is why the catalogue listings indicate a year, preceded by "Spring" or " Fall." The biannual order forms are standard in the pottery industry and allow for flexibility in seasonal introductions and room for rapid change.

The gift shows often functioned as a forum for judging the responsiveness of the public to an item, as, apparently, did Hagen-Renaker's display at Knotts Berry Farm at times. Several pieces are known to have failed the gift-show test, for example, Armae Conacher's child figures.

Sometimes a piece was ready for release before the order form was printed. Other explanations for the discrepancy between known availability and absence from the order form might be that the piece was missed

when the order form was assembled or was added to the line mid-season. We know that Hagen-Renaker provided its sales representatives with samples, and it is more than likely that certain pieces were available long before they appeared on the order forms.

"Our merchandise is very easy to sell." c.1952

Hagen-Renaker show, 1954

Hagen-Renaker sent out flyers introducing the new additions to the lines, along with the order forms, to its established accounts.

Hagen-Renaker did not retail any product until the limited-edition horses became available in the 1990s, and then only those horses. The main place to find Hagen-Renakers was gift stores, and even then there was no guarantee that there would be a fully representative selection. One notable collector did not know until years after the fact that Hagen-Renaker had created a Designer's Workshop line because the stores in his area did not retail them. Sadly, many collecting opportunities have been lost because pieces have not been available. Fortunately, more opportunities to purchase Hagen-Renakers by mail order are arising, and so collectors should not have to pass on a piece just because of a lack of knowledge or availability.

HOW TO READ THE LISTINGS

I have sorted the species alphabetically for the Designer's Workshop and Miniatures lists, and I have sorted the Pedigree dogs by breed. Emphasis has been placed on the species and breed of a given piece rather than on a mould number because these are the primary method of identification. Hagen-Renaker has never released colour catalogues or emphasized the mould number to the public; moreover, as will be seen in the catalogue, revised moulds do not always carry a revised mould number. I have tried to give a short description of the gender and pose of the Pedigree dogs to clarify, for instance, which of the many dachshund puppies I was discussing.

The model number, height, designer and colour sections should be self-explanatory. The "issued" section provides the list of seasons during which the piece was produced. These are in the six-month increments of spring and fall, according to the release of the spring and fall order forms, but there is no guarantee that any piece was made for a full six months even if it is listed as having been made for one season (for example, the pronghorn). If Hagen-Renaker had problems with a piece — a high level of breakage in the factory, difficulty removing the piece from the mould, or a high level of breakage during shipping — there was no point in losing money, and so the piece was quickly discontinued. Production terminology can be explained further using Rooster 'Alex' and Hen 'Elizabeth' as an example. These chicken models were made for a total of sixteen years (thirty-two seasons, as there are two seasons a year). They were introduced in fall 1955 and were made intermittently for another thirty-one seasons, until spring 1972. They were then re-introduced in San Marcos in spring 1982, and they last appeared on an order form in spring 1986.

Most San Marcos pieces were offered in both gloss and matte, while the previous offerings came in one finish only; for instance, the nine-inch Designer's Workshop Arabians were never offered in gloss from Monrovia or San Dimas.

In the Miniatures section, I have listed the total number of seasons during which a piece was issued and gave start, restart and last-produced dates if they were significant — for instance, if I knew there was a colour change or finish change. If a year is listed, it means the piece was made in the spring and fall of that year (as two seasons equal one year).

Eyes

The way in which the eyes are decorated is often used as an indication of the age of a Hagen-Renaker. In the earliest animals, the eyes were painted onto a face that did not have a great deal of intrinsic detail. Painters of eyes were able to indicate whimsy and charm with their brushstrokes. The *Calico Cat* (131) shows the finesse that a decorator needed to paint eyes. *The Gingham Dog* has been seen with eyes looking up and looking left, which indicates that the decorators were not just sticking to one pattern and painting by rote. Chances are good that Helen painted that gingham dog and the calico cat, as

Calico Cat (131) c.1946-c.1949

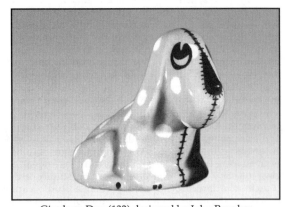
Gingham Dog (132) designed by John Renaker

she was a decorator long before she modelled her hippo. Maureen and Nell both put in their time decorating before they designed pieces.

Nell was responsible for initiating the extravagant eye white, eyebrows and wrinkles that are seen on early Designer's Workshop pieces, but each line had its own distinctive eye characteristics and, if the line was long-lived, the eyes sometimes changed during that time. The pixies and the Black Bisque, Disney and Little Horribles lines have very distinctive eyes and show little change for their short durations. (Please see the photos in each section for examples.) The Miniatures, Designer's Workshop and Pedigree dog lines, the three major and long lasting lines, all show a progression from early releases to late ones. Early eyes often had more work in them, with white eye corners, eyelashes and possibly eyebrows (usually associated with outlined nostrils as well), brown irises and white highlights. The fancier details were dropped over time, probably prompted by a combination of factors; new and less skilled employees, the change in look from cartoon to realistic, and competition from Japan all likely contributed to the simpler eye treatments. By the late 1950s and early 1960s, the eyes of the Designer's Workshop models and

Pedigree dogs mostly had white corners, possibly brown irises, black pupils, and a black line along the upper eyelid, like a lash. A few show the white corners and black pupils but no lash; some have the brown irises and black pupils but either no whites or no lash, or neither whites nor lash. Many pieces from the early to mid-1960s have only brown irises and black pupils. When the Designer's Workshop line came out in the 1980s, more time was put into details, and the eyes again showed more hand detailing.

In the Miniatures line, the eyes often had white corners and black pupils in the early days, unless the piece was very small. (For horse lovers, it is interesting to note that the majority of the foals in the Miniatures line never had whites to their eyes.) The eyes of even very recent or current miniatures with a dark face have whites, just to distinguish the eyes from the rest of the face. (Note the ant, for instance, or the black Lab). Thus, dating a piece based on whether its eyes have or lack whites is not a very accurate method.

Colours

Colours Used for Horses

Avidly sought after by collectors, the horse models have been analyzed from every angle, and they have engendered the most debate about colours. The debate is particularly difficult because some of the colours in which Hagen-Renaker produced its horses are simply not found in nature. Also, some of the horses that were produced in several different eras (Monrovia, San Dimas, and San Marcos) may be called by the same colour on lists while the colours are actually quite different. Let us look at 'Lippet.' He first came out in Monrovia in 1959 in brown and palomino. This brown is a soft, overall, warm colour with slightly darker brown body shadings. White is sprayed on his front legs and over his face. His knees, hocks, hooves and face are shaded with black. His eyes have white corners, black pupils, and a black line above the whites. In San Dimas, the same brown starts with a light tan slip colour. A stronger reddish brown is shaded overall, and the white front stocking and bald face remain. However, his hooves, knees, hocks, ears and face are shaded with the same reddish brown rather than with black. His eyes are simple black dots. In San Marcos, he has a yellowish-brown body rather than a red-brown one, and a black mane and tail. He may have black and white eyes. The first two colours can be called brown or chestnut, and chestnut is actually closer to the correct name. The last colour is a bay, as the horse has a black mane and tail and black legs. What about 'Honora,' which has a black mane and tail but light legs? It is something between a bay and a brown, and both words are often used to describe it. With Hagen-Renakers, knowledge of individual mould colours is important, as colours vary by mould and by factory.

Greys are also a problem for collectors of horse models. A grey horse is born black, bay or chestnut and gradually lightens to white, much like human hair does. Therefore, a grey horse is anything from a slightly greyed-out dark horse to a totally white one. However, Hagen-Renaker horses that are white with a grey mane and tail are called white, and horses that are tan with a dark brown mane and tail (doeskin) or light to dark brown with rosy shading (rose-grey) are called grey.

Below is a list of colour names used for Hagen-Renaker horses:

White: This refers to a white body with grey shading and/or grey points.

Grey: The term "rose-grey" refers to a tan, grey or brown slip colour with rosy and/or black shading; dark hooves, knees, hocks and ears; and a dark mane, tail and face. The term "doeskin" refers to a tan or grey body with dark brown points and no rosy shading on the body. Doeskin was actually a continuation of rose-grey, without the rosy shading, and was used in the 1960s and 1970s.

Appaloosa: This refers to any body colour with a white rump and spots. Only a few moulds were made in this colour.

Bay: This refers to a tan or light brown slip with darker brown or red body shading, a black mane and tail, black legs, black shaded ears and a black shaded face.

Black: This is usually a solid colour but there can be white markings.

Brown or chestnut: This refers to a tan to light brown slip, sometimes with darker brown body shading and always with a darker brown or black face and darker brown or black knees, hocks, hooves and ears. Such a horse may have a black mane and tail, white legs and a white face. An early brown horse may have a very light or white belly.

Buckskin: This refers to a tan, cream, or yellow body with a black mane and tail, black points and black legs.

Palomino: This refers to a yellow, tan or cream slip with a white mane and tail, white legs, sometimes a white face, and black or brown shading on points.

Pinto: This refers to any body colour with large areas of white on the body.

A few horses came in variations of these colours, which are described in their individual listings.

Colours Used for Other Models

Most of the wildlife that Hagen-Renaker produced was decorated in an approximation of the natural colours. As I am not familiar with the colours for all breeds of dogs and cats, the descriptions in these listings are generally concerned with slip and shading colour. At best, colours are approximate and, frequently, new colours that were not known to exist are brought to the collector's attention. Collectors should be aware that a piece in a colour that is not listed is not necessarily a rare piece or a copy.

Auerspurse Colours

For a short time, these colours were used to decorate bisque ware. The name apparently refers to a trade name of these stains, which were applied to plain white bisque ware by brushing or dipping and were not glazed. These colours are strong and vibrant, but it was ultimately decided to discontinue their use because they chipped off easily and because the pieces painted in these colours lacked presence.

Reds

In ceramics, red is a difficult colour to obtain as the chemicals that produce it tend to fire out in the kiln. In general, the reds that Hagen-Renaker used to decorate pieces were either painted on over the glaze and low-fired or were stains, such as the Auerspurse colours. Overglazed reds, such as those on a miniature rooster's comb, can chip or rub off with age. This is a problem experienced by all potteries.

Variations

As stated before, colours can change within a production run. Colours can also change from early to late releases. A colour change may appear depending on the density of application of the paint. I have already mentioned how colours and steps may be eliminated to reduce costs. Colours might also be modified because they just do not look right. The order forms do not often indicate a colour change, and so it is difficult to pinpoint the dates at which changes took place.

Values

I hope that I have expressed how variable the decoration, colour, shading and mould cleaning of a given Hagen-Renaker piece can be, but I have failed to mention that moulds do not last forever. A mould has a life span of about thirty castings. As it is used, the absorbed water softens the hard edges of the mould. The first pieces out of a mould will show the fabulous detail of the original (if it had good detail) — neck wrinkles, leg tendons, toe separations and feather engraving, for example — but, if the mould is overused, all of those details fade away. I have based the values on an unbroken B+ model, which is a very nice model but not a wonderfully crisp piece with superb decoration. The values tend to be conservative. This is not a fixed price list but only a guide. It is a given that price is an agreement between the buyer and the seller and is contingent on the economic situation, geography, desirability, popularity, and so on, all of which are variable factors.

Many Hagen-Renaker pieces have never been seen for sale, and so values have been extrapolated from known pieces and adjusted based on the length of production, survivability/breakability, aesthetics and complexity of moulding. Breakage and repair reduces the value of a piece, but not drastically, unless there is severe damage. Since Hagen-Renakers were not incredibly expensive — for example, a 'Swaps' sold for $2 in 1958 — they may not have been protected as they should have been, and it seems that a break or two may be a given. I would rather have a crisp, beautifully shaded model with a repaired leg break than a rather thick, coarse intact model. From my point of view, collecting Hagen-Renakers is a bit like doing archaeological work: over time, things break and are lost, but you have to be thankful for what you do find. Restoration is an option for pieces that are missing parts, and it is imperative that the piece be indelibly marked as having been restored. It is also a good idea to describe the amount of crackling on a piece. The presence of crackling is not generally a detriment — in fact, it is often seen as an enhancement as an indication of the age of the piece — but a collector might like to know the amount of crackling present to make a decision about a piece. For pieces that are too rare for even a guess to be made as to their value, the value indicated is "Rare" or "Extremely rare." If the piece is current, the value given is the manufacturer's suggested retail price (in U.S. dollars).

COPIES

Over the years, many Hagen-Renaker pieces have been copied. From the very earliest horses, such as the 1949 miniatures, competing potteries have tried to profit from Hagen-Renaker's designs. 'Clover,' 'Scamper' and 'Roughneck' have been copied in several different sizes, and the copies that are closest to the originals can fool even the most experienced collector. There are also copies of 'Sespe Violette,' but apparently they are decorated with jewels.

Potteries in Japan and China have probably produced most, if not all, of the copies. Collectors should look for white, dry-footed feet on a horse that should definitely be in coloured slip; chunkier legs; or any stamped number series, as Hagen-Renaker never stamped its animals with a number series.

Coloured slip can be an indication that the piece is indeed a Hagen-Renaker (please see the "Production, Step by Step" and "Techniques" sections for more details). However, a few other factories have used coloured slip, including Josef Originals, Renaker-Brazel, and a 1950s company that produced miniature animals with all the whimsy and detail of early Hagen-Renaker pieces. Moreover, some pieces were made in white so that they could be glazed or bisque-painted in colour (for a complete description of these methods, please see the "Colours" section).

RESTORING YOUR HAGEN-RENAKER PIECES

Repairs can be made to broken Hagen-Renaker pieces. This following information does not apply to stoneware pieces, as stoneware is harder to glue. If you need to repair a broken earthenware piece, you must first remove all of the old glue. You can dip the broken area in hot or boiling water, if you are careful not to let the pour hole fill with water or get water on the label. Most glues will soften in hot water and, if dipped repeatedly and wiped off, they can be removed fairly easily. If Krazy Glue was used, it will remain hard in the hot water and not come off. Contact an expert in that case.

When the glue is removed and the piece is dry again (sometimes this is a matter of days), check the fit on the pieces. A few bits of old glue may keep the fit from being perfect, and these can be removed carefully with a razor or straight pin. Be careful not to chip the outside edge. Reglue the pieces with Krazy Glue Gel, which does not absorb into the ceramic as quickly and gives a few seconds of extra time to get the fit just right.

If there are missing areas, or if the fit was not exact, you may wish to fill the gaps. This will be easier if you have done some crafts or art, as it takes some ability to mix colour and some previous knowledge of sanding and sealing. Use Martin Carbone Epoxy, which is available by mail but expensive for just one or two little repairs, or use the contour putty put out by Testors for a few very small repairs. This is not as strong as the epoxy but is all right for just filling gaps.

If you are using the epoxy, you must read the directions. Mix two little balls of epoxy of equal size by hand for several minutes. Then make a little "snake" and lay it into the gap. Work small and overfill the gap only slightly. This takes some practice. Smooth with a brush and alcohol. Let it set for several hours and then sand lightly with fine sandpaper.

If you are using the contour putty, carefully lay the putty into the gap, overfilling it a little, and smooth it with your wet fingertip. Let it dry very well, perhaps another day or two, and then sand lightly with very fine sandpaper.

If you are replacing a broken ear tip, you can use the same fillers, although the epoxy is really much better for this. Shape the tip to match the other one, and spread the edges of the epoxy slightly over the existing part of the ear so that you can sand them smooth.

Whether you use epoxy or contour putty, you should sand and fill until you cannot feel any gaps or bulges with your finger and the silhouette appears smooth when the piece is held up to a window. Wipe the piece off and prepare to paint.

You can use acrylics or oils for the colour. Acrylics are less expensive. There is not enough space here to list all of the colours, but you must remember that Hagen-Renaker clays are usually warm in tone. The white is not really white; it has a little beige in it. Grey is a mix of beige and black; add a little more brown if the colour you get is too greenish. Browns, tans and reds are all easier to match. Black usually has a little brown in it. Paint your mix on in very light, washy layers. Go slightly over the borders of the repair. Wash each layer over the last, and let the layers dry. Make adjustments as necessary. Remember that the colour will change when it dries and again when you seal it, and so try matching your sample colour by painting it on paper or cardboard, spraying it with the matte finish, cutting it out and holding it up to your piece. Colour matching is tedious and this is why restoration can be so expensive. When you have finished painting, let the piece dry and mist it lightly with Krylon matte finish. Glossy animals need a gloss finish spray; I cannot recommend one by name, but it must be non-yellowing and compatible with your paint. Try the spray on the samples and ask for advice at your local art-supply store. When spraying, try not to get too much spray on the rest of the piece. Cover all but the area in question using a plastic grocery bag and cutting a little hole to poke the leg or ear through. Hold the piece firmly within the bag and spray the exposed area.

For more extensive repairs, such as the replacement of missing body parts, castings can be made from intact pieces. This is an involved process requiring resins and moulds and will not be described here. I recommend that you consult books on pottery repair and restoration, such as David Everett's *Manual of Pottery and Porcelain Repair* (London: Robert Hale, 1992). Please note that the manufacturers listed in this book are British. You can also contact a person experienced in pottery repair.

Regardless of who repairs the piece, the repairer's initials and the date of repair must be marked somewhere on the model to indicate that the piece is not entirely original. This is especially important if you later sell the piece; restorations must not be sold as originals.

GLOSSARY OF CERAMIC TERMS

Auerspurse colours: This is a cold paint either put out by the the Auerspurse company or is a brand name, and used to decorate a selection of miniature figures in the early 1960s.

Bisque: This is greenware that has been fired once but not glazed.

Cast: To cast is to pour the slip into the plaster of Paris mould.

Casting: This is the dehydrated slip (clay body) removed from the mould.

Clay body: This refers to the contents of the clay slip and the properties.

Crazing: This is the pattern of cracks often seen in the glaze of a finished piece. It indicates that the glaze contracted more than the underlying body during cooling. It does not indicate age. It can also be created if the finished piece is subjected to moisture or environmental changes.

Decals or transfers: These are detailed colour patterns that are stuck over the glaze and then low-fired to make them adhere. The Specialties giraffes' spots are applied in this way.

Dry-footing: This is the process of wiping the glaze off the parts that touch the shelf so that the glaze does not adhere to the shelf while the piece is being fired.

Earthenware: This is a low-fired ceramic clay. Except where noted, all Hagen-Renakers are earthenware.

Glaze: This is a ground-glass mixture that is brushed onto bisque ware or into which the bisque ware is dipped to make the gloss or matte finish. If a piece is not glazed, it has a rough surface, like sandpaper.

Gloss/glossy: This terms refers to a highly reflective glaze finish.

Greenware: This is the raw clay that has been cast but not fired.

Leather-hard: With regard to greenware, this term refers to the malleability of the clay body.

Matte: This term refers to the non-reflective glaze finish.

Mould: These are the plaster negative forms that provide a shape for the clay slip to fill and maintain.

Slip: This is liquid clay that is poured into a mould.

Stain: This is a decorative paint that is not fired on. It is similar to acrylic paint.

Stoneware: This is a high-fired ceramic clay. Very few Hagen-Renakers are stoneware.

Underglaze: This is a mixture of clay, oxides and minerals that turn into colour when the piece is fired.

BIBLIOGRAPHY

Abelson, Cheryl. *Hagen-Renaker Collector's Catalog: 1949-1979*. Self-published, 1980.

Chipman, Jack. *Collector's Encyclopedia of California Pottery*. Collector Books, 1992.

Dog Collector (newsletter, now discontinued), Issues from 1983 and 1984.

Elber, Bonnie Sumser. *Hagen-Renaker Dogs*. Self-published, 1986.

Elber, Bonnie Sumser. "Hagen-Renaker of California." *American Clay Exchange*, Sept. 1983: 4

Frick, Devin and Tamara Hodge. Disneyana Collector's Guide to California Pottery, 1938-1960. Park Place Press 1999

"Hagen-Renaker Pottery Designer's Workshop." *Cat Collectors*, Dec./Jan. 1985.

Kennedy, Maggie. "Sculptress at Work." *Western Horseman*, Mar. 1962.

Lerner, Lois. *Lerner's Encyclopedia of U.S. Marks on Pottery, Porcelain and Clay*. Collector Books, 1988.

McCall, Jeanne. *The Hagen-Renaker Horse Reference Guide*. Self-published, 1988.

Roller, Gayle, Kathleen Rose and Joan Berkwitz. *The Hagen-Renaker Handbook*. Self-published, 1989.

Schneider, Mike. *California Potteries: The Complete Book*. Schiffer Publishing Co., 1995.

Tumbusch, Tom. *Tomart's Illustrated Disneyana: Catalog and Price Guide*. 2 Vols. Tomart Publishing, 1985.

Tumbusch, Tom. *Tomart's Disneyana Update*, No. 7, Feb./Mar. 1995.

Young, Nancy A. *Breyer Molds and Models: Horses, Riders and Animals (1950-1995)*. Schiffer Publishing Company, 1997.

Hagen-Renker Collector's Club

For the Hagen-Renaker collector who wishes to keep abreast of the happenings in the H-R world we suggest you consider joining the Hagen-Renaker Collector's Club. The newsletter is published six times a year and the annual fee is $20.00 U.S. funds. For Canadian and overseas fees please write to Jenny Palmer, 3651 Polish Line Road, Cheboygan, MI 49721, or e-mail: hrcc@freeway.net.

EARLY HAGEN-RENAKER

INDEX TO
EARLY HAGEN-RENAKER

Hagen-Renaker POTTERIES CALIFORNIA

ANIMALS

Calico Cat

Model No.:	131
Designer:	John Renaker
Height:	2 5/8", 6.6 cm
Colour:	Sand pink with yellow, green and blue patches
Issued:	c.1946 - c.1949

Description	U.S. $	Can. $	U.K. £
Calico Cat		Rare	

Gingham Dog

Model No.:	132
Designer:	John Renaker
Height:	2 ½", 6.4 cm
Colour:	1. Sand pink with white polka dots
	2. White with blue and yellow polka dots
Issued:	c.1946 - c.1949

Description	U.S. $	Can. $	U.K. £
Gingham Dog		Rare	

BELLS

Bells

Designer:	John Renaker
Height:	2 ½", 6.4 cm
Colour:	1. White background, orange duck, brown chicks, brown stripe around rim
	2. White background, brown grapes, and vines, green and orange leaves, brown trim
Issued:	c.1946 - c.1949

Description	U.S. $	Can. $	U.K. £
1. Ducks	30.00	60.00	50.00
2. Grapes	30.00	60.00	50.00

BOWL/FLOWER BOWL

Bowl

Designer:	John Renaker
Diameter:	6 ½", 16.5 cm
Colour:	White background, green and orange flowers, green and brown stylized leaves
Issued:	c.1946 - c.1949

Description	U.S. $	Can. $	U.K. £
Bowl	40.00	80.00	70.00

Flower Bowl with Frog

Designer:	John Renaker
Size:	1. Bowl — 12", 30.5 cm
	2. Frog — 6", 15.0 cm
Colour:	Turquoise
Issued:	c.1946 - c.1949

Description	U.S. $	Can. $	U.K. £
1. Flower bowl		Rare	
2. Frog		Rare	

BUTTER PATS

Butter Pats

Designer:	John Renaker
Diameter:	3 ½", 8.9 cm
Colour:	Dark brown, avocado green, orange-tan
Issued:	c.1946 - c.1949

Bird Design	U.S. $	Can. $	U.K. £
1. Drake	15.00	30.00	25.00
2. Duck	15.00	30.00	25.00
3. Hen	15.00	30.00	25.00
4. Rooster	15.00	30.00	25.00
5. Turkey, female	15.00	30.00	25.00
6. Turkey, male	15.00	30.00	25.00

Fruit Design	U.S. $	Can. $	U.K. £
1. Apples	15.00	30.00	25.00
2. Cherries	15.00	30.00	25.00
3. Grapes	15.00	30.00	25.00
4. Oranges	15.00	30.00	25.00
5. Pears	15.00	30.00	25.00
6. Plums	15.00	30.00	25.00

CUP AND SAUCER

Cup and Saucer

Designer:	John Renaker
Height:	2", 5.0 cm
Colour:	Dark brown, avocado green, orange
Issued:	c.1946 - c.1949

Description	U.S. $	Can. $	U.K. £
1. Cup	20.00	40.00	35.00
2. Cup and saucer	30.00	60.00	50.00

Note: The illustration also shows a large-sized plate with a rooster, hen and chick design; see page 8 for technical information.

DISHES

<table>
<tr><td rowspan="2">Photograph
not available
at press time</td><td colspan="4">Dishes, oval
Designer: John Renaker
Size: 4" x 6", 10.1 x 15.0 cm
Colour: Unknown
Issued: c.1946 - c.1949</td></tr>
<tr><td></td></tr>
</table>

Dishes, oval

Designer:	John Renaker
Size:	4" x 6", 10.1 x 15.0 cm
Colour:	Unknown
Issued:	c.1946 - c.1949

Description	U.S. $	Can. $	U.K. £
1. Chipmunk design		Rare	
2. Fairy wren design		Rare	

Note: These oval dishes have slotted handles.

PLAQUES/SHADOW BOXES

Plaques, oblong

Designer:	John Renaker
Size:	4" x 5", 10.1 x 12.7 cm
Colour:	Cream background; dark brown, avocado green and orange design
Issued:	c.1946 - c.1949

Description	U.S. $	Can. $	U.K. £
1. Anemone	40.00	80.00	70.00
2. Chrysanthemums	40.00	80.00	70.00
3. Iris	40.00	80.00	70.00
4. Rose, pink	40.00	80.00	70.00
5. Rose, yellow	40.00	80.00	70.00

Plaques, oval

Designer:	John Renaker
Size:	4" x 5", 10.1 x 12.7 cm
Colour:	Cream background; dark brown, avocado green and orange design
Issued:	c.1946 - c.1949

Description	U.S. $	Can. $	U.K. £
1. 18th century gentleman	40.00	80.00	70.00
2. 18th century lady	40.00	80.00	70.00
3. Sailor boy	40.00	80.00	70.00
4. Sailor girl	40.00	80.00	70.00

PLATES

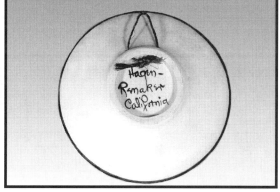

PLATES, large and small

Plates, large		Plates, small	
Designer:	John Renaker	Designer:	John Renaker
Diameter:	8 ¾", 22.2 cm	Diameter:	5 ½", 14.0 cm
Colour:	Dark brown, avocado green, orange	Colour:	Dark brown, avocado green, orange
Issued:	c.1946 - c.1949	Issued:	c.1946 - c.1949

Birds	U.S. $	Can. $	U.K. £	Birds	U.S. $	Can. $	U.K. £
Mallard drake	30.00	60.00	50.00	Mallard drake	20.00	40.00	35.00
Mallard hen with ducklings	30.00	60.00	50.00	Mallard hen with ducklings	20.00	40.00	35.00
Rooster	30.00	60.00	50.00	Rooster	20.00	40.00	35.00
Rooster, hen and chick	30.00	60.00	50.00	Rooster, hen and chick	20.00	40.00	35.00
Turkey and mallard hen	30.00	60.00	50.00	Turkey and mallard hen	20.00	40.00	35.00

Fruit	U.S. $	Can. $	U.K. £	Fruit	U.S. $	Can. $	U.K. £
Cherries	30.00	60.00	50.00	Cherries	20.00	40.00	35.00

TRAYS, leaf

Photograph
not available
at press time

Photograph
not available
at press time

Geranium Leaf		Maple Leaf	
Designer:	John Renaker	Designer:	John Renaker
Size:	3" x ½", 7.6 x 1.27 cm	Size:	5" x 1", 12.7 x 2.54 cm
Colour:	See below	Colour:	See below
Issued:	c.1946 - c.1949	Issued:	c.1946 - c.1949

Colourways	U.S. $	Can. $	U.K. £	Colourways	U.S. $	Can. $	U.K. £
1. Chartreuse				1. Chartreuse			
2. Mauve		Rare		2. Mauve		Rare	
3. Turquoise				3. Turquoise			
4. Wine				4. Wine			

BLACK BISQUE LINE

In spring 1959, the Black Bisque line was introduced as a "modern line of fanciful animals and birds. Black bisque body with bright blue-green jewelry enamel fired on for color accent. A brand new exciting approach to ceramic artware."

These black bisque pieces, which were available for six months, were not assigned model numbers on the order forms. There are only 22 black bisque pieces on the sales list; however, 29 pieces are shown in the mould book.

The following models do not appear on the order forms:

Cat, head cocked (Unk.); Dead Bird (29); Fish (11); Fox (8); Panther (17); Skunk (7); and Squirrel (Unk.).

INDEX TO
BLACK BISQUE LINE

HAGEN- MAKER Present. je New . . .

black bisque

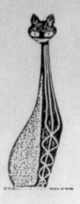

A modern line of fanciful animals and birds. Black bisque body with bright blue-green jewelry enamel fired on for color accent. A brand new exciting approach to ceramic artware. Popularly priced and sales tested in key giftware outlets. Send for our fast-selling, pre-tested assortment before the gift shows swamp us with orders. $35.00

Bull

Model No.:	13
Designer:	Maureen Love
Height:	4 ¼", 10.8 cm
Colour:	Black bisque, blue-green enamel
Issued:	1959

Description	U.S. $	Can.$	U.K. £
Bull	60.00	120.00	100.00

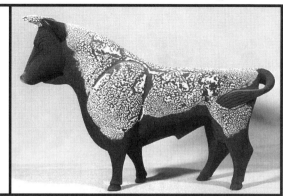

Cat, flat face

Model Nos.:	Large — 2
	Medium — 3
	Small — 4
Designer:	Tom Masterson
Height:	Large — 9", 22.9 cm
	Medium — 6 1/5", 15.7 cm
	Small — 3 ¾", 9.5 cm
Colour:	Black bisque, bright blue-green enamel
Issued:	1959

Description	U.S. $	Can.$	U.K. £
1. Large	70.00	140.00	120.00
2. Medium	50.00	100.00	85.00
3. Small	40.00	80.00	70.00

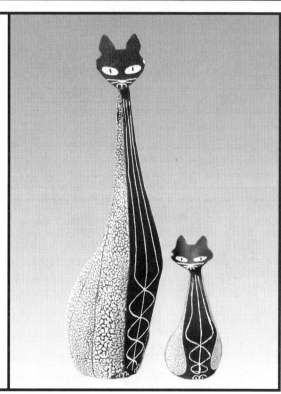

Cat, head cocked

Model No.:	Unknown
Designer:	Tom Masterson
Height:	4 7/8", 12.4 cm
Colour:	Black bisque, bright blue-green enamel
Issued:	1959

Description	U.S. $	Can.$	U.K. £
Cat, head cocked	40.00	80.00	70.00

Note: This model does not appear on the order forms.

Photograph
not available
at press time

Cormorant

Model No.:	1
Designer:	Will Climes
Height:	Unknown
Colour:	Black bisque, bright blue-green enamel
Issued:	1959

Description	U.S. $	Can.$	U.K. £
Cormorant		Rare	

Note: This model does not appear on the order forms.

Crowntail Bird

Model No.:	22
Designer:	Will Climes
Height:	3 ½", 8.9 cm
Colour:	Black bisque, white markings
Issued:	1959

Description	U.S. $	Can.$	U.K. £
Crowntail bird	45.00	90.00	80.00

Dachshund

Model No.:	26
Designer:	Helen Perrin Farnlund
Size:	3" x 9 ½", 7.6 x 24.0 cm
Colour:	Black bisque, white facial markings
Issued:	1959

Description	U.S. $	Can.$	U.K. £
Dachshund	120.00	240.00	200.00

Note: The head is a separate part to the body.

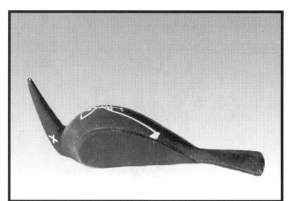

Dead Bird

Model No.:	29
Designer:	Will Climes
Height:	1 5/8", 4.1 cm
Colour:	Black bisque, white markings
Issued:	1959

Description	U.S. $	Can.$	U.K. £
Dead bird	45.00	90.00	80.00

Note: This model does not appear on the order forms.

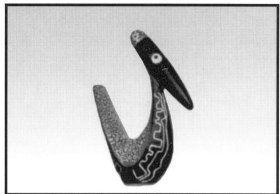

Dodo Bird

Model No.:	5
Designer:	Tom Masterson
Height:	3 ¼", 8.3 cm
Colour:	Black bisque, bright blue-green enamel
Issued:	1959

Description	U.S. $	Can.$	U.K. £
Dodo bird	45.00	90.00	80.00

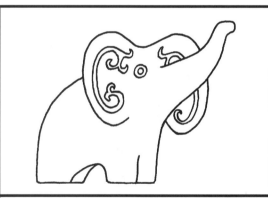

Elephant

Model No.:	19
Designer:	Will Climes
Height:	3", 7.6 cm
Colour:	Black bisque, bright blue-green enamel
Issued:	1959

Description	U.S. $	Can.$	U.K. £
Elephant	60.00	120.00	100.00

Featherduster Bird

Model No.:	19
Designer:	Tom Masterson
Height:	5", 12.7 cm
Colour:	Black bisque, bright blue-green enamel
Issued:	1959

Description	U.S. $	Can.$	U.K. £
Featherduster bird	70.00	140.00	120.00

Photograph not
available
at press time

Fish

Model No.:   11
Designer: Helen Perrin Farnlund
Height: Unknown
Colour: Black bisque, bright blue-green enamel
Issued: 1959

Description	U.S. $	Can.$	U.K. £
Fish		Rare	

Note: This model does not appear on the order forms.

Fox

Model No.:   8
Designer: Tom Masterson
Height: 3 ¾", 9.5 cm
Colour: Black bisque, bright blue-green enamel
Issued: 1959

Description	U.S. $	Can.$	U.K. £
Fox	45.00	90.00	80.00

Note: This model does not appear on the order forms.
The model illustrated has a broken nose.

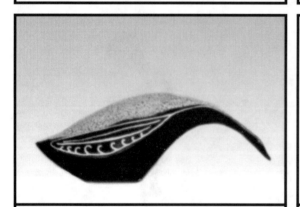

Goose

Model No.:   12
Designer: Tom Masterson
Height: 1 ½", 3.8 cm
Colour: Black bisque, bright blue-green enamel
Issued: 1959

Description	U.S. $	Can.$	U.K. £
Goose	40.00	80.00	70.00

Hen

Model No.:   28
Designer: Will Climes
Height: 2 ½", 6.4 cm
Colour: Black bisque, bright blue-green enamel
Issued: 1959

Description	U.S. $	Can.$	U.K. £
Hen	30.00	60.00	50.00

Note: This forms a pair with Rooster, small (27), page 17.

Horse

Model No.:	9
Designer:	Maureen Love
Height:	4 ½″, 11.9 cm
Colour:	Black bisque, bright blue-green enamel
Issued:	1959

Description	U.S. $	Can.$	U.K. £
Horse	90.00	180.00	155.00

Photograph not
available
at press time

Panther

Model No.:	17
Designer:	Helen Perrin Farnlund
Height:	Unknown
Colour:	Black bisque, bright blue-green enamel
Issued:	1959

Description	U.S. $	Can.$	U.K. £
Panther		Rare	

Pelican

Model No.:	10
Designer:	Tom Masterson
Height:	3 ½″, 8.9 cm
Colour:	Black bisque, bright blue-green enamel
Issued:	1959

Description	U.S. $	Can.$	U.K. £
Pelican	50.00	100.00	85.00

Pick-axe Bird

Model No.:	24
Designer:	Tom Masterson
Height:	3 ¼″, 8.3 cm
Colour:	Black bisque, bright blue-green enamel
Issued:	1959

Description	U.S. $	Can.$	U.K. £
Pick-axe bird	50.00	100.00	85.00

Pigeon

Model No.:	25
Designer:	Tom Masterson
Height:	3″, 7.6 cm
Colour:	Black bisque body, white markings
Issued:	1959

Description	U.S. $	Can.$	U.K. £
Pigeon	60.00	120.00	110.00

Poodle, seated

Model No.:	16
Designer:	Tom Masterson
Height:	3″, 7.6 cm
Colour:	Black bisque, bright blue-green enamel
Issued:	1959
Varieties:	'Rembrandt'

Description	U.S. $	Can.$	U.K. £
Poodle, seated	70.00	140.00	120.00

Note: The 'Rembrandt' mould was also used to make this model; see page 446.

Poodle, standing

Model No.:	14
Designer:	Tom Masterson
Height:	5″, 12.7 cm
Colour:	Black bisque, bright blue-green enamel
Issued:	1959
Varieties:	Also called Poodle 'Fifi' With crown

Description	U.S. $	Can.$	U.K. £
Poodle, standing	90.00	180.00	155.00

Note: See Pedigree section, page 445

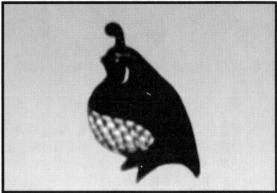

Quail

Model No.:	23
Designer:	Tom Masterson
Height:	Unknown
Colour:	Black bisque, bright blue-green enamel
Issued:	1959

Description	U.S. $	Can.$	U.K. £
Quail		Rare	

Rooster, large
Model No.: 23
Designer: Tom Masterson
Height: 2 ¾", 7.0 cm
Colour: Black bisque, bright blue-green enamel
Issued: 1959

Description	U.S. $	Can.$	U.K. £
Rooster, large		Rare	

Rooster, small
Model No.: 27
Designer: Will Climes
Height: Unknown
Colour: Black bisque, bright blue-green enamel
Issued: 1959

Description	U.S. $	Can.$	U.K. £
Rooster, small		Rare	

Note: This forms a pair with Hen (28), page 14.

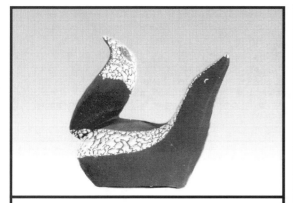

Skunk
Model No.: 7
Designer: Tom Masterson
Height: 2 7/16", 6.2 cm
Colour: Black bisque, bright blue-green enamel
Issued: 1959

Description	U.S. $	Can.$	U.K. £
Skunk	40.00	80.00	70.00

Note: This model does not appear on the order forms.

Snail
Model No.: 20
Designer: Tom Masterson
Height: 1 5/8", 4.1 cm
Colour: Black bisque, bright blue-green enamel
Issued: 1959

Description	U.S. $	Can.$	U.K. £
Snail	40.00	80.00	70.00

Squirrel

Model No.:	Unknown
Designer:	Unknown
Height:	4", 10.1 cm
Colour:	Black bisque, bright blue-green enamel
Issued:	1959

Description	U.S. $	Can.$	U.K. £
Squirrel		Rare	

Note: This model does not appear on the order forms.

Photograph not
available
at press time

Sign

Model No.:	14
Designer:	Nell Bortells
Height:	Unknown
Colour:	Unknown
Issued:	1959

Description	U.S. $	Can.$	U.K. £
Sign		Rare	

Zebra

Model No.:	6
Designer:	Maureen Love
Height:	5 3/8", 13.65 cm
Colour:	Black bisque, bright blue-green enamel
Issued:	1959

Description	U.S. $	Can.$	U.K. £
Zebra	80.00	160.00	140.00

Black bisque price ticket

DESIGNER'S WORKSHOP LINE

Designer's Workshop was launched under the direction of Nell Bortells and Bill Nicely in 1952 to produce a larger line of animal figurines. I believe the fantastic detail of many a Designer's Workshop piece makes the offerings from other ceramic companies pale in comparison. Who can resist the attitude and delicate legs of the Zilla foal? The way that the Hagen-Renaker is made — cast of coloured slip and shaded invites an appreciation of the nuances of the piece, as the sculptural details are not obscured by a thick layer of paint; thus there is an aesthetic immediacy.

Individuality was enhanced by the fact that most of the Designer's Workshop pieces were named, and given stickers of importance. Breed, sex and name were used consistently on the order forms from fall 1957 to fall 1967. By spring 1968, names were omitted from the order forms, except for the five famous thoroughbreds. If a colour choice was available, it was indicated on the price list, but if only one colour was available, it was not mentioned on the price list.

For Hagen-Renaker, the choice between glossy and matte glazes often came down to choosing between a glossy eye-catching flamboyant piece, to a more realistic matte model that really showed the artistic details. Not until San Marcos were most pieces offered in both matte and gloss so a collector could have the best of both worlds.

Information about colours and details appear earlier in this book. In 1954, a special line was created for dogs, "Pedigree Dogs." By fall 1968, the dogs were phased back into the Designer's Workshop list. Designer's Workshop was made until 1971. It was revived for a year in 1974. Once Hagen-Renaker acquired the San Marcos pottery, Designer's Workshop was again revived until that plant closed. This sign illustrated on the following page was made to complement the new designs.

INDEX TO
DESIGNER'S WORKSHOP LINE

Designer's Workshop label 'Cape Buffalo'   Hagen-Renaker ceramic sign

Attractive—Authentic Arabian Horse Models

You'll find it hard to believe that models of Arabian Horses can be so perfect. You'll probably want all three, but take your pick.

White Sheik is copied from the original horse —even his white coat, pink nose, eyes and hooves. 5½ inches high. A perfect ceramic model for only **$5.25.**

Sheik's colt is a little beauty as shown with his small dun color gray-brown body and tail —just like his mother. 2¾ inches high. Price only **$2.75.**

Sheik's Wife. Beautiful reproduction in pottery. Her true dun color and natural sheen are most life-like. 3¾ inches high. Price **$4.00.**

Entire Arabian Family—all three as above make a charming group. You save $1.25 by ordering all three for only **$10.95.** I pay postage. Money back if not delighted.

"little joe" WIESENFELD CO.

Dept. L4   Baltimore 1, Maryland

79

Early advertisement for Designer's Workshop horses
'Little Joe' renamed 'Abu Farwa'
'Tony' and 'Nancy'

BIRDS

Hagen-Renaker created a delightful collection of both wild and domestic birds and took great care in decorating the plumage.

Some very imaginative pieces were released from San Marcos, such as the *Little Red Hen* and *Mother Goose*, which utilized large added-on pieced such as Mother Goose's shawl and bonnet. Other San Marcos pieces such as the *Least Terns* and the *Roadrunner* are reminiscent of Maureen Love's own studio pieces.

INDEX TO
DESIGNER'S WORKSHOP BIRDS

CHICKS, DUCKS AND DUCKLINGS

Chick
Model No.:   B-747
Designer: Maureen Love
Height: 1. Large — 1 5/8", 4.1 cm
              2. Small — 1 ¼", 3.1 cm
Colour: Yellow; gloss or matte
Issued: Spring 1961 - fall 1963,
              spring 1979, spring 1982 - spring 1986

Description	U.S. $	Can. $	U.K.£
1. Monrovia	40.00	80.00	70.00
2. San Dimas	30.00	60.00	50.00
3. San Marcos	20.00	40.00	35.00

Note: Model B-747 was reworked.

Large size (left) Small size (right)

Chick 'Arthur', head down
Model No.:   B-619
Designer: Maureen Love
Height: 1 ½", 3.8 cm
Colour: Yellow; matte
Issued: Fall 1955, fall 1967

Description	U.S. $	Can. $	U.K.£
1. Monrovia	50.00	100.00	85.00
2. San Dimas	40.00	80.00	70.00

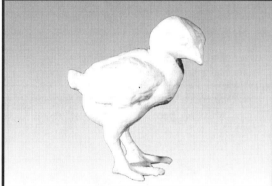

Chick 'Edna', head up
Model No.:   B-618
Designer: Maureen Love
Height: 1 7/8", 4.8 cm
Colour: Yellow; matte
Issued: Fall 1955, 1964, fall 1967

Description	U.S. $	Can. $	U.K.£
1. Monrovia	50.00	100.00	85.00
2. San Dimas	40.00	80.00	70.00

Note: The model illustrated is bisque.

Chick, large feet

Model No.:	B-523
Designer:	Helen Perrin Farnlund
Height:	2 ¼", 5.7 cm
Colour:	Yellow; gloss
Issued:	1. Fall 1952
	2 Spring 1979

Description	U.S. $	Can. $	U.K.£
1. Monrovia	50.00	100.00	85.00
2. San Dimas	40.00	80.00	70.00

Chick, wings up

Model No.:	B-524
Designer:	Helen Perrin Farnlund
Height:	1. 3", 7.6 cm
	2. 2 ¾", 7.0 cm
Colour:	Yellow; gloss
Issued:	1. Fall 1952
	2. Spring 1979

Description	U.S. $	Can. $	U.K.£
1. Monrovia	50.00	100.00	85.00
2. San Dimas	40.00	80.00	70.00

Note: This model was reworked, resulting in a smaller mould.

Duck 'Jack'
First Version (With curled tail feather)

Model No.:	B-723
Designer:	Maureen Love
Height:	5 ¾", 14.6 cm
Colour:	White; matte
Issued:	Spring 1960 - spring 1972

Description	U.S. $	Can. $	U.K.£
First version	40.00	80.00	70.00

Duck 'Jack'
Second Version (Without curled tail feather)

Model No.:	42
Designer:	Maureen Love
Height:	6 7/16", 16.3 cm
Colour:	White; gloss or matte
Issued:	Spring 1981 - spring 1986

Description	U.S. $	Can. $	U.K.£
Second version	30.00	60.00	50.00

Duck 'Jill'
First Version (Beak rests on chest)
Model No.:   B-724
Designer: Maureen Love
Height: 2 ¾", 7.0 cm
Colour: White, light brown shading; matte
Issued: Spring 1960 - spring 1972

Description	U.S. $	Can. $	U.K.£
First version	40.00	80.00	70.00

Duck' Jill'
Second Version (Beak away from chest)
Model No.:   43
Designer: Maureen Love
Height: 3 ¾", 9.5 cm
Colour: White, dark brown shading;
                gloss or matte
Issued: Spring 1981 - spring 1986

Description	U.S. $	Can. $	U.K.£
Second version	30.00	60.00	50.00

Duckling 'Beep'
First Version (Defined wings, tail points up)
Model No.:   B-573
Designer: Helen Perrin Farnlund
Height: 2", 5.1 cm
Colour: Yellow; gloss or matte
Issued: 1954, spring 1955, 1956

Description	U.S. $	Can. $	U.K.£
First version	30.00	60.00	50.00

Duckling 'Beep'
Second Version (Less definition)
Model No.:   745
Designer: Helen Perrin Farnlund
Height: 1 ¾", 4.4 cm
Colour: Yellow; gloss or matte
Issued: 1961, fall 1964 - spring 1968,
                fall 1981 - 1986

Description	U.S. $	Can. $	U.K.£
1. San Dimas	30.00	60.00	50.00
2. San Marcos	20.00	40.00	35.00

Note: 'Beep', models B-573 and 745, was made inter-
        mittently for 28 seasons between 1954 and 1986.

Duckling 'Bingo'
First Version (Squatting, head looks up)

Model No.:	B-571
Designer:	Helen Perrin Farnlund
Height:	1 ¼", 3.1 cm
Colour:	Yellow; gloss or matte
Issued:	1954, spring 1955, 1956

Description	U.S. $	Can. $	U.K.£
First version	30.00	60.00	50.00

Duckling 'Bingo'
Second Version (Upright, head looks forward)

Model No.:	B-746
Designer:	Helen Perrin Farnlund
Height:	1 ½", 3.8 cm
Colour:	Yellow; gloss or matte
Issued:	1961, fall 1964 - fall 1972, fall 1981 -spring 1986

Description	U.S. $	Can. $	U.K.£
1. San Dimas	30.00	60.00	50.00
2. San Marcos	20.00	40.00	35.00

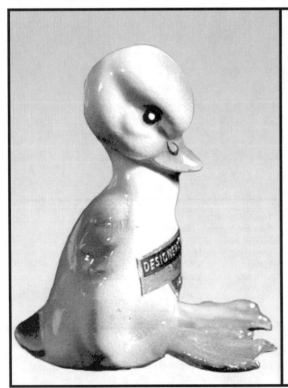

Duckling 'Willy', seated

Model No.:	B-574
Designer:	Helen Perrin Farnlund
Height:	1 7/8", 4.8 cm
Colour:	Yellow; gloss or matte
Issued:	Spring 1954 - spring 1956, spring 1979

Model No.	U.S. $	Can. $	U.K.£
B-574	40.00	80.00	70.00

GEESE

Little Girl Gosling (49)   Mother Goose (44)   Little Boy Gosling (48)

Mother Goose
Model No.:	44
Designer:	Helen Perrin Farnlund
Height:	6 ½", 16.5 cm
Colour:	Grey goose, pink shawl and bonnet, lavender ribbon; matte
Issued:	Fall 1982 - fall 1986

Model No.	U.S. $	Can. $	U.K. £
44	75.00	150.00	130.00

Note: This model is also known to have a yellow shawl and blue bonnet.

Little Boy Gosling
Model No.:	48
Designer:	Helen Perrin Farnlund
Height:	3 ¼", 8.3 cm
Colour:	Yellow gosling, blue hat; gloss or matte
Issued:	Spring 1983 - spring 1986

Model No.	U.S. $	Can. $	U.K. £
48	30.00	60.00	50.00

Little Girl Gosling
Model No.:	49
Designer:	Helen Perrin Farnlund
Height:	3", 7.6 cm
Colour:	Yellow gosling, pink bonnet with lavender ribbon; gloss or matte
Issued:	Spring 1983 - spring 1986

Model No.	U.S. $	Can. $	U.K. £
49	30.00	60.00	50.00

Canada Goose

Model No.:	127
Designer:	Maureen Love
Height:	7 ½", 19.1 cm
Colour:	Black head, neck and legs; tan wings with black markings; gloss or matte
Issued:	Spring 1986

Model No.	U.S. $	Can. $	U.K. £
127	125.00	250.00	220.00

Goose 'Toulouse'

Model No.:	B-636
Designer:	Maureen Love
Height:	7", 17.8 cm
Colour:	Grey, brown shading; matte
Issued:	Spring 1956 - fall 1956

Model No.	U.S. $	Can. $	U.K. £
B-636	150.00	300.00	260.00

HENS AND ROOSTERS

Banty Hen

Model No.:	B-767
Designer:	Maureen Love
Height:	4 1/8", 10.5 cm
Colour:	See below
Issued:	Fall 1962 - spring 1963, spring 1967

Colourways	U.S. $	Can. $	U.K.£
1. Black; matte (1967)	75.00	150.00	130.00
2. Brown/yellow/black	75.00	150.00	130.00
3. White; matte	75.00	150.00	130.00

Banty Rooster

Model No.:	B-766
Designer:	Maureen Love
Height:	5 ½", 14.0 cm
Colour:	See below
Issued:	Fall 1962 - spring 1963, spring 1967

Colourways	U.S. $	Can. $	U.K.£
1. Black; matte (1967)	75.00	150.00	130.00
2. Brown/yellow/black	75.00	150.00	130.00
3. White; matte	75.00	150.00	130.00

Fighting Cock

Model No.:	B-687
Designer:	Maureen Love
Size:	8 ¼"x 9", 21.0 x 22.9 cm
Colour:	1. Brown, red highlights on neck, green highlights on tail feathers
	2. Gold
	3. White
Issued:	Spring 1958, fall 1981

Colourways	U.S. $	Can. $	U.K.£
1. Brown (1958)			
2. Gold (1981)		Rare	
3. White (1981)			

Hen 'Elizabeth'

Model No.:	B-617
Designer:	Maureen Love
Height:	4 ¼", 10.8 cm
Colour:	See below
Issued:	Fall 1955 - spring 1972, spring 1982 - spring 1986

Colourways	U.S. $	Can. $	U.K.£
1. Banty (yellow/brown)	40.00	80.00	70.00
2. Red-brown	30.00	60.00	50.00
3. White; gloss/matte	25.00	50.00	45.00

Note: Model B-617 was made for 32 seasons between 1955-1972 and nine seasons between 1982-1986.

Little Red Hen

Model No.:	125
Designer:	Helen Perrin Farnlund
Height:	6 ½", 16.5 cm
Colour:	Brown; gloss or matte
Issued:	Spring 1986

Model No.	U.S. $	Can. $	U.K.£
125	125.00	250.00	220.00

Rooster 'Alex'

Model No.:	B-616
Designer:	Maureen Love
Height:	6 ¾", 17.2 cm
Colour:	See below
Issued:	Fall 1955 - spring 1972, spring 1982 - spring 1986

Colourways	U.S. $	Can. $	U.K.£
1. Banty	45.00	90.00	80.00
2. Red-brown	35.00	70.00	60.00
3. White	25.00	50.00	45.00

Note: Model B-616 was made for 32 seasons between 1955-1972 and nine seasons between 1982-1986.

LEAST TERNS

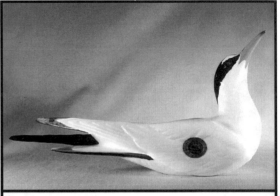

Least Tern, flying

Model No.:	128
Designer:	Maureen Love
Height:	Bird — 10", 25.4 cm
Colour:	White, black markings, orange bill; gloss or matte
Issued:	Spring 1986

Model No.	U.S. $	Can. $	U.K. £
128	75.00	150.00	130.00

Note: The bird rests on a metal rod supported by a base. Some bases are sand-glazed.

Least Tern, nesting

Model No.:	129
Designer:	Maureen Love
Height:	4 ½", 11.9 cm
Colour:	White, black markings, orange bill; gloss or matte
Issued:	Spring 1986

Model No.	U.S. $	Can. $	U.K. £
129	75.00	150.00	130.00

Note: The model illustrated shows a round San Marcos sticker on its wing.

MALLARDS

Mallard Hen With Ducklings

Model No.:	123
Designer:	Maureen Love
Height:	3 ¼", 8.3 cm
Colour:	Light brown with white, blue and black markings; gloss or matte
Issued:	Fall 1985 - spring 1986

Model No.	U.S. $	Can. $	U.K. £
123	60.00	120.00	105.00

Note: The ducklings were moulded separately and attached to the mother.

Mallard Drake

Model No.:	122
Designer:	Maureen Love
Height:	8", 20.3 cm
Colour:	Green head; white underbody; brown, white and black wings; gloss or matte
Issued:	Fall 1985 - spring 1986

Model No.	U.S. $	Can. $	U.K. £
122	70.00	140.00	120.00

Note: Set with Mallard Hen with Ducklings (123).

Mallard Drake

Model No.:	B-542
Designer:	Tom Masterson
Height:	6 ¼", 15.9 cm
Colour:	Green head, red-brown breast, brown and white wings; gloss
Issued:	Spring 1953 - spring 1955, spring 1967 - spring 1968

Description	U.S. $	Can. $	U.K. £
1. Monrovia	60.00	120.00	105.00
2. San Dimas	60.00	120.00	105.00

Mallard Hen, sharp-beaked

Model No.:	B-543
Designer:	Tom Masterson
Height:	2 ½", 6.4 cm
Colour:	Red-brown; gloss
Issued:	Spring 1953 - spring 1955

Model No.	U.S. $	Can. $	U.K. £
B-543	60.00	120.00	105.00

Mallard Drake

Model No.:	B-769
Designer:	Maureen Love
Height:	5 ½", 14.0 cm
Colour:	Green head, dark brown; gloss
Issued:	Fall 1962 - spring 1963

Model No.	U.S. $	Can. $	U.K. £
B-769	75.00	150.00	130.00

Mallard Hen

Model No.:	B-768
Designer:	Maureen Love
Height:	2 ¾", 7.0 cm
Colour:	1. Brown
	2. White; gloss
Issued:	Fall 1962 - spring 1963, 1981

Colourways	U.S. $	Can. $	U.K. £
1. Brown	75.00	150.00	130.00
2. White (1981)	40.00	80.00	70.00

Note: Model B-768 is illustrated in bisque.

OWLS

Owl

Model No.:	47
Designer:	Maureen Love
Height:	5½", 14.0 cm
Colour:	Brown with black and yellow eyes; gloss or matte
Issued:	Spring 1983 - spring 1986

Model No.	U.S. $	Can. $	U.K. £
47	60.00	120.00	105.00

Owlet

Model No.:	46
Designer:	Maureen Love
Height:	3", 7.6 cm
Colour:	Brown with black and yellow eyes; gloss or matte
Issued:	Spring 1983 - spring 1986

Model No.	U.S. $	Can. $	U.K. £
46	45.00	90.00	80.00

PHEASANTS

Pheasant, resting

Model No.:	18
Designer:	Maureen Love
Size:	4" x 13", 10.1 x 33.0 cm
Colour:	Green head, red face, brown body with green markings; gloss or matte
Issued:	1985 - spring 1986

Model No.	U.S. $	Can. $	U.K. £
18	50.00	100.00	85.00

Pheasant, standing, short legs

Model No.:	B-533
Designer:	Tom Masterson
Height:	5 ¼", 13.3 cm
Colour:	Green head, red eye, red-brown body with black markings; gloss
Issued:	Fall 1952 - spring 1955

Model No.	U.S. $	Can. $	U.K. £
B-533	75.00	150.00	130.00

Pheasant, standing, long legs

Model No.:	B-691
Designer:	Maureen Love
Height:	5 ½", 14.0 cm
Colour:	Red-brown, black markings, beige ring around neck; gloss or matte
Issued:	Spring 1962, 1969 - spring 1971

Description	U.S. $	Can. $	U.K. £
1. Monrovia	75.00	150.00	130.00
2. San Dimas	75.00	150.00	130.00

Note: In spring 1971, this pheasant was offered as a male or female, with or without neck-ring decoration.

QUAIL

Quail, standing

Model No.:	B-534
Designer:	Tom Masterson
Height:	5", 12.7 cm
Colour:	Brown, blue breast, yellow belly; gloss or matte
Issued:	5 seasons in the 1950s, spring 1962, 1969 - spring 1971

Description	U.S. $	Can. $	U.K. £
1. Monrovia	50.00	100.00	85.00
2. San Dimas	40.00	80.00	70.00

Quail Ma (98), Quail Boy (99), Quail Girl (100), Quail Pa (97)

QUAIL FAMILY

Quail Boy, mouth open, looking up

Model No.:   99
Designer: Maureen Love
Height: 1 ½", 3.8 cm
Colour: Light brown with dark brown markings; gloss or matte
Issued: Spring 1985 - spring 1986

Model No.	U.S. $	Can. $	U.K. £
99	20.00	40.00	35.00

Quail Girl, head turned

Model No.:   100
Designer: Maureen Love
Height: 1 ½", 3.8 cm
Colour: Light brown with dark brown markings; gloss or matte
Issued: Spring 1985 - spring 1986

Model No.	U.S. $	Can. $	U.K. £
100	20.00	40.00	35.00

Quail Ma

Model No.:   98
Designer: Maureen Love
Height: 3 ½", 8.9 cm
Colour: Dark brown head, dark brown body with white markings; gloss or matte
Issued: Spring 1985 - spring 1986

Model No.	U.S. $	Can. $	U.K. £
98	50.00	100.00	85.00

Quail Pa

Model No.:   97
Designer: Maureen Love
Height: 4 ½", 11.9 cm
Colour: Brown body with white markings; gloss or matte
Issued: Spring 1985 - spring 1986

Model No.	U.S. $	Can. $	U.K. £
97	50.00	100.00	85.00

ROADRUNNER

ROBIN

Roadrunner

Model No.:	45
Designer:	Maureen Love
Height:	4 ½", 11.9 cm
Colour:	Brown bird, wire legs; gloss or matte
Issued:	Spring 1982 - fall 1984

Model No.	U.S. $	Can. $	U.K. £
45	30.00	60.00	50.00

Robin Mama

Model No.:	B-662
Designer:	Will Climes
Height:	3 1/8", 7.9 cm
Colour:	Black back, rosy breast; gloss or matte
Issued:	Spring 1957, 1962, spring 1964 -1973, spring 1975, spring 1983 - spring 1986

Description	U.S. $	Can. $	U.K. £
1. Monrovia	40.00	80.00	70.00
2. San Dimas	30.00	60.00	50.00
3. San Marcos	30.00	60.00	50.00

SWAN

Swan

Model No.:	126
Designer:	Maureen Love
Height:	5 ¾", 14.6 cm
Colour:	White; gloss or matte
Issued:	Spring 1986

Model No.	U.S. $	Can. $	U.K. £
126	75.00	150.00	130.00

Little Red Hen (125)

CATS

INDEX TO
DESIGNER'S WORKSHOP CATS

Siamese kitten, playing, right paw up 'Khitti Kat' (B-530)
Re-issued 1957 to spring 1959 (matte) Original issue fall 1952 to fall 1954 (gloss)

PERSIAN CATS

Persian Cat 'Starlite'

Model No.:	B-683
Designer:	Martha Armstrong
Height:	6 ½", 16.5 cm
Colour:	White, black points; matte
Issued:	Spring 1958 - fall 1961, fall 1963 - fall 1975

Model No.	U.S. $	Can. $	U.K. £
B-683	40.00	80.00	70.00

Persian Cat, lying

Model No.:	B-676
Designer:	Tom Masterson
Size:	5" x 9 ¾", 12.7 x 24.7 cm
Colour:	White, green eyes, salmon nose; matte
Issued:	Fall 1957 - spring 1958

Model No.	U.S. $	Can. $	U.K. £
B-676	100.00	200.00	175.00

Persian Kitten 'Glitter'

Model No.:	B-685
Designer:	Martha Armstrong
Height:	3 ¼", 8.3 cm
Colour:	1. Marmalade; gloss or matte (San Marcos)
	2. White; gloss or matte
	3. White, black points; matte
Issued:	Spring 1958 - spring 1975, spring 1982 - spring 1984

Model No.	U.S. $	Can. $	U.K. £
B-685	30.00	60.00	50.00

Persian Kitten 'Sparkle'

Model No.:	B-684
Designer:	Martha Armstrong
Height:	2 ¼", 5.7 cm
Colour:	1. Marmalade; gloss or matte (San Marcos)
	2. White; gloss or matte
	3. White, black points; matte
Issued:	Spring 1958 - spring 1975, spring 1982 - spring 1984

Model No.	U.S. $	Can. $	U.K. £
B-684	30.00	60.00	50.00

'Madame Fluff'

Model No.:	B-580		
Designer:	Armae Conacher		
Height:	5", 12.7 cm		
Colour:	Tan; gloss		
Issued:	Fall 1954 - spring 1955		

Model No.	U.S. $	Can. $	U.K. £
B-580	100.00	200.00	175.00

'Puff'

Model No.:	B-588		
Designer:	Armae Conacher		
Height:	2 ½", 6.4 cm		
Colour:	Tan; gloss		
Issued:	Fall 1954 - spring 1955		

Model No.	U.S. $	Can. $	U.K. £
B-588	80.00	160.00	140.00

'Silver' (large)

Model No.:	B-661		
Designer:	Don Winton		
Height:	12 ¼", 31.1 cm		
Colour:	1. Black		
	2. White; gloss		
	3. White, brown points, green eyes; matte		
Issued:	Spring 1958, spring 1962 - fall 1963, spring 1981		

Colourways	U.S. $	Can. $	U.K. £
1. Black	100.00	200.00	175.00
2. White	60.00	120.00	105.00
3. White/brown	60.00	120.00	105.00

'Silver' (medium)

Model No.:	B-694		
Designer:	Don Winton		
Height:	9 ½", 24.0 cm		
Colour:	White, brown points, blue eyes; matte		
Issued:	Fall 1958 - spring 1968		

Colourways	U.S. $	Can. $	U.K. £
White/brown	50.00	100.00	85.00

Note: 'Silver' medium size not illustrated.

Persian Kitten, crouched, 'Moonbeam'

Model No.:	B-695
Designer:	Tom Masterson
Height:	3 7/8", 9.8 cm
Colour:	White, black points; matte
Issued:	Fall 1958 - fall 1968

Description	U.S. $	Can. $	U.K. £
1. Monrovia	30.00	60.00	50.00
2. San Dimas	30.00	60.00	50.00

PUSS IN BOOTS

Puss in Boots
First and Second Versions

Model No.:	82
Designer:	Helen Perrin Farnlund
Height:	6 ½", 16.5 cm
Colour:	1. Grey cat, pink cloak and hat, black boots, cream cane; matte
	2. Grey cat, pink cloak, green hat, blue boots, black cane; gloss
Issued:	Fall 1984 - spring 1986

Description	U.S. $	Can. $	U.K. £
1. First version, matte	100.00	200.00	175.00
2. Second version, gloss	100.00	200.00	175.00

Note: Earlier models had slip-coated lace. Later pieces had glued-coated lace. Other colourways exist. See also Puss in Boots (3236), Specialties section, page 461.

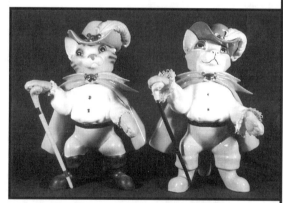

First Version (left), Second Version (right)

SIAMESE

Siamese Cat, climbing
First Version (smooth fur)

Model No.:	B-525
Designer:	Tom Masterson
Height:	6 ½", 16.5 cm
Colour:	Siamese; gloss or matte
Issued:	Fall 1952 - spring 1973, spring 1974, spring 1975

Description	U.S. $	Can. $	U.K. £
1. Monrovia	40.00	80.00	70.00
2. San Dimas	25.00	50.00	45.00

Siamese Cat, climbing
Second Version (textured fur)

Model No.:	21
Designer:	Freeman-McFarlin design
Height:	9 ½", 24.0 cm
Colour:	Siamese; gloss or matte
Issued:	Fall 1981 - spring 1983

Description	U.S. $	Can. $	U.K. £
Second version	30.00	60.00	50.00

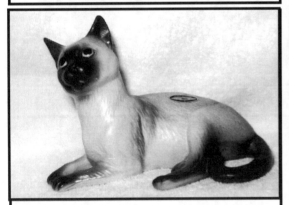

Siamese Cat, lying, 'Harry'

Model No.:	B-729
Designer:	Will Climes
Height:	4 5/6", 12.3 cm
Colour:	Siamese; matte
Issued:	1960

Model No.	U.S. $	Can. $	U.K. £
B-729	75.00	150.00	130.00

Note: This forms a set with 'Dick' (B-728), page 42, and 'Tom' (B-727), page 43.

Siamese Cat, seated, 'Dick'

Model No.:	B-728
Designer:	Will Climes
Height:	6 ½", 17.8 cm
Colour:	Siamese; matte
Issued:	1960

Model No.	U.S. $	Can. $	U.K. £
B-728	75.00	150.00	130.00

Note: This forms a set with 'Harry' (B-729), page 42 and 'Tom' (B-727), page 43.

Siamese Cat, seated, 'Kwei Li'

Model No.:	B-667
Designer:	Tom Masterson
Height:	8", 20.3 cm
Colour:	Siamese; gloss or matte
Issued:	Fall 1956 - 1957
	spring 1965 - fall 1972

Model No.	U.S. $	Can. $	U.K. £
B-667	40.00	80.00	70.00

Siamese Cat, seated, 'Quan Yen'

Model No.:	B-700
Designer:	Tom Masterson
Height:	5 ½", 14.0 cm
Colour:	Siamese; matte
Issued:	Spring 1959, fall 1965

Description	U.S. $	Can. $	U.K. £
1. Eyes closed	65.00	130.00	115.00
2. Eyes open	60.00	120.00	105.00

Note: This model was decorated with the eyes either open or closed.

Siamese Cat, seated, 'Sookie'

Model No.:	B-757
Designer:	Helen Perrin Farnlund
Height:	7", 17.8 cm
Colour:	Siamese; gloss and matte
Issued:	Fall 1961, spring 1965 - spring 1973,
	spring 1975

Model No.	U.S. $	Can. $	U.K. £
B-757	65.00	130.00	115.00

Siamese Cat, walking, 'Tom'

Model No.:	B-727
Designer:	Will Climes
Height:	5 ¾", 14.6 cm
Colour:	Siamese; matte
Issued:	1960

Model No.	U.S. $	Can. $	U.K. £
B-727	75.00	150.00	130.00

Note: This forms a set with 'Dick' (B-728) and 'Harry' (B-729); see page 42.

Siamese Formal Cats

Siamese Cat, seated, 'Choo San' (tall formal)

Model No.: B-646
Designer: Tom Masterson
Height: 10 ¾", 27.8 cm
Colour: Siamese; gloss
Issued: Fall 1956 - spring 1957,
spring 1965 - fall 1972,
fall 1974 - spring 1975

Model No.	U.S. $	Can. $	U.K. £
B-646	40.00	80.00	70.00

Siamese Cat, seated, 'Ching Li' (short formal)

Model No.: B-647
Designer: Tom Masterson
Height: 7 ", 17.8 cm
Colour: Siamese gloss
Issued: Fall 1956 - spring 1957,
spring 1965 - fall 1972

Description	U.S. $	Can. $	U.K. £
1 'Ching Li'	35.00	70.00	60.00
2. Base	20.00	40.00	35.00

Note: A black base, 1¾" x 4½" x 3¼", was issued from 1956 to 1957 for 'Ching Li'.

Climbing Kittens

These cats, designed by Maureen Love, were issued in either a gloss or matte Siamese colourway.

Kitten, right paw reaching, 'Chessie'

Model No.: B-753
Size: 4" x 3", 10.1 x 7.6 cm
Issued: Fall 1961, spring 1962,
spring 1965 - spring 1973

Model No.	U.S. $	Can. $	U.K. £
B-753	30.00	60.00	50.00

Kitten, tail out, 'Tink'

Model No.: B-752
Size: 4" x 2 7/8", 10.1 x 7.3 cm
Issued: Fall 1961, spring 1962,
spring 1965 - spring 1973

Model No.	U.S. $	Can. $	U.K. £
B-752	30.00	60.00	50.00

Siamese Kitten, hair pointed on chest, 'Quan Tiki'
Model No.:   B-660
Designer: Helen Perrin Farnlund
Height: 4", 10.1 cm
Colour: Siamese; gloss or matte
Issued: 1957, spring 1965 - spring 1973,
   spring 1975

Description	U.S. $	Can. $	U.K. £
1. Monrovia	30.00	60.00	50.00
2. San Dimas	30.00	60.00	50.00

Siamese Kitten, on hind legs, 'Pitti Pat'
Model No.:   B-528/83
Designer: Helen Perrin Farnlund
Height: 5", 12.7 cm
Colour: Siamese; gloss or matte
Issued: Fall 1952 - fall 1954,
   1957 - fall 1958, spring 1959
   spring 1984, fall 1985

Description	U.S. $	Can. $	U.K. £
1. Monrovia	40.00	80.00	70.00
2. San Marcos	30.00	60.00	50.00

Siamese Kitten, playing, 'Quan Yen'
Model No.:   B-657
Designer: Helen Perrin Farnlund
Size: 3 ¾" x 5", 9.5 x 12.7 cm
Colour: Siamese; gloss or matte
Issued: 1957, fall 1982 - spring 1986

Model No.	U.S. $	Can. $	U.K. £
B-657	40.00	80.00	70.00

Note: Model B-657 was also used to make tabby cat
'Sassy', page 48.

Siamese Kitten, standing, 'An How'
Model No.:   B-737
Designer: Helen Perrin Farnlund
Height: 3 ½", 8.9 cm
Colour: Siamese; gloss or matte
Issued: Fall 1960, spring 1965 - spring 1973,
   fall 1974 - spring 1975,
   spring 1981 - spring 1986

Description	U.S. $	Can. $	U.K. £
1. Monrovia	30.00	60.00	50.00
2. San Dimas	40.00	80.00	70.00
3. San Marcos	30.00	60.00	50.00

Note: Some kittens were decorated with crossed eyes.

Siamese 'Calypso Cats With Hats' and 'Daniel,' The Bongo Rat

Calypso Cat 'Tabbie'

Model No.:	B-664
Designer:	Will Climes
Height:	4 ¼", 10.8 cm
Colour:	Siamese, light blue eyes; gloss
Issued:	Fall 1957 - spring 1958, 1964

Description	U.S. $	Can. $	U.K. £
1. 1957/58	75.00	150.00	130.00
2. 1964	60.00	120.00	105.00

Bongo Rat 'Daniel'

Model No.:	B-678
Designer:	Will Climes
Height:	2 ¼", 5.7 cm
Colour:	Brown, white belly, pink inner ears; gloss
Issued:	Fall 1957

Model No.	U.S. $	Can. $	U.K. £
B-678		Rare	

Calypso Cat 'Tom' (Eyes closed)

Model No.:	B-663
Designer:	Will Climes
Height:	4 1/8", 10.5 cm
Colour:	Siamese; gloss
Issued:	Fall 1957 - spring 1958, 1964

Description	U.S. $	Can. $	U.K. £
1. 1957/58	75.00	150.00	130.00
2. 1964	60.00	120.00	105.00

Bongo

Model No.:	B-678A
Designer:	Will Climes
Height:	1", 2.5 cm
Colour:	1. Blue, white top; gloss
	2. Grey, white top; gloss
Issued:	Fall 1957

Colourways	U.S. $	Can. $	U.K. £
1. Blue/white		Rare	
2. Grey/white		Rare	

Hat

Model No.:	B-663A
Designer:	Will Climes
Height:	1", 2.5 cm
Colour:	Yellow straw hat with pink, yellow and blue flowers
Issued:	Fall 1957 - spring 1958

Model No.	U.S. $	Can. $	U.K. £
B-663A	20.00	40.00	35.00

Siamese Kitten, lying on back

Model No.: B-529
Designer: Helen Perrin Farnlund
Size: 3″ x 1 ½″, 7.6 x 3.8 cm
Colour: Siamese; gloss
Issued: Fall 1952 - spring 1954

Model No.	U.S. $	Can. $	U.K. £
B-529	50.00	100.00	85.00

Siamese Kitten, playing, right paw up, 'Khitti Kat'

Model No.: B-530
Designer: Helen Perrin Farnlund
Height: 2 ¼″, 5.7 cm
Colour: Siamese; gloss or matte
Issued: Fall 1952 - fall 1954, 1957, fall 1958 - spring 1959

Description	U.S. $	Can. $	U.K. £
1. Original (matte)	40.00	80.00	70.00
2. Re-issue (gloss)	40.00	80.00	70.00

Siamese Cat, 'tail watching'

Model No.: B-526
Designer: Tom Masterson
Height: 3″, 7.6 cm
Colour: Siamese; gloss
Issued: Fall 1952 - spring 1954

Model No.	U.S. $	Can. $	U.K. £
B-526	50.00	100.00	85.00

Note: Model B-530 was revised and re-issued with the head upright and the right paw held away from the cat's body.

TABBY CATS

Tabby Kitten, reaching, 'Sassy'

Model No.: B-657
Designer: Helen Perrin Farnlund
Height: 3 ¾", 8.3 cm
Colour: Brown tabby
Issued: 1965 - 1966

Model No.	U.S. $	Can. $	U.K. £
B-657	50.00	100.00	85.00

Note: Model B-657 was also used to make Siamese Kitten 'Quan Yen', page 45.

Tabby Kitten, seated, 'Sassy'

Model No.: B-719
Designer: Tom Masterson
Height: 3", 7.6 cm
Colour: Brown tabby
Issued: Fall 1959 - spring 1960

Model No.	U.S. $	Can. $	U.K. £
B-719	50.00	100.00	85.00

Tabby Kitten, seated, 'Sophie'

Model No.: B-718
Designer: Tom Masterson
Height: 3 ¾", 9.5 cm
Colour: Brown tabby; matte
Issued: Fall 1959 - spring 1960

Model No.	U.S. $	Can. $	U.K. £
B-718	65.00	130.00	115.00

MISCELLANEOUS CATS

Cat, walking, 'Tom'

Model No.:	B-631
Designer:	Maureen Love
Height:	5", 12.7 cm
Colour:	1. Grey; matte
	2. Orange tabby, green eyes; matte
Issued:	Spring 1956, fall 1967

Colourways	U.S. $	Can. $	U.K. £
1. Grey	75.00	150.00	130.00
2. Orange	75.00	150.00	130.00

Kitten, standing, 'Sugar'

Model No.:	B-634
Designer:	Maureen Love
Height:	2 ¼", 5.7 cm
Colour:	1. Light brown, dark brown stripes; gloss or matte
	2. Grey, blue eyes; matte
	3. Orange tabby, green eyes; matte
Issued:	1956, 1959, fall 1967

Colourways	U.S. $	Can. $	U.K. £
1. Brown 'Alley Cat'	40.00	80.00	70.00
2. Grey	40.00	80.00	70.00
3. Orange	40.00	80.00	70.00

Cat, tongue out, 'Tabbie'

Model No.:	B-632
Designer:	Maureen Love
Height:	5 ½", 14.0 cm
Colour:	1. Grey, blue eyes; matte
	2. Orange tabby, green eyes; matte
Issued:	Spring 1956

Colourways	U.S. $	Can. $	U.K. £
1. Grey	75.00	150.00	130.00
2. Orange	75.00	150.00	130.00

Kitten, climbing, 'Spice'

Model No.:	B-633
Designer:	Maureen Love
Height:	2 3/8", 6.0 cm
Colour:	Grey, blue eyes; matte
Issued:	1956, fall 1957

Model No.	U.S. $	Can. $	U.K. £
B-633	40.00	80.00	70.00

Note: The grey colourway was produced at Monrovia and the orange colourway at San Dimas. In 1959, model B-634, 'Sugar' was released as a pair with Tabby Cat, model B-699. Model B-632 has a distinctive 'squirrel tail.'

Cat, lying, 'San Su'

Model No.:	B-659
Designer:	Will Climes
Height:	5 ½", 14.0 cm
Colour:	1. Grey tabby
	2. Siamese
Issued:	Spring 1957, spring 1965 - fall 1966

Colourways	U.S. $	Can. $	U.K. £
1. Grey tabby	90.00	180.00	155.00
2. Siamese	90.00	180.00	155.00

Cat, lying

Model No.:	121
Designer:	Maureen Love
Height:	7", 17.8 cm
Colour:	1. Black and white; gloss or matte
	2. Grey; gloss or matte
Issued:	1985 - spring 1986

Colourways	U.S. $	Can. $	U.K. £
1. Black/white	40.00	80.00	70.00
2. Grey	40.00	80.00	70.00

Cat, seated, 'Ah Choo'

Model No.:	B-582
Designer:	Maureen Love
Height:	6", 15.0 cm
Colour:	See below
Issued:	Fall 1954 - fall 1956, 1958 - 1959, 1965, fall 1967, fall 1969

Colourways	U.S. $	Can. $	U.K. £
1. Abyssinian; gloss	75.00	150.00	130.00
2. Blue point; gloss/matte	60.00	120.00	105.00
3. Siamese; gloss/matte	50.00	100.00	85.00

Note: Model B-582 was revised so that the tail curved more towards the cat's body.

Cat, seated

Model No.:	B-699
Designer:	Unknown
Height:	4 ¾", 12.1 cm
Colour:	See below
Issued:	1959, fall 1982 - fall 1983

Colourways	U.S. $	Can. $	U.K. £
1. Calico; gloss/matte	40.00	80.00	70.00
2. Light and dark brown	50.00	100.00	85.00
3. Grey; gloss/matte	40.00	80.00	70.00
4. Marmalade; gloss	40.00	80.00	70.00

Cat, standing, 'Ching Wu'
Model No.:   B-585
Designer: Maureen Love
Height: 6 3/8", 16.2 cm
Colour: 1. Abyssinian; gloss
        2. Blue point; gloss or matte
        3. Siamese; gloss or matte
Issued: Fall 1954 - fall 1956, 1958, 1959, 1965,
        fall 1967, fall 1969

Description	U.S. $	Can. $	U.K. £
1. Abyssinian	75.00	150.00	130.00
2. Blue point	60.00	120.00	105.00
3. Siamese	50.00	100.00	85.00

Cat, walking, 'Yay Long'
Model No.:   B-736
Designer: Helen Perrin Farnlund
Height: 7", 17.8 cm
Colour: 1. Grey tabby; gloss
        2. Siamese
Issued: Fall 1960, spring 1965 - fall 1966

Model No.	U.S. $	Can. $	U.K. £
1. Grey tabby	75.00	150.00	130.00
2. Siamese	75.00	150.00	130.00

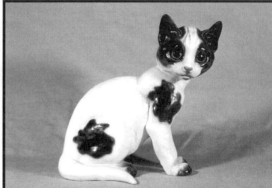

Kitten, arched back, 'Kwei Li'
Model No.:   B-587
Designer: Maureen Love
Height: 3 ¾", 9.5 cm
Colour: 1. Black; gloss or matte
        2. Siamese; gloss or matte
Issued: c.1950, fall 1967,
        fall 1982 - fall 1983

Colourways	U.S. $	Can. $	U.K. £
1. Black	30.00	60.00	50.00
2. Siamese	30.00	60.00	50.00

Note: This kitten was produced for 12 seasons.

Kitten, seated
Model No.:   B-748
Designer: Maureen Love
Height: 5 ¼", 13.3 cm
Colour: 1. Brown, rust shading; matte
        2. White, black spots; matte
Issued: Spring 1961, spring 1967

Colourways	U.S. $	Can. $	U.K. £
1. Brown/rust	50.00	100.00	85.00
2. White/black	50.00	100.00	85.00

Kitten, standing, 'Bing Bong'
Model No.:   B-586
Designer: Maureen Love
Height: 3 ½", 8.9 cm
Colour: See below
Issued: Fall 1954 - 1956, 1959, 1965,
               fall 1967, fall 1969, fall 1982 - 1983

Colourways	U.S. $	Can. $	U.K. £
1. Abysinnian (San Dimas)	50.00	100.00	85.00
2. Black (San Marcos)	65.00	130.00	115.00
3. Blue (San Dimas)	50.00	100.00	85.00
4. Siamese (All)	30.00	60.00	50.00

Note: Model B-586 is also known as 'Scaredy Cat'.

Kitten, walking, 'Fuzzy'
Model No.:   B-758
Designer: Helen Perrin Farnlund
Height: 3", 7.6 cm
Colour: 1. Calico; gloss
               2. Siamese; matte
Issued: Fall 1961, 1965, 1966

Description	U.S. $	Can. $	U.K. £
1. Calico	50.00	100.00	85.00
2. Siamese	40.00	80.00	70.00

Note: The calico kitten was released in 1966.

Loving Cats With Kitten

Loving Cats
Model No.:   132
Designer: Freeman-McFarlin design
Height: 10 ½", 26.7 cm
Colour: 1. Gold
               2. Siamese; gloss or matte
               3. White; gloss
Issued: Fall 1981 - spring 1986

Colourways	U.S. $	Can. $	U.K. £
1. Gold	50.00	100.00	85.00
2. Siamese	50.00	100.00	85.00
3. White	50.00	100.00	85.00

Kitten
Model No.:   133
Designer: Freeman-McFarlin design
Height: 4", 10.1 cm
Colour: 1. Gold
               2. Siamese; gloss or matte
               3. White; gloss
Issued: Fall 1981 - spring 1986

Colourways	U.S. $	Can. $	U.K. £
1. Gold	30.00	60.00	50.00
2. Siamese	30.00	60.00	50.00
3. White	30.00	60.00	50.00

Note: Freeman-McFarlin also produced Loving Cats (132);
see page 536.

Cat, on hind legs, 'Fuzzy'

Model No.:	B-713
Designer:	Tom Masterson
Height:	4 ¾", 12.1 cm
Colour:	1. Muted brown tabby
	2. Siamese
Issued:	Fall 1959

Colourways	U.S. $	Can. $	U.K. £
1. Tabby	50.00	100.00	85.00
2. Siamese		Rare	

Kitten, seated, 'Sookie'

Model No.:	B-715
Designer:	Tom Masterson
Height:	1 ½", 3.8 cm
Colour:	1. Muted brown tabby
	2. Siamese
Issued:	Fall 1959 - spring 1960

Colourways	U.S. $	Can. $	U.K. £
1. Tabby	30.00	60.00	50.00
2. Siamese	30.00	60.00	50.00

Cat, walking, 'Pom Pom'

Model No.:	B-714
Designer:	Tom Masterson
Height:	3", 7.6 cm
Colour:	1. Muted brown tabby
	2. Siamese
Issued:	Fall 1959 - spring 1960, spring 1965 - fall 1966

Colourways	U.S. $	Can. $	U.K. £
1. Tabby	50.00	100.00	85.00
2. Siamese	50.00	100.00	85.00

Kitten, walking, 'Tink'

Model No.:	B-716
Designer:	Tom Masterson
Height:	1 ½", 3.8 cm
Colour:	1. Muted brown tabby
	2. Siamese
Issued:	Fall 1959 - spring 1960

Colourways	U.S. $	Can. $	U.K. £
1. Tabby	30.00	60.00	50.00
2. Siamese	30.00	60.00	50.00

Kitten, paw up, 'Chessie'

Model No.:	B-717
Designer:	Tom Masterson
Height:	1 ¼", 3.1 cm
Colour:	1. Muted brown tabby
	2. Siamese
Issued:	Fall 1959 - spring 1960

Colourways	U.S. $	Can. $	U.K. £
1. Tabby	30.00	60.00	50.00
2. Siamese	30.00	60.00	50.00

Siamese cat, seated, 'Sookie' (B-757)

FARM ANIMALS AND CATTLE

INDEX TO DESIGNER'S WORKSHOP
FARM ANIMALS

INDEX TO DESIGNER'S WORKSHOP
FARM CATTLE

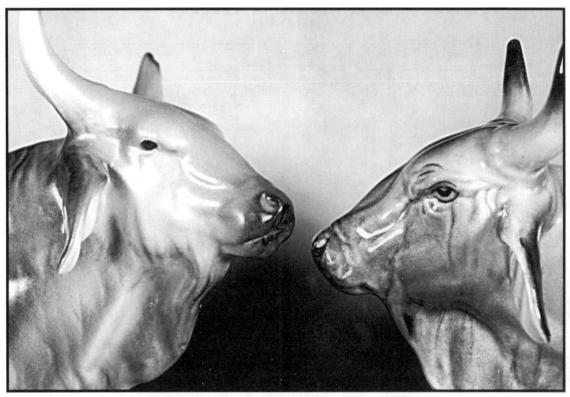

Brahma Bull 'Geronimo' ((B-579)
Variation in detail

GOATS

Doe 'Gretchen'

Model No.:	B-608
Designer:	Helen Perrin Farnlund
Height:	4 ½", 11.9 cm
Colour:	1. Brown, black and white; gloss
	2. White and black; matte
Issued:	Spring 1955, 1967
Varieties:	'Heidi's Goat'

Colourways	U.S. $	Can. $	U.K.£
1. Brown/black/white	75.00	150.00	130.00
2. White/black	75.00	150.00	130.00

Kid, scratching, 'Heidi'

Model No.:	B-603
Designer:	Helen Perrin Farnlund
Height:	2 ½", 6.4 cm
Colour:	Brown, black and white; gloss
Issued:	Spring 1955

Colourways	U.S. $	Can. $	U.K.£
Brown/black/white	85.00	170.00	150.00

Kid, standing, 'Peterli'

Model No.:	B-596
Designer:	Helen Perrin Farnlund
Height:	3", 7.6 cm
Colour:	1. Brown, black and white; gloss
	2. White and black; matte
Issued:	Spring 1955, 1967

Colourways	U.S. $	Can. $	U.K.£
1. Brown/black/white	75.00	150.00	130.00
2. White/black	75.00	150.00	130.00

'Heidi's Goat'

Model No.:	79
Designer:	Helen Perrin Farnlund
Height:	4 ½", 11.9 cm
Colour:	White, decorated with flowers; gloss or matte
Issued:	Fall 1984 - spring 1986
Varieties:	Doe 'Gretchen'

Model No.	U.S. $	Can. $	U.K.£
79	45.00	90.00	80.00

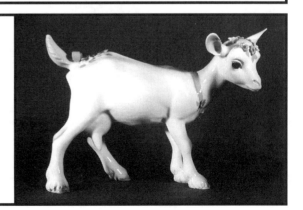

NUBIAN GOATS

Nubian Kid, standing

Model No.:	77
Designer:	Maureen Love
Height:	3", 7.6 cm
Colour:	Brown; gloss or matte
Issued:	Fall 1984 - spring 1986

Model No.	U.S. $	Can. $	U.K.£
77	20.00	40.00	35.00

Nubian Kid, walking

Model No.:	78
Designer:	Maureen Love
Height:	3", 7.6 cm
Colour:	Brown; gloss or matte
Issued:	Fall 1984 - spring 1986

Model No.	U.S. $	Can. $	U.K.£
78	20.00	40.00	35.00

Nubian Doe

Model No.:	76
Designer:	Maureen Love
Height:	5", 12.7 cm
Colour:	Brown; gloss or matte
Issued:	Fall 1984 - spring 1986

Model No.	U.S. $	Can. $	U.K.£
76	50.00	100.00	85.00

PIGS

Pig Family — 1970

Piglet, standing
Style One

Model No.:	B-510
Designer:	Tom Masterson
Height:	1 ¾", 3.1 cm
Colour:	Pink
Issued:	Fall 1970

Model No.	U.S. $	Can. $	U.K.£
B-510		Rare	

Piglet, seated
Style One

Model No.:	B-511
Designer:	Tom Masterson
Height:	2 ¾", 7.0 cm
Colour:	Pink
Issued:	Fall 1970

Model No.	U.S. $	Can. $	U.K.£
B-511	Possibly not put into production		

Pig Mama

Model No.:	B-512
Designer:	Tom Masterson
Height:	3 ¼", 8.3 cm
Colour:	Pink
Issued:	Fall 1970

Model No.	U.S. $	Can. $	U.K.£
B-512		Rare	

Note: Model B-511 is believed to have been used by Walker-Renaker.
For information on miniature pig illustrated on extreme left (model A-166(a)), see miniature farm animals, page 257.

Pig Family — 1984 - 1986

Piglet, standing
Style Two

Model No.: 57
Designer: Maureen Love
Height: 1 ¾", 4.4 cm
Colour: Pink and white; gloss or matte
Issued: Spring 1984 - spring 1986

Model No.	U.S. $	Can. $	U.K.£
57	20.00	40.00	35.00

Piglet, seated
Style Two

Model No.: 56
Designer: Maureen Love
Height: 1 ¾", 4.4 cm
Colour: Pink and white; gloss or matte
Issued: Spring 1984 - spring 1986

Model No.	U.S. $	Can. $	U.K.£
56	20.00	40.00	35.00

Sow

Model No.: 55
Designer: Maureen Love
Size: 3" x 7", 7.6 x 17.8 cm
Colour: Pink and white; gloss or matte
Issued: Spring 1984 - spring 1986

Model No.	U.S. $	Can. $	U.K.£
55	40.00	80.00	70.00

SHEEP

Bighorn Sheep on Base

Model No.:	B-726
Designer:	Tom Masterson
Height:	7 ¼", 18.4 cm
Colour:	See below
Issued:	Spring 1960 - spring 1961, spring 1966 - spring 1968, fall 1971 - fall 1972, fall 1981

Colourways	U.S. $	Can. $	U.K.£
1. Gold	175.00	350.00	300.00
2. Tan	175.00	350.00	300.00
3. White	175.00	350.00	300.00

Note: The gold colourway was available in 1981.

Tan colourway (left) White colourway (right)

Ewe 'Lady Jane'

Model No.:	B-591
Designer:	Maureen Love
Height:	4", 10.1 cm
Colour:	White with black face; gloss or matte
Issued:	Spring 1955 - spring 1956, 1967, Spring 1983 - spring 1986

Description	U.S. $	Can. $	U.K.£
1. Monrovia	75.00	150.00	130.00
2. San Dimas	75.00	150.00	130.00
3. San Marcos	50.00	100.00	85.00

Lamb 'Son John'

Model No.:	B-592
Designer:	Maureen Love
Height:	2 ¾", 7.0 cm
Colour:	White with black face; gloss or matte
Issued:	Spring 1955 - spring 1956, 1967, spring 1983 - spring 1986

Description	U.S. $	Can. $	U.K.£
1. Monrovia	60.00	120.00	105.00
2. San Dimas	60.00	120.00	105.00
3. San Marcos	30.00	60.00	50.00

Note: Early versions of B-591 have a moulded bell. The San Marcos version has a ceramic gold bell attached by a wire.

BRAHMA CATTLE

Brahma Bull 'Geronimo'
Model No.:   B-579
Designer: Maureen Love
Height: 6", 15.0 cm
Colour: Grey; gloss or matte
Issued: 1. Fall 1954 - fall 1956 — Monrovia
               2. Fall 1981 — San Marcos

Description	U.S. $	Can. $	U.K. £
1. Monrovia	100.00	200.00	175.00
2. San Marcos	100.00	200.00	175.00

HEREFORD CATTLE

These cattle, in a brown and white colourway, were designed by Maureen Love.

Hereford Calf, standing, 'Dandy'
Model No.:   B-589
Height: 3", 7.6 cm
Issued: Fall 1954 - fall 1956, fall 1966 - spring 1967

Description	U.S. $	Can. $	U.K. £
1. Monrovia	60.00	120.00	105.00
2. San Dimas	50.00	100.00	85.00

Hereford Calf, lying, 'Candy'
Model No.:   B-590
Height: 2", 5.1 cm
Issued: Fall 1954 - fall 1956

Description	U.S. $	Can. $	U.K. £
1. Monrovia	60.00	120.00	105.00
2. San Dimas	50.00	100.00	85.00

Hereford Bull 'Domino'
Model No.:   B-581
Height: 5 ¼", 13.3 cm
Issued: Fall 1954 - fall 1956, spring 1962,
               fall 1966 - spring 1967

Description	U.S. $	Can. $	U.K. £
1. Monrovia	125.00	250.00	220.00
2. San Dimas	100.00	200.00	175.00

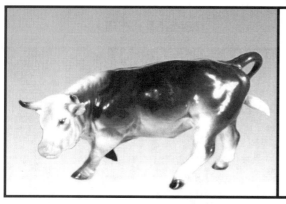

Hereford Cutting Steer

Model No.:	B-690/24
Designer:	Maureen Love
Height:	3 ½", 8.9 cm
Colour:	Brown and white; gloss or matte
Issued:	Fall 1958 - spring 1966, fall 1981 - spring 1986

Description	U.S. $	Can. $	U.K. £
1. Monrovia	75.00	150.00	130.00
2. San Dimas	50.00	100.00	90.00

Note: This model forms a pair with 'Cutter' page 83.

HOLSTEIN CATTLE

Holstein Cow

Model No.:	53
Designer:	Maureen Love
Height:	5", 12.7 cm
Colour:	Black and white; gloss or matte
Issued:	Fall 1983 - spring 1986

Model No.	U.S. $	Can. $	U.K. £
53	75.00	150.00	130.00

Holstein Calf

Model No.:	54
Designer:	Maureen Love
Height:	3 ¼", 8.3 cm
Colour:	Black and white; gloss or matte
Issued:	Fall 1983 - spring 1986

Model No.	U.S. $	Can. $	U.K. £
54	40.00	80.00	70.00

HOLY COW

Holy Cow
Model No.: 124
Designer: Maureen Love
Height: 7", 17.8 cm
Colour: Light brown; gloss or matte
Issued: Fall 1985 - spring 1986
Varieties: Jersey Cow

Model No.	U.S. $	Can. $	U.K. £
124	125.00	250.00	220.00

Note: This is the Jersey cow (95) with a bonnet and halo added.

Jersey Cow
Model No.: 95
Designer: Maureen Love
Height: 5", 12.7 cm
Colour: Light brown; gloss or matte
Issued: Spring 1985 - spring 1986
Varieties: Holy Cow

Model No.	U.S. $	Can. $	U.K. £
95	100.00	200.00	175.00

JERSEY CATTLE

Jersey Calf
Model No.: 96
Designer: Maureen Love
Height: 4", 10.1 cm
Colour: Light brown; gloss or matte
Issued: Spring 1985 - spring 1986

Model No.	U.S. $	Can. $	U.K. £
96	40.00	80.00	70.00

LONGHORN

Longhorn
Model No.: B-740
Designer: Maureen Love
Height: 5 ¾", 14.6 cm
Colour: Light brown, dark brown shading
Issued: Spring 1961 - fall 1962, fall 1981

Model No.	U.S. $	Can. $	U.K. £
B-740	150.00	300.00	260.00

HORSES

INDEX TO
DESIGNER'S WORKSHOP HORSES

AMERICAN SADDLE BRED HORSES

American Saddle Bred
'Honora', large
Model No.: B-679
Designer: Maureen Love
Height: 8", 20.3 cm
Colour: 1. Brown
2. White
Issued: Spring 1958 - fall 1961

Colourways	U.S. $	Can. $	U.K.£
1. Brown	400.00	800.00	700.00
2. White	400.00	800.00	700.00

American Saddle Bred
'Honora', small
Model No.: B-759
Designer: Maureen Love
Height: 6 ¾", 17.2 cm
Colour: See below
Issued: 1962, 1964 - spring 1967, 1968, 1969, spring 1982 - fall 1983, 1984

Colourways	U.S. $	Can. $	U.K.£
1. Bay; gloss/matte	125.00	250.00	220.00
2. Brown	150.00	300.00	260.00
3. Palomino; gloss/matte	175.00	350.00	300.00
4. White	150.00	300.00	260.00

Note: The ribbon colours were blue, lime, purple or white. A special edition of one hundred palomino matte and one hundred gloss were issued in 1984 for the Black Horse Ranch.

APPALOOSAS

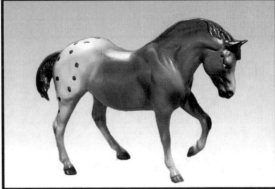

Appaloosa 'Jamboree'

Model No.:	Unknown
Designer:	Maureen Love
Height:	5", 12.7 cm
Colour:	1. Bay; gloss
	2. Grey; gloss
	3. Tan; gloss
Issued:	August 1993 - February 1994
	in a limited edition of 262

Colourways	U.S. $	Can. $	U.K.£
1. Bay	125.00	250.00	220.00
2. Grey	125.00	250.00	220.00
3. Tan	125.00	250.00	220.00

Note: This was the first limited-edition horse issued by Hagen-Renaker. The mould was originally released as a Maureen Love original.

Appaloosa 'Love'

Model No.:	B-749
Designer:	Maureen Love
Height:	4 ¾", 12.1 cm
Colour:	Chestnut; matte
Issued:	Fall 1961 - fall 1962,
	spring 1964 - spring 1968

Model No.	U.S. $	Can. $	U.K.£
B-749	400.00	800.00	700.00

Note: Early models had indentations for the decorators to paint as spots; later models did not.

ARABIANS

Arabian Family
Style One — 9"

These Arabian horses, designed by Maureen Love, were released from Monrovia in grey or white matte; from San Dimas in brown, and from San Marcos in grey, palomino or white, gloss or matte.

Arabian Stallion 'Amir'

Model No.:	B-656/38
Height:	9", 22.9 cm
Issued:	1957, 1962, spring 1968,
	fall 1981 - fall 1984

Colourways	U.S. $	Can. $	U.K.£
1. Monrovia	400.00	800.00	700.00
2. San Dimas		Rare	
3. San Marcos	200.00	400.00	350.00

Arabian Mare 'Zara'

Model No.:	B-655
Height:	9", 22.9 cm
Issued:	1957, 1962, spring 1968,
	spring 1981 - fall 1984

Colourways	U.S. $	Can. $	U.K.£
1. Monrovia	400.00	800.00	700.00
2. San Dimas		Rare	
3. San Marcos	200.00	400.00	350.00

Arabian Foal 'Zilla'

Model No.:	B-645
Height:	7", 17.8 cm
Issued:	1957, 1962, spring 1968,
	spring 1981 - fall 1984

Colourways	U.S. $	Can. $	U.K.£
1. Monrovia	200.00	400.00	350.00
2. San Dimas		Rare	
3. San Marcos	100.00	200.00	175.00

'Amir' produced at San Dimas in a very 'light doeskin' grey;
'Zilla' produced at San Dimas in a 'dark doeskin' grey;
'Zara' produced at Monrovia in a 'rose-grey' grey

Arabian Family
Style Two — 6"

Arabian Stallion 'Amir'

Model No.:	B-707
Designer:	Maureen Love
Height:	6", 15.0 cm
Colour:	1. Grey; matte
	2. White; matte
Issued:	Fall 1959 - spring 1973, spring 1975

Description	U.S. $	Can. $	U.K.£
1. Monrovia	175.00	350.00	300.00
2. San Dimas	125.00	250.00	210.00

Arabian Mare 'Zara'

Model No.:	B-708
Designer:	Maureen Love
Height:	6½", 16.5 cm
Colour:	1. Grey; matte
	2. White; matte
Issued:	Fall 1959 - spring 1973, spring 1975

Description	U.S. $	Can. $	U.K.£
1. Monrovia	175.00	350.00	300.00
2. San Dimas	125.00	125.00	210.00

Arabian Foal 'Zilla'

Model No.:	B-709
Designer:	Maureen Love
Height:	5", 12.7 cm
Colour:	1. Grey; matte
	2. White; matte
Issued:	Fall 1959 - spring 1973, spring 1975

Description	U.S. $	Can. $	U.K.£
1. Monrovia	100.00	200.00	175.00
2. San Dimas	80.00	160.00	135.00

Arabian, head turned, 'Abu-Farwa'

Model No.:	B-621
Designer:	Maureen Love
Height:	6", 15.0 cm
Colour:	1. White with detailed eyes and nostrils
	2. White, grey shading, dot eyes
Issued:	Fall 1955 - spring 1957

Description	U.S. $	Can. $	U.K.£
1. Detailed eyes	600.00	1,200.00	1,000.00
2. Dot eyes	400.00	800.00	700.00

Arabian, rearing, 'Fez'
First Version

Model No.:	B-612
Designer:	Maureen Love
Height:	8 ½", 21.6 cm
Colour:	1. Chestnut; matte
	2. White; matte
Issued:	Fall 1955 - spring 1957

Colourways	U.S. $	Can. $	U.K.£
1. Chestnut	400.00	800.00	700.00
2. White	400.00	800.00	700.00

Arabian, rearing, 'Fez'
Second Version

Model No.:	B-648
Designer:	Maureen Love
Height:	7 ¾", 19.7 cm
Colour:	White
Issued:	1968

Description	U.S. $	Can. $	U.K.£
Second version	400.00	800.00	700.00

Arabian, standing, 'Abdullah'
First Version

Model No.:	B-635
Designer:	Maureen Love
Height:	6 ¼", 15.9 cm
Colour:	White; matte
Issued:	Spring 1956 - spring 1957

Model No.	U.S. $	Can. $	U.K.£
B-649	400.00	800.00	700.00

Note: Model B-635 was revised to make model B-649. Model illustrated is a test colourway.

Arabian, standing, 'Abdullah'
Second Version

Model No.:	B-649
Designer:	Maureen Love
Height:	6", 15.0 cm
Colour:	1. Chestnut; white mane and tail; matte
	2. White
Issued:	1968 - spring 1969

Colourways	U.S. $	Can. $	U.K.£
1. Chestnut	400.00	800.00	700.00
2. White	400.00	800.00	700.00

Note: Model B-649 is a revision of model B-635.

Arabian, standing, 'Encore'

Model No.:	Unknown
Designer:	Maureen Love
Height:	5 ½", 14.0 cm
Colour:	See below; gloss
Issued:	May to November 1994 in a limited edition of 418

Colourways	U.S. $	Can. $	U.K.£
1. Bay	200.00	400.00	350.00
2. Chestnut	200.00	400.00	350.00
3. Dapple-grey	225.00	450.00	390.00
4. White	200.00	400.00	350.00

Arabian, standing, 'Nataf'

Model No.:	11
Designer:	Maureen Love
Height:	12", 30.5 cm
Colour:	White; gloss or matte
Issued:	Spring 1981 - spring 1986

Description	U.S. $	Can. $	U.K.£
1. Gloss	300.00	600.00	525.00
2. Matte	300.00	600.00	525.00

Arabian, turning

Model No.:	B-650
Designer:	Maureen Love
Height:	6", 15.0 cm
Colour:	1. Chestnut; matte
	2. White; matte
Issued:	1968 - spring 1969

Colourways	U.S. $	Can. $	U.K.£
1. Chestnut	400.00	800.00	700.00
2. White	400.00	800.00	700.00

Arabian Foal, lying, 'Fez'

Model No.:	B-710
Designer:	Maureen Love
Height:	2 ¾", 7.0 cm
Colour:	1. Grey
	2. White
Issued:	Fall 1959 - spring 1968, 1970, 1971

Model No.	U.S. $	Can. $	U.K.£
B-710	150.00	300.00	260.00

Arabian Foal, standing, 'Sherif'

Model No.:	B-658
Designer:	Maureen Love
Height:	4 ½", 11.9 cm
Colour:	1. Grey; matte (Monrovia)
	2. White; matte (San Dimas)
Issued:	Spring 1957 - spring 1959,
	1966 - spring 1967

Description	U.S. $	Can. $	U.K.£
1. Monrovia	250.00	500.00	435.00
2. San Dimas	150.00	300.00	260.00

Arabian Mare 'Sheba'

Model No.:	B-698
Designer:	Maureen Love
Height:	7", 17.8 cm
Colour:	1. Grey (steel grey, doe skin);
	matte (Monrovia)
	2. White; matte (San Dimas)
Issued:	Fall 1958 - spring 1959,
	spring 1965 - spring 1967, 1970

Description	U.S. $	Can. $	U.K.£
1. Monrovia	400.00	800.00	700.00
2. San Dimas	300.00	600.00	525.00

Arabian Stallion 'Ferseyn'

Model No.:	B-697
Designer:	Maureen Love
Height:	7 ¾", 19.7 cm
Colour:	1. Grey (steel grey, doe skin);
	matte; (San Dimas)
	2. White; matte (Monrovia)
Issued:	Fall 1958 - spring 1959,
	spring 1965 - spring 1967, 1970

Description	U.S. $	Can. $	U.K.£
1. Monrovia	300.00	600.00	525.00
2. San Dimas	400.00	800.00	700.00

BELGIAN

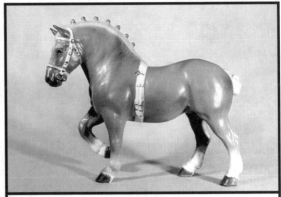

Bedouin

Model No.:	B-642
Designer:	Maureen Love
Height:	9 ½", 24.0 cm
Colour:	Grey horse; rider wears yellow shirt, light green pants, white robe; matte
Issued:	Fall 1956 - spring 1958

Model No.	U.S. $	Can. $	U.K.£
B-642	1,000.00	2,000.00	1,750.00

Note: The tassels and gun were separately added pieces.

Belgian Mare 'Sespe Violette'

Model No.:	B-567
Designer:	Maureen Love
Height:	6", 15.0 cm
Colour:	1. Chestnut; matte
	2. Palomino; gloss
Issued:	1954, 1955, fall 1967 - spring 1968

Colourways	U.S. $	Can. $	U.K.£
1. Chestnut	900.00	1,750.00	1,500.00
2. Palomino	900.00	1,750.00	1,500.00

CLYDESDALE

HACKNEY

Clydesdale

Model No.:	50
Designer:	Maureen Love
Height:	7 ½", 19.1 cm
Colour:	Bay; gloss or matte
Issued:	Spring 1983 - spring 1986

Description	U.S. $	Can. $	U.K.£
1. Gloss	300.00	600.00	525.00
2. Matte	300.00	600.00	525.00

Note: This model was based on Bennie, a Clydesdale horse in San Marcos.

Hackney Pony 'Brookside Stella'

Model No.:	B-644
Designer:	Maureen Love
Height:	5 ½", 14.0 cm
Colour:	1. Bay horse on wooden plinth; gloss
	2. Bay horse on ceramic plinth; matte
Issued:	Fall 1956 - spring 1958,
	fall 1983 - spring 1985

Desription	U.S. $	Can. $	U.K.£
1. Bay/wooden	500.00	1,000.00	875.00
2. Bay/ceramic	300.00	600.00	525.00

LIPIZZANER

Lipizzaner

Model No.:	B-653
Designer:	Maureen Love
Height:	6 ½", 16.5 cm
Colour:	See below
Issued:	Spring 1957 - spring 1958, fall 1963 - spring 1968, fall 1983 - fall 1984

Colourways	U.S. $	Can. $	U.K.£
1. Bay	400.00	800.00	700.00
2. White (Monrovia)	300.00	600.00	525.00
3. White; gloss or matte	150.00	300.00	260.00

Note: Monrovia models had wooden or ceramic bases and San Marcos models, ceramic only.

MORGAN HORSES

Morgan Foal, bucking, 'Peggy Lou'

Model No.:	B-702
Designer:	Maureen Love
Height:	4", 10.1 cm
Colour:	1. Chestnut; matte
	2. Palomino; matte
Issued:	1959

Colourways	U.S. $	Can. $	U.K.£
1. Chestnut	400.00	800.00	700.00
2. Palomino	400.00	800.00	700.00

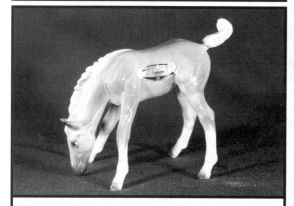

Morgan Foal, grazing, 'Scamper'

Model No.:	B-562
Designer:	Maureen Love
Height:	3", 7.6 cm
Colour:	See below
Issued:	Spring 1954 - fall 1958

Colourways	U.S. $	Can. $	U.K.£
1. Brown; gloss or matte	150.00	300.00	260.00
2. Palomino; gloss or matte	150.00	300.00	260.00
3. White; matte	150.00	300.00	260.00

Note: The white matte colourway was produced in 1958.

Morgan Foal, lying, 'Clover'

Model No.:	B-561
Designer:	Maureen Love
Height:	2 ½", 6.4 cm
Colour:	See below
Issued:	Spring 1954 - fall 1958

Colourways	U.S. $	Can. $	U.K.£
1. Brown; gloss or matte	150.00	300.00	500.00
2. Palomino; gloss or matte	150.00	300.00	500.00
3. White; matte	150.00	300.00	500.00

Note: The white matte colourway was produced in 1958.

Morgan Foal, lying, 'Miss Pepper'

Model No.:	B-701
Designer:	Maureen Love
Height:	2 ¾", 7.0 cm
Colour:	1. Chestnut; matte
	2. Palomino; matte
Issued:	Spring 1959 - fall 1971

Colourways	U.S. $	Can. $	U.K.£
1. Chestnut	100.00	200.00	175.00
2. Palomino	100.00	200.00	175.00

Note: Model B-701 was later re-modelled as a Unicorn, see page 91.

Morgan Horse 'Tria'

Model No.:	Unknown
Designer:	Maureen Love
Height:	4", 10.1 cm
Colour:	See below
Issued:	October 1995 to March 1996 in a limited edition of 200. Third in the series.

Colourways	U.S. $	Can. $	U.K.£
1. Bay; gloss	125.00	250.00	220.00
2. Palomino; gloss	125.00	250.00	220.00

Note: These models are signed, dated and numbered on the base.

Morgan Mare 'Heather'

Model No.:	B-548
Designer:	Maureen Love
Height:	5", 12.7 cm
Colour:	See below
Issued:	1954 - 1957

Colourways	U.S. $	Can. $	U.K.£
1. Brown; gloss or matte	400.00	800.00	700.00
2. Palomino; gloss or matte	400.00	800.00	700.00
3. White; matte	400.00	800.00	700.00

Note: The white matte colourway was produced in 1958.

Morgan Stallion 'Lippet'

Model No.:	B-704
Designer:	Maureen Love
Height:	6 ¼", 15.9 cm
Colour:	See below
Issued:	Spring 1959 - spring 1974, fall 1983 - spring 1986

Colourways	U.S. $	Can. $	U.K.£
1. Chestnut (Monrovia)	150.00	300.00	260.00
2. Chestnut (San Dimas)	110.00	220.00	185.00
3. Dark bay (San Marcos)	100.00	200.00	175.00
4. Palomino (Monrovia)	175.00	350.00	300.00
5. Palomino (San Dimas)	125.00	250.00	220.00

<table>
<tr><td colspan="4">Morgan Stallion 'Thunder'
Model No.: B-549
Designer: Maureen Love
Height: 5 ½", 14.0 cm
Colour: See below
Issued: Spring 1954 - fall 1958</td></tr>
</table>

Colourways	U.S. $	Can. $	U.K.£
1. Brown; gloss or matte	300.00	600.00	525.00
2. Palomino; gloss or matte	300.00	600.00	525.00
3. White; matte	300.00	600.00	525.00

Note: The white colourway was produced in 1958.

Morgan Mare and Foal

Morgan Foal 'Roughneck'
Model No.: B-550
Designer: Maureen Love
Height: 4 ½", 11.9 cm
Colour: See below
Issued: Spring 1954 - fall 1974, fall 1983 - spring 1986

Colourways	U.S. $	Can. $	U.K.£
1. Brown; gloss or matte	95.00	190.00	160.00
2. Chestnut; matte	50.00	100.00	85.00
3. Dark bay; gloss or matte	50.00	100.00	85.00
4. Palomino; gloss or matte	95.00	190.00	160.00
5. Palomino; matte (SD)	50.00	100.00	85.00
6. White; matte (1958)	95.00	190.00	160.00

Morgan Mare 'Forever Amber'
Model No.: B-703
Designer: Maureen Love
Height: 5", 12.7 cm
Colour: See below
Issued: Spring 1959 - spring 1974, fall 1983 - spring 1986

Colourways	U.S. $	Can. $	U.K.£
1. Chestnut; matte	110.00	225.00	185.00
2. Dark bay; gloss or matte	100.00	200.00	175.00
3. Palomino; matte	110.00	225.00	185.00

MUSTANGS

Mustang Foal, standing, 'Butch'

Model No.: B-732
Designer: Maureen Love
Height: 4 ½", 11.9 cm
Colour: See below
Issued: Fall 1960 - fall 1961,
spring 1964 - spring 1965,
spring 1968, 1969, spring 1970

Colourways	U.S. $	Can. $	U.K.£
1. Bay	175.00	350.00	300.00
2. Buckskin	175.00	350.00	300.00
3. Red-brown pinto	175.00	350.00	300.00
4. Tan	175.00	350.00	300.00

Mustang Mare 'Daisy'

Model No.: B-731
Designer: Maureen Love
Height: 5 ½", 14.0 cm
Colour: See below
Issued: Fall 1960 - fall 1961, spring 1964 -
spring 1965, spring 1968 - spring 1970

Colourways	U.S. $	Can. $	U.K.£
1. Bay	300.00	600.00	525.00
2. Buckskin	300.00	600.00	525.00
3. Red-brown pinto	300.00	600.00	525.00
4. Tan	300.00	600.00	525.00
5. White		Very rare	

Mustang Stallion 'Comanche'

Model No.: B-730
Designer: Maureen Love
Height: 6 ¼", 15.9 cm
Colour: See below
Issued: Fall 1960 - fall 1961, spring 1964 -
spring 1965, spring 1968 - spring 1970

Colourways	U.S. $	Can. $	U.K.£
1. Buckskin; matte	400.00	800.00	700.00
2. Dark brown; matte	300.00	600.00	525.00
3. Red-brown; matte	300.00	600.00	525.00

Mustang, head up, 'Don Cortez'

Model No.: B-673/39
Designer: Maureen Love
Height: 6 ½", 16.5 cm
Colour: For colourways see 'King Cortez' (p. 79)
Issued: Fall 1957 - spring 1959, spring 1968,
spring 1982 - fall 1984

Description	U.S. $	Can. $	U.K.£
1. Monrovia	250.00	500.00	425.00
2. San Marcos	175.00	350.00	300.00

Mustang, rearing, 'King Cortez'
Model No.: B-672/41
Designer: Maureen Love
Height: 8", 20.3 cm
Colour: Monrovia:
   1. Black; matte
   2. Palomino; matte
   3. White; matte
   San Marcos:
   1. Black; gloss or matte
   2. Chestnut; gloss or matte
   3. Grey; gloss or matte
   4. White; gloss or matte
Issued: Fall 1957 - fall 1967,
   spring 1982 - fall 1984

Desription	U.S. $	Can. $	U.K.£
1. Monrovia	250.00	500.00	425.00
2. San Marcos	175.00	350.00	295.00

Mustang, turning, 'Sun Cortez'
Model No.: B-674/40
Designer: Maureen Love
Height: 6", 15.0 cm
Colour: For colourways see 'King Cortez' above
Issued: Fall 1957 - spring 1959, spring 1968

Desription	U.S. $	Can. $	U.K.£
1. Monrovia	250.00	500.00	435.00
2. San Marcos	150.00	300.00	260.00

PERCHERON

Percheron 'Crusader'
Model No.: B-706
Designer: Maureen Love
Height: 6 ¼", 15.9 cm
Colour: White; matte
Issued: Spring 1959 - spring 1960,
   spring 1966 - spring 1967

Model No.	U.S. $	Can. $	U.K.£
B-706	800.00	1,600.00	1,400.00

Note: Model illustrated was decorated in dapple grey by Maureen Love.

QUARTER HORSES

Quarter Horse Foal 'Shamrock'

Model No.:	B-756
Designer:	Maureen Love
Height:	5", 12.7 cm
Colour:	1. Bay; gloss or matte
	2. Buckskin; matte
Issued:	Fall 1961 - spring 1972,
	fall 1983 - spring 1986

Colourways	U.S. $	Can. $	U.K.£
1. Bay	75.00	150.00	130.00
2. Buckskin	125.00	250.00	220.00

Note: See also Quarter Horse Family, page 82, for the palomino colourway.

Quarter Horse Mare 'Erin'

Model No.:	B-755
Designer:	Maureen Love
Height:	6", 15.0 cm
Colour:	1. Bay; gloss or matte
	2. Buckskin; matte
Issued:	Fall 1961 - spring 1963
	fall 1983 - spring 1986

Colourways	U.S. $	Can. $	U.K.£
1. Bay	125.00	250.00	210.00
2. Buckskin	200.00	400.00	350.00

Note: See also Quarter Horse Family, page 82, for the palomino colourway.

Quarter Horse Mare

Model No.:	75
Designer:	Maureen Love
Height:	8", 20.3 cm
Colour:	See below
Issued:	Fall 1984 - spring 1986

Colourways	U.S. $	Can. $	U.K.£
1. Appaloosa; matte	250.00	500.00	435.00
2. Bay; gloss or matte	175.00	350.00	300.00
3. Chestnut; gloss or matte	175.00	350.00	300.00
4. Grey; gloss or matte	175.00	350.00	300.00

Note: Only one colour was offered at a time between 1984 and 1986. The Appaloosa colourway was issued in 1985 in a limited edition of 100 and numbered in gold on the belly. Several unnumbered pieces have been seen. The mare was sculptured after 'Coco Silk,' a quarter horse in San Marcos.

Quarter Horse Stallion 'Topper'

Model No.:   B-575
Designer: Maureen Love
Height: 5 ¾", 14.6 cm
Colour: Palomino; gloss
Issued: Fall 1954 - spring 1957

Model No.	U.S. $	Can. $	U.K.£
B-575	300.00	600.00	525.00

Quarter Horse Stallion 'Two Bits'

Model No.:   B-712
Designer: Maureen Love
Height: 5 ¾", 14.6 cm
Colour: 1. Bay; gloss or matte
               2. Buckskin; matte
Issued: Fall 1959 - fall 1962,
               fall 1963 - spring 1972,
               fall 1983 - spring 1986

Colourways	U.S. $	Can. $	U.K.£
1. Bay	125.00	250.00	210.00
2. Buckskin	200.00	400.00	350.00

Note: See also Quarter Horse Family, page 82.

Quarter Horse 'Maverick'

Model No.:   B-688
Designer: Maureen Love
Height: 6", 15.0 cm
Colour: Buckskin; matte
Issued: 1958 - spring 1959,
               1967 - spring 1968

Model No.	U.S. $	Can. $	U.K.£
B-688	500.00	1,000.00	875.00

Quarter Horse 'Metalchex'

Model No.:   25
Designer: Maureen Love
Height: 11 ¾", 29.8 cm
Colour: 1. Buckskin; gloss or matte
               2. Chestnut; gloss or matte
Issued: Fall 1981 - spring 1986

Colourways	U.S. $	Can. $	U.K.£
1. Buckskin	300.00	600.00	525.00
2. Chestnut	300.00	600.00	525.00

Quarter Horse Family (Palomino)

Quarter Horse Mare

Model No.:	B-755
Designer:	Maureen Love
Height:	6", 15.0 cm
Colour:	Palomino; gloss or matte
Issued:	November 1985 in a limited edition of 25
Varieties:	Also called Quarter Horse Mare 'Erin'

Model No.	U.S. $	Can. $	U.K.£
B-775	150.00	300.00	250.00

Quarter Horse Stallion

Model No.:	B-712
Designer:	Maureen Love
Height:	5 ¾", 14.6 cm
Colour:	Palomino; gloss or matte
Issued:	November 1985 in a limited edition of 25
Varieties:	Also called Quarter Horse Stallion 'Two Bits'

Model No.	U.S. $	Can. $	U.K.£
B-712	200.00	400.00	350.00

Quarter Horse Foal

Model No.:	B-756
Designer:	Maureen Love
Height:	5", 12.7 cm
Colour:	Palomino; gloss or matte
Issued:	November 1985 in a limited edition of 25
Varieties:	Also called Quarter Horse Foal 'Shamrock'

Model No.	U.S. $	Can. $	U.K.£
B-756	150.00	300.00	250.00
Complete set	400.00	800.00	700.00

Note: See also Quarter Horse Foal 'Shamrock' and Quarter Horse Mare 'Erin', page 80; and Quarter Horse Stallion 'Two Bits', page 81.

Cutting Quarter Horse and Rider 'Cutter'

Model No.:	B-689/23
Designer:	Maureen Love
Height:	8 ½", 21.6 cm
Colour:	1. Bay; matte
	2. Black; matte
	3. Buckskin; gloss or matte
	4. Chestnut; matte
Issued:	Fall 1958 - spring 1966,
	fall 1981 - spring 1986

Colourways	U.S. $	Can. $	U.K.£
1. Monrovia	500.00	1,000.00	875.00
2. San Dimas	300.00	600.00	525.00
3. San Marcos	200.00	400.00	350.00

Note: Monrovia/San Dimas models – one-piece mould. Rider and horse cast separately at San Marcos.

SHETLAND PONIES

These models, designed by Maureen Love, were available from spring 1954 to fall 1955, from fall 1956 to spring 1957, and in 1967.

Shetland Stallion 'Wrangler'

Model No.:	B-566
Height:	4", 10.1 cm
Colours:	See below

Colourways	U.S. $	Can. $	U.K. £
1. Brown pinto; gloss	300.00	600.00	525.00
2. Chestnut; matte	300.00	600.00	525.00
3. Grey pinto; gloss	300.00	600.00	525.00

Shetland Mare 'Maydee'

Model No.:	B-565
Height:	3 ½", 8.9 cm
Colours:	See below

Colourways	U.S. $	Can. $	U.K. £
1. Brown pinto; gloss	300.00	600.00	525.00
2. Chestnut; matte	300.00	600.00	525.00
3. Grey pinto; gloss	300.00	600.00	525.00

Shetland Foal 'Rascal'

Model No.:	B-564
Height:	2 ¾", 7.0 cm
Colours:	See below

Colourways	U.S. $	Can. $	U.K. £
1. Brown pinto; gloss	200.00	400.00	350.00
2. Chestnut; matte	200.00	400.00	350.00
3. Grey pinto; gloss	200.00	400.00	350.00

TENNESSEE WALKING HORSE

THOROUGHBREDS

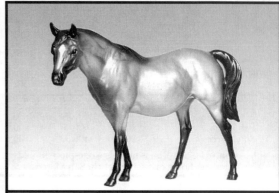

Tennessee Walking Horse Mare 'Roan Lady'

Model No.:	B-705
Designer:	Maureen Love
Height:	7 ¼", 18.4 cm
Colour:	See below
Issued:	Spring 1959 - fall 1960, 1966, 1967, 1970, spring 1971

Colourways	U.S. $	Can. $	U.K.£
1. Grey; matte	500.00	1,000.00	875.00
2. White; matte	500.00	1,000.00	875.00

Note: Monrovia ribbons — blue with black checks; San Dimas – lime or turquoise with black checks.

Thoroughbred 'Comella'

Model No.:	B-750
Designer:	Maureen Love
Height:	5 ½", 14.0 cm
Colour:	1. Bay; matte
	2. Buckskin; matte
Issued:	Fall 1961 - spring 1972

Colourways	U.S. $	Can. $	U.K.£
1. Bay	300.00	600.00	525.00
2. Buckskin	300.00	600.00	525.00

Thoroughbred Race Horse 'Kelso'

Model No.:	B-772
Designer:	Maureen Love
Height:	6 ½", 16.5 cm
Colour:	Dark bay; matte
Issued:	Spring 1965 - spring 1971, fall 1974 - spring 1975

Description	U.S. $	Can. $	U.K.£
1. Monrovia	300.00	600.00	525.00
2. San Dimas	250.00	500.00	435.00

Note: A Thoroughbred Race Ticket was issued with this model.

Thoroughbred 'Man O' War'

Model No.:	B-742
Designer:	Maureen Love
Height:	7", 17.8 cm
Colour:	Chestnut; matte
Issued:	Spring 1961 - spring 1971, fall 1974 - fall 1975

Description	U.S. $	Can. $	U.K.£
1. Monrovia	200.00	400.00	350.00
2. San Dimas	125.00	250.00	220.00

Note: A Thoroughbred Race Ticket was issued with this model.

Thoroughbred Stallion 'Payday'

Model No.:	B-577
Designer:	Maureen Love
Height:	6 ¼", 15.9 cm
Colour:	Bay; gloss
Issued:	Fall 1954 - spring 1957

Model No.	U.S. $	Can. $	U.K.£
B-577	300.00	600.00	525.00

Thoroughbred 'Silky Sullivan'

Model No.:	B-770
Designer:	Maureen Love
Height:	6 ½", 16.5 cm
Colour:	Chestnut; matte
Issued:	Fall 1962 - spring 1971, fall 1974 - spring 1975

Description	U.S. $	Can. $	U.K.£
1. Monrovia	200.00	400.00	350.00
2. San Dimas	125.00	250.00	220.00

Note: A Thoroughbred Race Ticket was issued with this model.

Thoroughbred 'Swaps'

Model No.:	B-671
Designer:	Maureen Love
Height:	6 ¾", 17.2 cm
Colour:	Chestnut; matte
Issued:	Fall 1957 - spring 1971, fall 1974 - spring 1975

Description	U.S. $	Can. $	U.K.£
1. Monrovia	200.00	400.00	350.00
2. San Dimas	125.00	250.00	220.00

Note: A Thoroughbred Race Ticket was issued with this model.

Thoroughbred 'Terrang'

Model No.:	B-741
Designer:	Maureen Love
Height:	6 ¼", 15.9 cm
Colour:	Dark bay; matte
Issued:	Spring 1961 - spring 1971, fall 1974 - fall 1975

Description	U.S. $	Can. $	U.K.£
1. Monrovia	200.00	400.00	350.00
2. San Dimas	125.00	250.00	220.00

Note: A Thoroughbred Race Ticket was issued with this model.

Thoroughbred and Jockey

Model No.:	B-760
Designer:	Maureen Love
Height:	6 ½", 16.5 cm
Colour:	Bay horse; jockey's silks are lavender; yellow saddle blanket
Issued:	Fall 1962

Model No.	U.S. $	Can. $	U.K.£
B-760		Extremely rare	

Note: Other horse colourways are possible.
The model illustrated is not on the original base.

Thoroughbred Foal 'Vanguard'

Model No.:	B-751
Designer:	Maureen Love
Height:	4 ¾", 12.1 cm
Colour:	1. Bay; matte
	2. Buckskin; matte
Issued:	Fall 1961 - spring 1972

Colourways	U.S. $	Can. $	U.K.£
1. Bay	200.00	400.00	350.00
2. Buckskin	200.00	400.00	350.00

YEARLINGS

Yearling, head down, 'Mischief'

Model No.:	B-680
Designer:	Maureen Love
Height:	4", 10.1 cm
Colour:	See below
Issued:	Spring 1958 - spring 1959

Colourways	U.S. $	Can. $	U.K.£
1. Palomino; matte	300.00	600.00	525.00
2. White; matte	300.00	600.00	525.00

Note: Model B-680 was later re-modelled as a Unicorn; see page 91.

Yearling, head up, 'Drum Major'

Model No.:	B-681
Designer:	Maureen Love
Height:	5 ¼", 13.3 cm
Colour:	See below
Issued:	Spring 1958 - spring 1959, spring 1968

Colourways	U.S. $	Can. $	U.K.£
1. Buckskin; matte	300.00	600.00	525.00
2. Palomino; matte	300.00	600.00	525.00
3. White; matte	300.00	600.00	525.00

MISCELLANEOUS HORSES

Yearling, turning, 'Sky Chief'

Model No.:	B-682
Designer:	Maureen Love
Height:	4 ¾", 13.3 cm
Colour:	See below
Issued:	Spring 1958 - spring 1959, spring 1968

Colourways	U.S. $	Can. $	U.K.£
1. Buckskin; matte	300.00	600.00	525.00
2. Palomino; matte	300.00	600.00	525.00
3. White; matte	300.00	600.00	525.00

Note: Model B-682 was later re-modelled as a Unicorn; see page 91.

Foal, head down

Model No.:	B-537
Designer:	Tom Masterson
Height:	2", 5.0 cm
Colour:	See below
Issued:	Fall 1952 - 1953

Colourways	U.S. $	Can. $	U.K.£
1. Chestnut; gloss	60.00	120.00	105.00
2. Palomino; gloss	60.00	120.00	105.00

Foal, head up

Model No.:	B-538
Designer:	Tom Masterson
Height:	3", 7.6 cm
Colour:	See below
Issued:	Fall 1952 - 1953

Colourways	U.S. $	Can. $	U.K.£
1. Chestnut; gloss	60.00	120.00	105.00
2. Palomino; gloss	60.00	120.00	105.00

Horse, half-rearing

Model No.:	B-536
Designer:	Tom Masterson
Height:	5", 12.7 cm
Colour:	See below
Issued:	Fall 1952 - 1953

Colourways	U.S. $	Can. $	U.K.£
1. Chestnut; gloss	75.00	150.00	130.00
2. Palomino; gloss	75.00	150.00	130.00

Horse, rearing

Model No.:	B-535
Designer:	Tom Masterson
Height:	5 ½", 14.0 cm
Colour:	See below
Issued:	Fall 1952 - 1953

Colourways	U.S. $	Can. $	U.K.£
1. Chestnut; gloss	75.00	150.00	130.00
2. Palomino; gloss	75.00	150.00	130.00

Note: Good-quality copies of model B-535 exist.

Modern Horse

Model No.:	B-771
Designer:	Maureen Love
Height:	13 ½", 13.3 cm
Colour:	1. Gold
	2. White; gloss
Issued:	Fall 1962

Model No.	U.S. $	Can. $	U.K.£
B-771		Rare	

Pony, head down

Model No.:	17
Designer:	Maureen Love
Height:	5 ½", 15.9 cm
Colour:	1. Chestnut; gloss or matte
	2. White; gloss or matte
Issued:	Spring 1981 - fall 1984

Colourways	U.S. $	Can. $	U.K.£
1. Chestnut	125.00	250.00	220.00
2. White	100.00	200.00	175.00

Pony, head up

Model No.:	16
Designer:	Maureen Love
Height:	7", 17.8 cm
Colour:	1. Chestnut; gloss or matte
	2. White; gloss or matte
Issued:	Spring 1981 - fall 1984

Colourways	U.S. $	Can. $	U.K.£
1. Chestnut	125.00	250.00	220.00
2. White	100.00	200.00	175.00

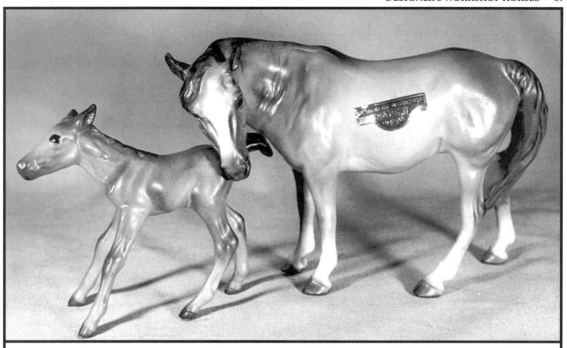

Newborn Foal, 'Tony'
Model No.:	B-627
Designer:	Maureen Love
Height:	3 ¼", 8.3 cm
Colour:	Grey; black or brown shading; matte
Issued:	Fall 1955 - spring 1957, spring 1958, 1964, 1965

Model No.	U.S. $	Can. $	U.K.£
B-627	200.00	400.00	350.00

Mare 'Nancy'
Model No.:	B-626
Designer:	Maureen Love
Height:	3 ¾", 9.5 cm
Colour:	Grey; black or brown shading; matte
Issued:	Fall 1955 - spring 1957, spring 1958, 1964, 1965

Model No.	U.S. $	Can. $	U.K.£
B-626	350.00	700.00	600.00

Note: These models were called Arabians on the 1964 release.

DONKEYS/MULES

Mule
Model No.:	58
Designer:	Maureen Love
Height:	8", 20.3 cm
Colour:	Bay; gloss or matte
Issued:	Spring 1984 - spring 1986

Model No.	U.S. $	Can. $	U.K.£
58	225.00	450.00	390.00

Note: This model was based on *Big Red Loretta*, a San Marcos mule.

Donkey Jenny With Hat, 'Adelaide'

Model No.:	B-641	
Designer:	Maureen Love	
Height:	5 ¼", 13.3 cm	
Colour:	Grey; gloss or matte	
Issued:	Spring 1956 - spring 1958,	
	spring 1962 - spring 1973,	
	spring 1975, spring 1983 - spring 1986	

Description	U.S. $	Can. $	U.K.£
1. Monrovia	100.00	200.00	175.00
2. San Dimas	80.00	160.00	140.00
3. San Marcos	75.00	150.00	130.00

Donkey Foal, 'Harry'

Model No.:	B-643	
Designer:	Maureen Love	
Height:	3 ¾", 9.5 cm	
Colour:	Grey; gloss or matte	
Issued:	Spring 1956 - spring 1958,	
	spring 1962 - spring 1973,	
	spring 1975, spring 1983 - spring 1986	

Description	U.S. $	Can. $	U.K.£
1. Monrovia	50.00	100.00	85.00
2. San Dimas	40.00	80.00	70.00
3. San Marcos	40.00	80.00	70.00

Hat

Model No.:	B-641A	
Designer:	Maureen Love	
Height:	1", 2.5 cm	
Colour:	Yellow; gloss or matte	
Issued:	Spring 1956 - spring 1958,	
	spring 1962 - spring 1973,	
	spring 1975, spring 1983 - spring 1986	

Description	U.S. $	Can. $	U.K.£
1. Monrovia	30.00	60.00	50.00
2. San Dimas	20.00	40.00	35.00
3. San Marcos	20.00	40.00	35.00

Note: The hat fits both 'Adelaide' and Mouse 'Timothy' (B-696), page 107. Handmade flowers were applied to hats made at Monrovia.

UNICORNS

Unicorn, turning

Model No.:	B-682
Designer:	Maureen Love
Height:	5", 12.7 cm
Colours:	White; gold hooves and horns; blue, pink and yellow flowers and ribbons; gloss
Issued:	Spring 1981 - spring 1986

Model No.	U.S. $	Can. $	U.K. £
B-682	95.00	190.00	165.00

Unicorn, head down

Model No.:	B-680
Designer:	Maureen Love
Height:	4", 10.1 cm
Colours:	White; gold hooves and horns; blue, pink and yellow flowers and ribbons; gloss
Issued:	Spring 1981 - spring 1986

Model No.	U.S. $	Can. $	U.K. £
B-680	95.00	190.00	165.00

Unicorn, lying

Model No.:	B-701
Designer:	Maureen Love
Height:	3", 7.6 cm
Colours:	White; gold hooves and horns; blue, pink and yellow flowers and ribbons; gloss
Issued:	Spring 1981 - spring 1986

Model No.	U.S. $	Can. $	U.K. £
B-701	95.00	190.00	165.00

Note: Earlier versions of these models have ribbon streamers. Moulds used to make these unicorns were 'Sky Chief' (B-682), page 87; 'Miss Pepper' (B-701), page 76; and 'Mischief' (B-680), page 86.

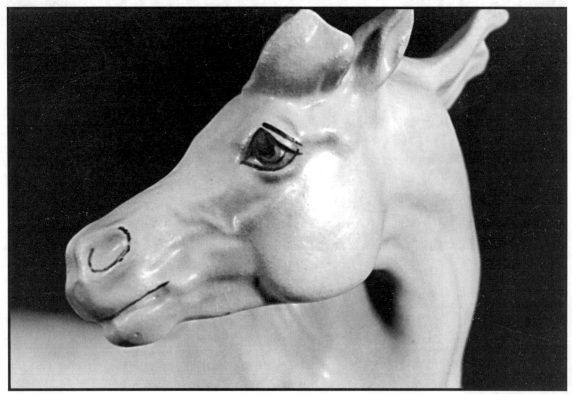

Arabian, head turned, 'Abu Farwa' (B-621),
illustrating fine eye detail

WILD ANIMALS

INDEX TO
DESIGNER'S WORKSHOP
WILD ANIMALS

BEAR

Grizzly Bear
Model No.: B-738
Designer: Maureen Love
Height: 7 ¾", 19.7 cm
Colour: 1. Brown; matte (Monrovia)
2. Brown; gloss (San Dimas)
3. Gold (San Marcos)
4. White; gloss (San Marcos)
Issued: 1961, spring 1966 - spring 1968,
fall 1971 - fall 1972, fall 1981

Colourways	U.S. $	Can. $	U.K. £
1. Brown; matte	175.00	350.00	300.00
2. Brown; gloss	150.00	300.00	260.00
3. Gold (1981)	125.00	250.00	220.00
4. White; gloss (1981)	125.00	250.00	220.00

Note: See also Grizzly Bear (738), page 556.

BISON

Bison
Model No.: B-739
Designer: Maureen Love
Height: 5 ¾", 14.6 cm
Colour: 1. Brown, black shading; matte
2. Red-chestnut, dot eyes; matte
3. White and grey; gloss
Issued: 1961, spring 1966 - spring 1968,
fall 1971 - fall 1972, fall 1981

Colourways	U.S. $	Can. $	U.K. £
1. Brown/black (Monrovia)	175.00	350.00	300.00
2. Red-chestnut	175.00	350.00	300.00
3. White/grey		Rare	

CAPE BUFFALO

Cape Buffalo
Model No.: B-602
Designer: Tom Masterson
Size: 4 ¾" x 9", 12.1 x 22.9 cm
Colour: Grey; black and brown shading
Issued: Spring 1955

Model No.	U.S. $	Can. $	U.K. £
B-602	300.00	600.00	525.00

CHIPMUNKS (1952 - 1953)

Chipmunk Papa, standing

Model No.:	B-505
Designer:	Helen Perrin Farnlund
Height:	1 7/8", 4.8 cm
Colour:	Brown and white; gloss
Issued:	Fall 1952 - 1953

Model No.	U.S. $	Can. $	U.K. £
B-505	40.00	80.00	70.00

Chipmunk Mama, seated, with nut

Model No.:	B-506
Designer:	Helen Perrin Farnlund
Height:	2 ¾", 7.0 cm
Colour:	Brown and white; gloss
Issued:	Fall 1952 - 1953

Model No.	U.S. $	Can. $	U.K. £
B-506	40.00	80.00	70.00

Chipmunk Baby, seated, facing left

Model No.:	B-504
Designer:	Helen Perrin Farnlund
Height:	1 ¾", 4.4 cm
Colour:	Brown and white; gloss
Issued:	Fall 1942 - 1953

Model No.	U.S. $	Can. $	U.K. £
B-504	30.00	60.00	50.00

Chipmunk Baby, seated, with acorn

Model No.:   B-669
Designer: Martha Armstrong
Height: 2 ¼", 5.7 cm
Colour: 1. Red-brown and white; matte
               2. Yellow-brown and white; semi-gloss
Issued: Fall 1957, spring 1967

Description	U.S. $	Can. $	U.K. £
1. Monrovia	40.00	80.00	70.00
2. San Dimas	30.00	60.00	50.00

Chipmunk Baby, walking

Model No.:   B-670
Designer: Martha Armstrong
Height: 1 5/16", 3.3 cm
Colour: Red-brown and white; matte
Issued: Fall 1957

Model No.	U.S. $	Can. $	U.K. £
B-670	40.00	80.00	70.00

Chipmunk Mama, seated, tail stretched behind

Model No.:   B-668
Designer: Martha Armstrong
Size: 3" x 4 ¼", 7.6 x 10.8 cm
Colour: 1. Red-brown and white; matte
               2. Yellow-brown and white; semi-gloss
Issued: Fall 1957, spring 1967

Description	U.S. $	Can. $	U.K. £
1. Monrovia	45.00	90.00	80.00
2. San Dimas	40.00	80.00	70.00

DEER
Deer Family

Buck 'Sentinel' Second Version (left), First Version (right)

Doe 'Patience' First Version (left), Second Version (right)

Fawns 'Twinkle' (B-559), 'Snowflake' (B-558) and 'Raindrop' (B-555);
Buck 'Sentinel', Second Version (B-52); Doe 'Patience', Second Version (B-51)

Buck 'Sentinel'
First Version (Small antlers)

Model No.:	B-553
Designer:	Tom Masterson
Height:	6 ¾", 17.2 cm
Colour:	Red-brown; gloss
Issued:	Spring 1954 - spring 1956, 1963 - 1972 (fall only)

Description	U.S. $	Can. $	U.K. £
1. Monrovia	150.00	300.00	260.00
2. San Dimas	150.00	300.00	260.00

Buck 'Sentinel'
Second Version (Large antlers)

Model No.:	B-52
Designer:	Helen Perrin Farnlund
Height:	8", 20.3 cm
Colour:	Brown; matte
Issued:	Spring 1984 - spring 1986

Description	U.S. $	Can. $	U.K. £
First version	100.00	200.00	175.00

Doe 'Patience'
First Version (Small ears)

Model No.:	B-554
Designer:	Tom Masterson
Height:	3 ¾", 9.5 cm
Colour:	Brown; gloss
Issued:	Spring 1954 - spring 1956, 1963 - 1972 (fall only)

Description	U.S. $	Can. $	U.K. £
1. Monrovia	30.00	60.00	50.00
2. San Dimas	30.00	60.00	50.00

Doe 'Patience'
Second Version (Large ears)

Model No.:	B-51
Designer:	Helen Perrin Farnlund
Height:	4", 10.1 cm
Colour:	Brown, dark brown shading; gloss or matte
Issued:	Spring 1983 - spring 1986

Description	U.S. $	Can. $	U.K. £
Second version	25.00	50.00	45.00

Fawn, head down, 'Raindrop'

Model No.:	B-555
Designer:	Helen Perrin Farnlund
Height:	2 ½", 6.4 cm
Colour:	Brown; gloss or matte
Issued:	Spring 1954 - spring 1956, 1963 - 1968 (fall only), spring 1983 - spring 1986

Description	U.S. $	Can. $	U.K. £
1. Monrovia	35.00	70.00	60.00
2. San Dimas	30.00	60.00	50.00
3. San Marcos	30.00	60.00	50.00

Fawn, prancing, 'Snowflake'

Model No.:	B-558
Designer:	Helen Perrin Farnlund
Height:	3 ¼", 8.3 cm
Colour:	Brown; gloss or matte
Issued:	Spring 1954 - spring 1956, 1967 - 1972 (fall only), spring 1983 - spring 1986

Description	U.S. $	Can. $	U.K. £
1. Monrovia	35.00	70.00	60.00
2. San Dimas	30.00	60.00	50.00
3. San Marcos	30.00	60.00	50.00

Fawn, standing, 'Twinkle'

Model No.:	B-559
Designer:	Helen Perrin Farnlund
Height:	3 ½", 8.9 cm
Colour:	Brown; gloss or matte
Issued:	Spring 1954 - spring 1956, spring 1983 - spring 1986

Description	U.S. $	Can. $	U.K. £
1. Monrovia	35.00	70.00	60.00
2. San Dimas	30.00	60.00	50.00
3. San Marcos	30.00	60.00	50.00

Note: In the first version of Buck 'Sentinel', the antlers were attached to the head before the model was fired and glazed. In the second version the antlers were separate to the body, with the retailer glueing them on. This reduced breakage.

Deer Family (1960)

Doe

Model No.:	B-734
Designer:	Maureen Love
Height:	4 1/8", 10.5 cm
Colour:	Dark brown; matte
Issued:	Fall 1960 - spring 1961

Model No.	U.S. $	Can. $	U.K. £
B-734	150.00	300.00	260.00

Buck

Model No.:	B-733
Designer:	Maureen Love
Height:	4 ¾", 12.1 cm
Colour:	Dark brown; matte
Issued:	Fall 1960 - spring 1961

Model No.	U.S. $	Can. $	U.K. £
B-733	150.00	300.00	260.00

Fawn

Model No.:	B-735
Designer:	Maureen Love
Height:	3", 7.6 cm
Colour:	Dark brown; matte
Issued:	Fall 1960 - spring 1961

Model No.	U.S. $	Can. $	U.K. £
B-735	75.00	150.00	130.00

White-tailed Deer (1956)

Doe

Model No.:	B-639
Designer:	Maureen Love
Height:	5 ½", 14.0 cm
Colour:	Light red-brown; gloss
Issued:	Fall 1956 - spring 1957

Model No.	U.S. $	Can. $	U.K. £
B-639		Rare	

Buck

Model No.:	B-638
Designer:	Maureen Love
Height:	8", 20.3 cm
Colour:	Light red-brown; gloss
Issued:	Fall 1956 - spring 1957

Model No.	U.S. $	Can. $	U.K. £
B-638		Rare	

Fawn

Model No.:	B-640
Designer:	Maureen Love
Height:	2 ¼", 5.7 cm
Colour:	Light red-brown; gloss
Issued:	Fall 1956 - spring 1957

Model No.	U.S. $	Can. $	U.K. £
B-640		Rare	

ELEPHANT FAMILY

Elephant Baby, right front leg to side

Model No.:	B-501
Designer:	Tom Masterson
Height:	3 ½", 8.9 cm
Colour:	Grey; gloss
Issued:	Fall 1952 - fall 1953

Model No.	U.S. $	Can. $	U.K. £
B-501	50.00	100.00	85.00

Elephant Baby, right front leg up

Model No.:	B-502
Designer:	Tom Masterson
Height:	3 ¼", 8.3 cm
Colour:	Grey; gloss
Issued:	Fall 1952 - fall 1953

Model No.	U.S. $	Can. $	U.K. £
B-502	50.00	100.00	85.00

Elephant Mama

Model No.:	B-503
Designer:	Tom Masterson
Height:	5", 12.7 cm
Colour:	Grey; gloss
Issued:	Fall 1952 - fall 1953

Model No.	U.S. $	Can. $	U.K. £
B-503	60.00	120.00	105.00

Elephant Baby, front legs crossed

Model No.:	B-500
Designer:	Tom Masterson
Height:	3 ½", 8.9 cm
Colour:	Grey; gloss
Issued:	Unknown

Model No.	U.S. $	Can. $	U.K. £
B-500	Possibly not put into production		

Elephant 'Rajah'

Model No.:	B-605
Designer:	Maureen Love
Height:	8 ¾", 22.2 cm
Colour:	Grey; matte
Issued:	Spring 1955 - spring 1958, 1962, spring 1966 - spring 1968, fall 1981

Description	U.S. $	Can. $	U.K. £
1. Monrovia	100.00	200.00	175.00
2. San Marcos	75.00	150.00	130.00

Elephant Baby 'Pasha'

Model No.:	B-628
Designer:	Maureen Love
Height:	3 ½", 8.9 cm
Colour:	Grey; gloss or matte
Issued:	Fall 1955 - fall 1956, spring 1966 - spring 1968, fall 1981 - spring 1984

Description	U.S. $	Can. $	U.K. £
1. Monrovia (matte)	60.00	120.00	105.00
2. San Marcos (gloss)	40.00	80.00	70.00
3. San Marcos (matte)	40.00	80.00	70.00

'Mahout' (Elephant with Rider)

Model No.:	B-604
Designer:	Nell Bortells
Height:	9 ½", 24.0 cm
Colour:	Grey elephant; Mahout wears white clothing; matte
Issued:	Spring 1955 - fall 1956, 1966

Model No.	U.S. $	Can. $	U.K. £
B-604	160.00	320.00	280.00

GIRAFFES

Giraffe Baby

Model No.:	B-520
Designer:	Helen Perrin Farnlund
Height:	5″, 12.7 cm
Colour:	Yellow-tan with brown spots
Issued:	Fall 1952 - spring 1954

Description	U.S. $	Can. $	U.K. £
1. Giraffe Baby	80.00	160.00	140.00
2. Set	250.00	500.00	435.00

Giraffe Mama

Model No.:	B-519
Designer:	Helen Perrin Farnlund
Height:	8 ½″, 21.6 cm
Colour:	Yellow-tan with brown spots
Issued:	Fall 1952 - spring 1954

Description	U.S. $	Can. $	U.K. £
1. Giraffe Mama	140.00	275.00	200.00
2. Set	250.00	500.00	435.00

IMPALA

Impala

Model No.:	B-595
Designer:	Tom Masterson
Height:	6 ¾″, 17.2 cm
Colour:	Brown with black details, grey horns; gloss or matte
Issued:	1. Fall 1955 — gloss
	2. Spring 1966 — matte

Model No.	U.S. $	Can. $	U.K. £
B-595	300.00	600.00	525.00

KOALA

Koala

Model No.:	130
Designer:	Maureen Love
Height:	5″, 12.7 cm
Colour:	Grey; gloss or matte
Issued:	Spring 1986

Model No.	U.S. $	Can. $	U.K. £
130	95.00	190.00	165.00

MICE

City Mouse Family

City Mouse, Mama

Model No.:	B-541/33
Designer:	Helen Perrin Farnlund
Height:	3", 7.6 cm
Colour:	Grey mouse, purple shoes and gloves
Issued:	Fall 1952 - fall 1955, spring 1967, fall 1981 - spring 1985

Description	U.S. $	Can. $	U.K. £
1. Monrovia	50.00	100.00	85.00
2. San Dimas	40.00	80.00	70.00
3. San Marcos	40.00	80.00	70.00

City Mouse, Papa

Model No.:	B-544/32
Designer:	Helen Perrin Farnlund
Height:	3 ¼", 8.3 cm
Colour:	Grey mouse, white cravat and spats
Issued:	Spring 1953 - fall 1955, fall 1981 - spring 1985

Description	U.S. $	Can. $	U.K. £
1. Monrovia	50.00	100.00	85.00
2. San Marcos	40.00	80.00	70.00

City Mouse, Baby

Model No.:	B-545/34
Designer:	Helen Perrin Farnlund
Height:	2", 5.0 cm
Colour:	Grey mouse
Issued:	Spring 1953 - fall 1955, fall 1981 - spring 1985

Description	U.S. $	Can. $	U.K. £
1. Monrovia	30.00	60.00	50.00
2. San Marcos	20.00	40.00	35.00

Note: Models illustrated were produced in Monrovia.

Country Mouse Family

Country Mouse, Mama

Model No.:	B-540/36
Designer:	Helen Perrin Farnlund
Height:	3", 7.6 cm
Colour:	Grey mouse, yellow shawl
Issued:	Fall 1952 - fall 1955, spring 1967, fall 1981 - spring 1985

Description	U.S. $	Can. $	U.K. £
1. Monrovia	50.00	100.00	85.00
2. San Dimas	40.00	80.00	70.00
3. San Marcos	40.00	80.00	70.00

Country Mouse, Papa

Model No.:	B-546/35
Designer:	Helen Perrin Farnlund
Height:	3 1/8", 7.9 cm
Colour:	Grey mouse, blue overalls and yellow hat
Issued:	Spring 1953 - fall 1955, fall 1981 - spring 1985

Description	U.S. $	Can. $	U.K. £
1. Monrovia	50.00	100.00	85.00
2. San Marcos	40.00	80.00	70.00

Country Mouse, Baby

Model No.:	B-539/37
Designer:	Helen Perrin Farnlund
Height:	1 ¾", 4.4 cm
Colour:	Grey mouse, blue overalls
Issued:	Fall 1952 - fall 1955, fall 1981 - spring 1985

Description	U.S. $	Can. $	U.K. £
1. Monrovia	30.00	60.00	50.00
2. San Marcos	20.00	40.00	35.00

Note: Models illustrated were produced in Monrovia.

Mouse 'Timothy'

Model No.:	B-696
Designer:	Tom Masterson
Height:	2 ½", 6.4 cm
Colour:	1. Brown, gloss or matte (Monrovia)
	2. Grey, pink inner ears; gloss or matte (San Dimas)
	3. White, pink eyes (San Marcos)
Issued:	Fall 1958 - spring 1975, spring 1981 - spring 1986

Description	U.S. $	Can. $	U.K. £
1. Monrovia	30.00	60.00	50.00
2. San Dimas	25.00	50.00	45.00
3. San Marcos	20.00	40.00	35.00

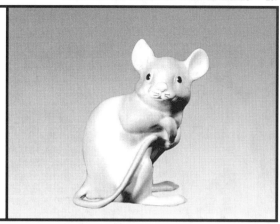

MOUNTAIN LIONS

Mountain Lion, lying

Model No.:	B-652
Designer:	Maureen Love
Size:	5" x 9", 12.7 x 22.9 cm
Colour:	1. Cream-tan; rust and black eyes
	2. Cream-tan; green and black eyes
Issued:	1. Spring 1957 - spring 1958
	2. Spring 1966 - spring 1968

Description	U.S. $	Can. $	U.K. £
1. Rust eyes	250.00	500.00	435.00
2. Green eyes	250.00	500.00	435.00

Mountain Lion, standing

Model No.:	B-651
Designer:	Maureen Love
Size:	5 ¼" x 15", 13.3 x 38.1 cm
Colour:	1. Cream-tan; rust and black eyes
	2. Cream-tan; green and black eyes
Issued:	1. Spring 1957 - spring 1958
	2. Spring 1966 - spring 1968

Description	U.S. $	Can. $	U.K. £
1. Rust eyes	300.00	600.00	525.00
2. Green eyes	300.00	600.00	525.00

POLAR BEAR

Polar Bear

Model No.:	B-725
Designer:	Tom Masterson
Height:	3 ¾", 9.5 cm
Colour:	White; matte
Issued:	Spring 1960, fall 1966

Model No.	U.S. $	Can. $	U.K. £
B-725	175.00	350.00	300.00

PRONGHORN

Pronghorn

Model No.:	B-754
Designer:	Maureen Love
Height:	6", 15.0 cm
Colour:	Brown; matte
Issued:	Fall 1961

Model No.	U.S. $	Can. $	U.K. £
B-754		Rare	

RABBITS AND HARES

Hare 'Harry'

Model No.:	B-568
Designer:	Nell Bortells
Height:	1 ½", 3.8 cm
Colour:	1. Brown hare, yellow shirt
	2. Dark grey-brown hare, light blue shirt
Issued:	1955

Colourways	U.S. $	Can. $	U.K. £
1. Brown		Rare	
2. Grey-brown		Rare	

Note: Pair with 'Tommy' the Tortoise (B-593), page 120.

Rabbit Baby, mouth open

Model No.:	B-637
Designer:	Helen Perrin Farnlund
Height:	2 ¼", 5.7 cm
Colour:	See below
Issued:	c.1955, spring 1979, spring 1981 - spring 1986

Colourways	U.S. $	Can. $	U.K. £
1. Brown; gloss	15.00	30.00	25.00
2. Brown; matte	15.00	30.00	25.00
3. White; gloss	15.00	30.00	25.00
4. White; matte	15.00	30.00	25.00

Note: Model is a reworked version of 'Flopsy' (B-569).

'Mopsy' (B-572), 'Cottontail' (B-576), 'Flopsy' (B-569), Mama 'Molly' (B-570)

Rabbit 'Cottontail'

Model No.: B-576
Designer: Helen Perrin Farnlund
Height: 2 ½", 6.4 cm
Colour: Brown, white chest; gloss
Issued: Spring 1954 - spring 1956

Model No.	U.S. $	Can. $	U.K. £
B-576	40.00	80.00	70.00

Rabbit 'Flopsy'

Model No.: B-569
Designer: Helen Perrin Farnlund
Height: 1 ½", 3.8 cm
Colour: Brown, white chest; gloss
Issued: Spring 1954 - spring 1955

Model No.	U.S. $	Can. $	U.K. £
B-569	40.00	80.00	70.00

Rabbit 'Mopsy'

Model No.: B-572
Designer: Helen Perrin Farnlund
Height: 2 ½", 6.4 cm
Colour: Brown, white chest; gloss
Issued: Spring 1954 - spring 1956

Model No.	U.S. $	Can. $	U.K. £
B-572	40.00	80.00	70.00

Rabbit Mama 'Molly'

Model No.: B-570
Designer: Helen Perrin Farnlund
Height: 4", 10.1 cm
Colour:
1. Brown, white chest; gloss (Monrovia)
2. Brown; gloss or matte (San Marcos)
3. Blue-grey; matte (San Dimas)
4. Rose-pink; matte (San Dimas)
5. White; gloss or matte (San Marcos)
6. White; black points (Monrovia)
Issued: Spring 1954 - spring 1956,
spring 1981 -spring 1986

Colourways	U.S. $	Can. $	U.K. £
1. Brown	50.00	100.00	85.00
2. Brown	30.00	60.00	50.00
3. Blue-grey	40.00	80.00	70.00
4. Rose-pink	40.00	80.00	70.00
5. White	30.00	60.00	50.00
6. White	50.00	100.00	85.00

Note: 'Molly', also known as Mama Rabbit, was produced in blue and pink as Easter specials, c.1975.

Rabbit Family

Rabbit Baby, facing right

Model No.:	B-765
Designer:	Helen Perrin Farnlund
Height:	2 ½", 6.4 cm
Colour:	See below
Issued:	Fall 1962, spring 1968, 1969, 1970, spring 1979 - spring 1984

Colourways	U.S. $	Can. $	U.K. £
1. Blue-grey; gloss/matte	25.00	50.00	40.00
2. Brown; gloss/matte	15.00	30.00	25.00
3. Grey; matte	25.00	50.00	40.00
4. Rose-pink, matte	25.00	50.00	40.00
5. White; gloss/matte	15.00	30.00	25.00

Rabbit Papa

Model No.:	B-763
Designer:	Helen Perrin Farnlund
Height:	3 ½", 8.9 cm
Colour:	See below
Issued:	Spring 1981 - spring 1986

Colourways	U.S. $	Can. $	U.K. £
1. Blue-grey; gloss/matte	40.00	80.00	70.00
2 Brown; gloss/matte	30.00	60.00	50.00
3. Grey; matte	40.00	80.00	70.00
4. Rose-pink; matte	40.00	80.00	70.00
5. White; gloss/matte	35.00	70.00	60.00

Rabbit Baby, facing left

Model No.:	B-764
Designer:	Helen Perrin Farnlund
Height:	3", 7.6 cm
Colour:	See below
Issued:	Fall 1962, spring 1966 - spring 1967, spring 1971, spring 1972, spring 1979, fall 1983 - spring 1985

Colourways	U.S. $	Can. $	U.K. £
1. Blue-grey; gloss	25.00	50.00	40.00
2. Brown; gloss /matte	15.00	30.00	25.00
3. Grey; matte	25.00	50.00	40.00
4. Rose-pink; matte	25.00	50.00	40.00
5. White; gloss/matte	15.00	30.00	25.00

Note: Models B-763, B-764 and B-765 were produced as Easter Specials, c.1975, in blue or pink colourways.

SQUIRRELS

Chatter Family

The 'Chatter Family' was designed by Robyn Sikking. They were produced in fall 1955 in a grey matte colourway.

Name	Height	U.S. $	Can. $	U.K. £
1. 'Mr. Chatter', adult, standing	3 7/8", 9.8 cm	30.00	60.00	50.00
2. 'Chit', squirrel baby, standing, tail behind body	1 3/8", 3.5 cm	20.00	40.00	35.00
3. 'Chew', squirrel baby, standing, tail curled	1 13/16", 4.6 cm	20.00	40.00	35.00
4. 'Chat', squirrel baby, on hind legs	2 ½", 6.4 cm	20.00	40.00	35.00
5. 'Chunk', squirrel baby, standing, tail over back	1 ¾", 4.4 cm	20.00	40.00	35.00
6. 'Mrs. Chatter', seated, with nut	4", 10.1 cm	30.00	60.00	50.00

Squirrel 'Peggy' (B-721); Squirrel Baby (B-761); Squirrel, seated (B-762); Squirrel 'Betty' (B-722)

Squirrel, walking, 'Peggy'

Model No.: B-721
Designer: Maureen Love
Height: 4 3/8", 11.1 cm
Colour: 1. Brown; gloss
2. Grey; bisque
3. White
Issued: Spring 1960 - spring 1962,
spring 1965, spring 1966

Colourways	U.S. $	Can. $	U.K. £
1. Brown	30.00	60.00	50.00
2. Grey	30.00	60.00	50.00
3. White	30.00	60.00	50.00

Squirrel Baby, standing

Model No.: B-761
Designer: Helen Perrin Farnlund
Height: 1 1/2", 3.8 cm
Colour: Brown; gloss or matte
Issued: 1962, fall 1965, spring 1966,
fall 1969 - fall 1972

Model No.	U.S. $	Can. $	U.K. £
B-761	20.00	40.00	35.00

Squirrel With Acorn 'Betty'

Model No.: B-722
Designer: Maureen Love
Height: 3 1/4", 8.3 cm
Colour: 1. Brown;, gloss
2. Grey; bisque
3. White
Issued: Spring 1960 - fall 1962,
fall 1965 - spring 1966

Colourways	U.S. $	Can. $	U.K. £
1. Brown	30.00	60.00	50.00
2. Grey	30.00	60.00	50.00
3. White	30.00	60.00	50.00

Squirrel Baby, seated

Model No.: B-762
Designer: Helen Perrin Farnlund
Height: 1 3/4", 4.4 cm
Colour: Brown; gloss or matte
Issued: Spring 1962, fall 1965,
spring 1966

Model No.	U.S. $	Can. $	U.K. £
B-762	30.00	60.00	50.00

Squirrel 'Jane'

Model No.:	B-720
Designer:	Maureen Love
Height:	5 ¼", 13.3 cm
Colour:	1. Brown; gloss
	2. Grey; bisque
Issued:	Spring 1960 - fall 1961,
	fall 1965 - spring 1966,
	fall 1969 - fall 1972

Description	U.S. $	Can. $	U.K. £
1. Monrovia	85.00	170.00	145.00
2. San Dimas	75.00	150.00	130.00

Squirrel on Branch

Model No.:	31
Designer:	Maureen Love
Height:	7 ¾", 19.7 cm
Colour:	1. Grey; gloss
	2. Red-brown; matte
Issued:	Fall 1981 - spring 1982,
	fall 1983 - spring 1984

Colourways	U.S. $	Can. $	U.K. £
1. Grey	150.00	300.00	260.00
2. Red-brown	150.00	300.00	260.00

ZEBRAS

Zebra Ma
Model No.: B-517
Designer: Helen Perrin Farnlund
Height: 5 ½", 14.0 cm
Colour: Black and white; gloss
Issued: Fall 1952, spring 1953

Model No.	U.S. $	Can. $	U.K. £
B-517	150.00	300.00	260.00

Zebra Baby
Model No.: B-518
Designer: Helen Perrin Farnlund
Height: 3 ¾", 9.5 cm
Colour: Black and white; gloss
Issued: Fall 1952, spring 1953

Model No.	U.S. $	Can. $	U.K. £
B-518	75.00	150.00	130.00

Note: Excellent copies of these models exist.

MISCELLANEOUS ITEMS

INDEX TO
DESIGNER'S WORKSHOP
MISCELLANEOUS ITEMS

Frog Prince (13)
illustrating sgraffito eye detail

CATERPILLARS

Caterpillar Family

Caterpillar Papa 'Horace'

Model No.:	B-623
Designer:	Nell Bortells
Height:	3 1/8", 7.95 cm
Colour:	1. Light green
	2. Light green with purple spots, light brown hat
Issued:	Fall 1955, fall 1969 - spring 1973

Colourways	U.S. $	Can. $	U.K. £
1. Green	20.00	40.00	35.00
2. Green/purple/brown	45.00	90.00	80.00

Caterpillar Mama 'Clarabelle'

Model No.:	B-624
Designer:	Nell Bortells
Height:	3", 7.6 cm
Colour:	1. Light green
	2. Light green with purple spots, yellow hat with pink ribbon, lavender purse
Issued:	Fall 1955, fall 1969 - spring 1973

Colourways	U.S. $	Can. $	U.K. £
1. Green	20.00	40.00	35.00
2. Green/purple/yellow	45.00	90.00	80.00

Caterpillar Baby 'Genevieve'

Model No.:	B-625
Designer:	Nell Bortells
Height:	2 ¼", 5.7 cm
Colour:	1. Light green
	2. Light green with purple spots, white hat with pink flowers
Issued:	Fall 1955, fall 1969 - spring 1973

Colourways	U.S. $	Can. $	U.K. £
1. Green	10.00	20.00	17.00
2. Green/purple/white	30.00	60.00	50.00

Note: Early models of 'Horace' (B-623) may have an umbrella.

FROGS

Frog 'Clem', small

Model No.:	B-629/744
Designer:	Maureen Love
Height:	1 ¾", 4.4 cm
Colour:	1. Green; gloss
	2. Green, yellow belly, light green and brown shading; matte
Issued:	Fall 1955, spring 1956, spring 1961 - spring 1973, spring 1975

Model No.	U.S. $	Can. $	U.K. £
B-629/744	30.00	60.00	45.00

Frog 'Daniel', large

Model No.:	B-620/743/12
Designer:	Maureen Love
Height:	2 5/8", 6.6 cm
Colour:	1. Green; gloss
	2. Green, yellow belly, light green and brown shading; matte
Issued:	Fall 1955, spring 1956, spring 1961 - spring 1973, spring 1975

Model No.	U.S. $	Can. $	U.K. £
B-620/743/12	30.00	60.00	45.00

Frog 'Samuel', medium

Model No.:	B-622
Designer:	Maureen Love
Height:	2", 5.0 cm
Colour:	Green, yellow belly, light green and brown shading; matte
Issued:	Fall 1955, spring 1956

Model No.	U.S. $	Can. $	U.K. £
B-622	75.00	150.00	130.00

Note: Model B-622 is illustrated in a bisque finish.

Frog Prince
Model No.: 13
Designer: Maureen Love
Height: 2 ½", 6.4 cm
Colour: Brown frog, yellow and white hat;
gloss or matte
Issued: Spring 1981 - fall 1983

Model No.	U.S. $	Can. $	U.K. £
13	75.00	150.00	130.00

Lily Pad
Model No.: 14
Designer: Maureen Love
Size: 1" x 6", 2.54 x 15.0 cm
Colour: Green lily pad,
yellow flower
Issued: Spring 1981 - fall 1983

Model No.	U.S. $	Can. $	U.K. £
14	30.00	60.00	50.00

DRAGON

Dragon

Model No.:	28
Designer:	Helen Perrin Farnlund
Height:	9", 22.9 cm
Colour:	1. Green; gloss or matte
	2. Purple; gloss or matte
Issued:	Spring 1981 - spring 1986

Colourways	U.S. $	Can. $	U.K. £
1. Green	300.00	600.00	525.00
2. Purple	300.00	600.00	525.00

MOTH

Cecropia Moth

Model No.:	B-630
Designer:	Maureen Love
Size:	6 ¼" x 5 1/8", 15.9 x 13.0 cm
Colour:	Unknown
Issued:	Spring 1956

Model No.	U.S. $	Can. $	U.K. £
B-630		Rare	

Note: Model illustrated is bisque.

TORTOISES

'Tommy' the Tortoise

Model No.:	B-593
Designer:	Nell Bortells
Height:	1 ½", 3.81 cm
Colour:	Tan body; black, white and pink shell
Issued:	1955

Model No.	U.S. $	Can. $	U.K. £
B-593		Rare	

Note: Pair with Hare 'Harry' (B-568), page 108.

Tortoise

Model No.:	B-560
Designer:	Tom Masterson
Height:	3 ¼", 8.3 cm
Colour:	Brown
Issued:	Spring 1966

Model No.	U.S. $	Can. $	U.K. £
B-560		Rare	

Note: Model illustrated is bisque.

TOADSTOOLS

Toadstools, large
Model No.: 2501
Designer: Millesan Drews
Height: 1. Curved — 3", 7.6 cm
        2. Straight — 2", 5.0 cm
Colour: Off-white; matte
Issued: Spring 1969 - fall 1972, spring 1973

Model No.	U.S. $	Can. $	U.K. £
2501	20.00	40.00	35.00

Toadstools, medium
Model No.: 2502
Designer: Millesan Drews
Height: 1. Curved — 1 ¾", 4.4 cm
        2. Straight — 1 ½", 3.81 cm
Colour: Off-white; matte
Issued: Spring 1969 - fall 1972, spring 1973

Model No.	U.S. $	Can. $	U.K. £
2502	15.00	30.00	25.00

Toadstools, small
Model No.: 2503
Designer: Millesan Drews
Height: 1. Curved — 5/8", 1.58 cm
        2. Straight — ½", 1.27 cm
Colour: Off-white; matte
Issued: Spring 1969 - fall 1972, spring 1973

Model No.	U.S. $	Can. $	U.K. £
2503	8.00	16.00	14.00

Note: These models were originally offered with the Pixies.
See page 572 for Pixies.

Squirrel on Branch (31)
Issued from San Marcos in grey gloss

LITTLE HORRIBLES

One day in the late 1950s, John Renaker asked Nell Bortells to make a vulture to give to a friend in the hospital. Her first vulture was not "hungry enough," so she returned to the clay to sculpt a ravenous vulture, which was just perfect. History does not record what the friend had to say. About this time, the song *The Purple People Eater* was popular and John suggested that Nell design such a creature, which she did. Thus, the Little Horribles collection was born.

Alternatively, the story goes that David Renaker, John's son, was the source of inspiration. Portuguese fishing boats often had an eye painted on their sides, and he saw one that had legs added to the eye in a Dali-esque manner. He was the one to ask Nell to create "Eye Spider."

In any case, Nell Bortells was the sole designer for the line, while David Renaker named the models and came up with the pun that was printed on the studio card. The Little Horribles were made for four seasons. They were big sellers for about one year and were packed in various sizes of plastic boxes, pre-labelled and pre-priced. The pieces themselves were given 5/16" round gold stickers printed with "Hagen-Renaker U.S.A. ©." A studio card, and often a flyer showing the Little Horribles collection, came in the box. Individual Little Horribles were cast in blue, green, grey, purple or tan and then decorated in blue, bright orange, coloured glazes, flesh tones or green. Eyes, teeth and wrinkles were outlined in black. Some pieces were meant to be shelf sitters.

Nell Bortells has said that she was mildly offended that her creatures were considered "horrible." She felt that they were mostly goofy, unlovely people, and she would make other clay partners to keep them company. For example, "Little Old Man" has a pet frog and "Little Purple Man" has a buddy, "Moose." She would listen to soap operas for inspiration as she worked. Surely that sense of overwrought emotion is perfectly personified in "Hard Working Harry" and "Ribbon Clerk." In any case, an article in a British paper used the Little Horribles as an example of the typical vulgar excesses of Americans.

INDEX TO
LITTLE HORRIBLES

Photograph
not available
at press time

Anxious

Model No.:	D-443
Designer:	Nell Bortells
Height:	Unknown
Colour:	Unknown
Issued:	Fall 1959
Pun:	Unknown

Model No.	U.S. $	Can. $	U.K. £
D-443	70.00	140.00	120.00

Ashes to Ashes

Model No.:	D-438
Designer:	Nell Bortells
Height:	1 ¾", 4.4 cm
Colour:	Brown garbage can and feet, pink flesh tone face, black hair and facial markings
Issued:	Spring 1959 - fall 1959
Pun:	"Why rush it, I was gonna resign anyway."

Model No.	U.S. $	Can. $	U.K. £
D-438	55.00	110.00	95.00

Bag in a Sack

Model No.:	D-398
Designer:	Nell Bortells
Height:	2 ¼", 5.7 cm
Colour:	See below
Issued:	Spring 1958 only
Pun:	"Who needs Dior?"

Colourways	U.S. $	Can. $	U.K. £
1. Dark green	55.00	110.00	95.00
2. Light green	55.00	110.00	95.00
3. Orange	55.00	110.00	95.00

Note: Models may or may not have a bow on their behind.

Batty

Model No.:	D-387
Designer:	Nell Bortells
Height:	1 5/8", 4.12 cm
Colour:	Black and brown bat, salmon hat
Issued:	Unknown
Pun:	Unknown

Description	U.S. $	Can. $	U.K. £
Batty		Rare	

Note: This model does not appear on the order forms.

Beautiful Baby

Model No.:	D-439
Designer:	Nell Bortells
Height:	1 3/8", 3.49 cm
Colour:	Pink flesh tones
Issued:	Spring 1959 - fall 1959
Pun:	"You're the only one who knows the real me."

Model No.	U.S. $	Can. $	U.K. £
D-439	55.00	110.00	95.00

Big Foot

Model No.:	D-406
Designer:	Nell Bortells
Height:	2 ¼", 5.7 cm
Colour:	Green body, pink flesh tone foot with painted nails
Issued:	Spring 1958 - fall 1958
Pun:	"Fallout? It never bothered me none."

Model No.	U.S. $	Can. $	U.K. £
D-406	65.00	130.00	115.00

Bongo Player

Model No.:	D-418
Designer:	Nell Bortells
Height:	1 ½", 3.81 cm
Colour:	Blue-green body, gold bongos with white tops
Issued:	Fall 1959
Pun:	Unknown

Model No.	U.S. $	Can. $	U.K. £
D-418	85.00	170.00	150.00

Note: This forms a set with Cornet Player (D-417), page 127, and Piano Player (D-442), page 132.

Cave, The

Model No.:	D-392
Designer:	Nell Bortells
Height:	3 ¼", 8.3 cm
Colour:	Brown; matte
Issued:	1959 - fall 1960
Pun:	Unknown

Model No.	U.S. $	Can. $	U.K. £
D-392	65.00	130.00	115.00

Note: Cave was revised and released with Cavemen, page 399.

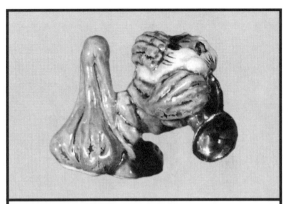

Cornet Player

Model No.:	D-417
Designer:	Nell Bortells
Height:	1 5/8", 4.12 cm
Colour:	Blue-green, gold cornet
Issued:	Fall 1959
Pun:	Unknown

Model No.	U.S. $	Can. $	U.K. £
D-417	75.00	150.00	130.00

Note: This forms a set with Bongo Player (D-418), page 126, and Piano Player (D-442), page 132.

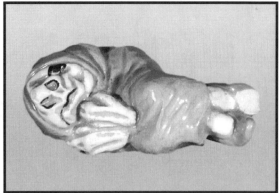

Dark Eyes

Model No.:	D-404
Designer:	Nell Bortells
Height:	1", 2.54 cm
Colour:	Pink flesh tones, grey-green slip
Issued:	Fall 1958
Pun:	"Are you sure the parade goes by here?"

Model No.	U.S. $	Can. $	U.K. £
D-404	60.00	120.00	105.00

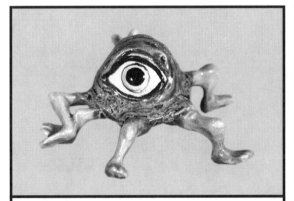

Eye Spider

Model No.:	D-386
Designer:	Nell Bortells
Height:	7/8", 2.2 cm
Colour:	Green body
Issued:	Spring 1958 - fall 1959
Pun:	"Lately, Doc…Everybody seems to stare at me."

Model No.	U.S. $	Can. $	U.K. £
D-386	60.00	120.00	105.00

FHA

Model No.:	D-434
Designer:	Nell Bortells
Height:	1 3/8", 3.49 cm
Colour:	Green
Issued:	Fall 1959
Pun:	Unknown

Model No.	U.S. $	Can. $	U.K. £
D-434	65.00	130.00	115.00

Footsore and Weary

Model No.:	D-402
Designer:	Nell Bortells
Height:	1 5/8", 4.12 cm
Colour:	Green
Issued:	Fall 1959
Pun:	"Oh my feet are killing me."

Model No.	U.S. $	Can. $	U.K. £
D-402	55.00	110.00	95.00

Guitar Player

Model No.:	D-436
Designer:	Nell Bortells
Height:	1 ½", 3.81 cm
Colour:	Blue-green body, pink mouth
Issued:	Fall 1959
Pun:	Unknown

Model No.	U.S. $	Can. $	U.K. £
D-436	85.00	170.00	150.00

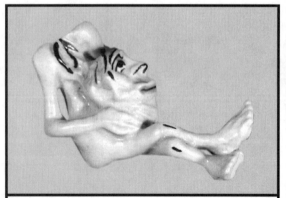

Hangover Bob

Model No.:	D-407
Designer:	Nell Bortells
Height:	1 3/8", 3.49 cm
Colour:	Pink flesh tone, black facial markings
Issued:	Fall 1958 - fall 1959
Pun:	"Not today Bob, I'm nursing a headache."

Model No.	U.S. $	Can. $	U.K. £
D-407	60.00	120.00	105.00

Hard Working Harry

Model No.:	D-424
Designer:	Nell Bortells
Height:	1", 2.54 cm
Colour:	Golden brown, orange nose, black fingernails and toenails
Issued:	Fall 1958 - fall 1959
Pun:	"This …is the story of my life."

Model No.	U.S. $	Can. $	U.K. £
D-424	55.00	110.00	95.00

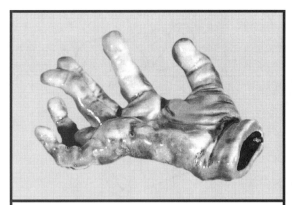

Helping Hand

Model No.:	D-396
Designer:	Nell Bortells
Height:	1″, 2.54 cm
Colour:	Green with paler green highlights
Issued:	Spring 1959 - fall 1959
Pun:	"Can you use an extra hand around the place?"

Model No.	U.S. $	Can. $	U.K. £
D-396	60.00	120.00	105.00

Note: "THINK" is spelled out over the knuckles.

High Jumper

Model No.:	D-420
Designer:	Nell Bortells
Height:	1 3/8″, 3.49 cm
Colour:	Blue-green
Issued:	Fall 1958
Pun:	"Frankly, I'm on the fence."

Model No.	U.S. $	Can. $	U.K. £
D-420	65.00	130.00	115.00

Hole in the Head

Model No.:	D-422
Designer:	Nell Bortells
Height:	2 ¼″, 5.7 cm
Colour:	Pink flesh tone, black markings and nails, peach eyes and nose
Issued:	Fall 1958 - fall 1959
Pun:	"Bang! Bang! Got you with both barrels."

Model No.	U.S. $	Can. $	U.K. £
D-422	75.00	150.00	130.00

Horse Laugh

Model No.:	D-431
Designer:	Nell Bortells
Height:	2 ½″, 6.4 cm
Colour:	Pink flesh tones, green hat
Issued:	Spring 1959 - fall 1959
Pun:	"It only hurts when I laugh."

Model No.	U.S. $	Can. $	U.K. £
D-431	55.00	110.00	95.00

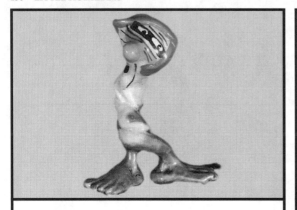

Hula Hooper

Model No.:	D-432
Designer:	Nell Bortells
Height:	2 1/8″, 5.39 cm
Colour:	Pink flesh tone, brown hair and nose, black eye mask
Issued:	Spring 1959 - fall 1959
Pun:	Unknown

Model No.	U.S. $	Can. $	U.K. £
D-432	55.00	110.00	95.00

Note: The metal hoop is missing from this illustration.

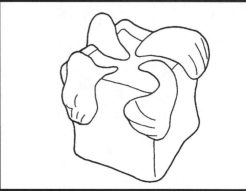

John and Marsha

Model No.:	D-440
Designer:	Nell Bortells
Height:	Unknown
Colour:	Unknown
Issued:	Fall 1959
Pun:	Unknown

Model No.	U.S. $	Can. $	U.K. £
D-440	70.00	140.00	120.00

Knotty

Model No.:	D-416
Designer:	Nell Bortells
Height:	1 ¾″, 4.4 cm
Colour:	Brown
Issued:	Fall 1959
Pun:	"I feel like I've been pulled through a knot."

Model No.	U.S. $	Can. $	U.K. £
D-416	75.00	150.00	130.00

Note: Model D-416 is a shelf sitter.

Little Blue Man

Model No.:	D-390
Designer:	Nell Bortells
Height:	1 ¼″, 3.1 cm
Colour:	Pink flesh tones, blue hair
Issued:	Spring 1958 - fall 1959
Pun:	"Please, Ma… Can I have a flattop?"

Model No.	U.S. $	Can. $	U.K. £
D-390	50.00	100.00	85.00

Note: Model D-390 was also used to make Beach Boy Junior (A-071), page 398.

Little Horribles Sign

Model No.:	Unknown
Designer:	Nell Bortells
Size:	2" x 7", 5.0 x 17.8 cm
Colour:	White with black lettering
Issued:	Unknown

Description	U.S. $	Can. $	U.K. £
Little Horribles Sign	100.00	200.00	175.00

Little Purple Man

Model No.:	D-419
Designer:	Nell Bortells
Height:	1 1/8", 2.85 cm
Colour:	Maroon
Issued:	Fall 1958 - spring 1959
Pun:	"Go ahead…search me!"

Model No.	U.S. $	Can. $	U.K. £
D-419	50.00	100.00	85.00

Note: This forms a pair with Moose (D-389), page 132.
Photo LH4bLittle Old Man and His Frog Friend

Model No.:	D-383
Designer:	Nell Bortells
Height:	Old Man — 2", 5.0 cm
	Frog — 7/8", 2.2 cm
Colour:	Old Man — Mustard face and legs,
	brown and white beard
	Frog — Green with orange spots
Issued:	Old Man — Spring 1958 - fall 1959
	Frog — Unknown
Pun:	"Just what I wanted.. a necktie!"

Description	U.S. $	Can. $	U.K. £
1. Little Old Man	55.00	110.00	95.00
2. Frog Friend	Possibly not put into production		

Note: Frog Friend does not appear on the order forms.

Moose

Model No.:	D-389
Designer:	Nell Bortells
Height:	1 1/8", 2.85 cm
Colour:	Green, pink face
Issued:	Spring 1958 - fall 1958
Pun:	"I think I'm nearly over the hump."

Model No.	U.S. $	Can. $	U.K. £
D-389	55.00	110.00	95.00

Note: This forms a pair with Little Purple Man (D-419), page 131.

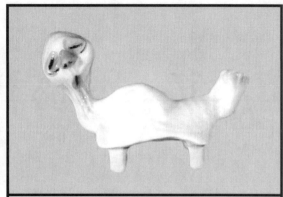

Patient, The

Model No.:	D-395
Designer:	Nell Bortells
Height:	1 3/8", 3.49 cm
Colour:	White
Issued:	Fall 1959
Pun:	Unknown

Model No.	U.S. $	Can. $	U.K. £
D-395	75.00	150.00	130.00

Peeping Tom

Model No.:	D-435
Designer:	Nell Bortells
Height:	1 5/8", 4.12 cm
Colour:	Green body, pink face
Issued:	Fall 1959
Pun:	"If I had the wings of an angel, I could look over transoms."

Model No.	U.S. $	Can. $	U.K. £
D-435	55.00	110.00	95.00

Photograph
not available
at press time

Piano Player

Model No.:	D-442
Designer:	Nell Bortells
Height:	Unknown
Colour:	Unknown
Issued:	Fall 1959
Pun:	Unknown

Model No.	U.S. $	Can. $	U.K. £
D-442	85.00	170.00	150.00

Note: This forms a set with Bonjo Player (D-418), page 126, and Cornet Player (D-417), page 127.

Pruneface

Model No.:	D-391
Designer:	Nell Bortells
Height:	2 ¼", 5.7 cm
Colour:	Yellow-green clothing, pink face with black markings
Issued:	Spring 1958 - spring 1959
Pun:	"Fix me a Martini, Fred. The children have been monsters!"

Model No.	U.S. $	Can. $	U.K. £
D-391	55.00	110.00	95.00

Purple People Eater

Model No.:	D-405
Designer:	Nell Bortells
Height:	1 ¼", 3.1 cm
Colour:	Purple with green highlights
Issued:	Fall 1958 - fall 1959
Pun:	"Take me to your leader, Earthman."

Model No.	U.S. $	Can. $	U.K. £
D-405	75.00	150.00	130.00

Note: The model illustrated has the wings missing.

RH Negative

Model No.:	D-437
Designer:	Nell Bortells
Height:	1 ¾", 4.44 cm
Colour:	Unknown
Issued:	Spring 1959 - fall 1959
Pun:	"Take me to your bleeder."

Model No.	U.S. $	Can. $	U.K. £
D-437	55.00	110.00	95.00

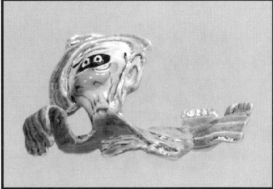

Ribbon Clerk

Model No.:	D-430
Designer:	Nell Bortells
Height:	1 ¼", 3.17 cm
Colour:	Blue
Issued:	Spring 1959 - fall 1959
Pun:	Unknown

Model No.	U.S. $	Can. $	U.K. £
D-430	55.00	110.00	95.00

September Morn

Model No.:	D-421
Designer:	Nell Bortells
Height:	1 ½", 3.81 cm
Colour:	Pink flesh tones on blue slip
Issued:	Spring 1959 - fall 1959
Pun:	"Couldn't you have knocked?"

Model No.	U.S. $	Can. $	U.K. £
D-421	55.00	110.00	95.00

Silent Sam

Model No.:	D-428
Designer:	Nell Bortells
Height:	1 2/3", 4.23 cm
Colour:	Pink flesh tones
Issued:	Spring 1959 - fall 1959
Pun:	"Say, did I say the wrong thing?"

Model No.	U.S. $	Can. $	U.K. £
D-428	55.00	110.00	95.00

Skindiver or Octopus

Model No.:	D-423
Designer:	Nell Bortells
Height:	1 1/8", 2.85 cm
Colour:	Green with paler green highlights, red feet
Issued:	Fall 1958 - fall 1959
Pun:	"Some guys are pretty hard to take!"

Model No.	U.S. $	Can. $	U.K. £
D-423	55.00	110.00	95.00

Spectator

Model No.:	D-441
Designer:	Nell Bortells
Height:	2", 5.0 cm
Colour:	Blue-green
Issued:	Fall 1959
Pun:	"Yeah! team."

Model No.	U.S. $	Can. $	U.K. £
D-441	60.00	120.00	105.00

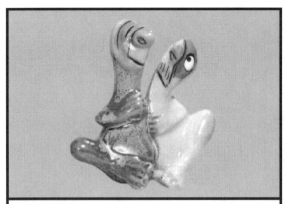

Split Personality

Model No.:	D-429
Designer:	Nell Bortells
Height:	1 ¾", 4.44 cm
Colour:	Left side – green; right side – pink flesh tones
Issued:	Spring 1959 - fall 1959
Pun:	"You're alright, how am I?"

Model No.	U.S. $	Can. $	U.K. £
D-429	55.00	110.00	95.00

Strictly From Hunger

Model No.:	D-399
Designer:	Nell Bortells
Height:	1 ¾", 4.4 cm
Colour:	Green
Issued:	Spring 1958
Pun:	"And how long do you think I been standing in line?"

Model No.	U.S. $	Can. $	U.K. £
D-399	65.00	130.00	115.00

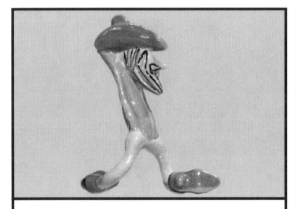

Tex

Model No.:	D-433
Designer:	Nell Bortells
Height:	2 ¼", 5.7 cm
Colour:	Pink flesh tones, brown hat and boots
Issued:	Spring 1959 - fall 1959
Pun:	"I still say martini is a sissy drink."

Model No.	U.S. $	Can. $	U.K. £
D-433	55.00	110.00	95.00

Three-Armed Pete

Model No.:	D-397
Designer:	Nell Bortells
Height:	1 1/8", 2.85 cm
Colour:	Green and blue, pink face with black markings
Issued:	Spring 1958
Pun:	"Sometimes you tickle me half to death."

Model No.	U.S. $	Can. $	U.K. £
D-397	55.00	110.00	95.00

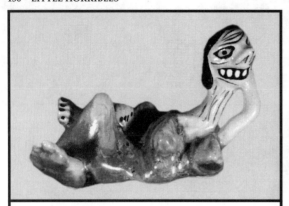

Tia Juana Rosie

Model No.:	D-400
Designer:	Nell Bortells
Height:	1 ¾", 4.4 cm
Colour:	Green dress; blue skin; black hair, mouth and nails; white teeth
Issued:	Spring 1958 - fall 1959
Pun:	"What's my line?"

Model No.	U.S. $	Can. $	U.K. £
D-400	55.00	110.00	95.00

Toothy

Model No.:	Unknown
Designer:	Nell Bortells
Height:	1 ¼", 3.17 cm
Colour:	Green and blue
Issued:	Unknown
Pun:	Unknown

Description	U.S. $	Can. $	U.K. £
Toothy	Possibly not put into production		

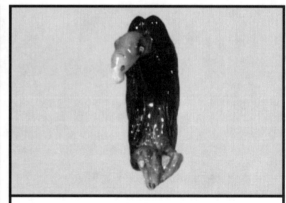

Tycoon

Model No.:	D-425
Designer:	Nell Bortells
Height:	1 7/8", 4.76 cm
Colour:	Green slip, striped shorts
Issued:	Spring 1959
Pun:	Unknown

Model No.	U.S. $	Can. $	U.K. £
D-425	60.00	120.00	105.00

Note: This model is also known without the decorated shorts.

Vulture, large

Model No.:	Unknown
Designer:	Nell Bortells
Height:	2 3/8", 6.03 cm
Colour:	Black and pink
Issued:	Unknown
Pun:	Unknown

Description	U.S. $	Can. $	U.K. £
Vulture, large	Possibly not put into production		

Vulture, small

Model No.: D-394
Designer: Nell Bortells
Height: 1 7/8", 4.76 cm
Colour: Black and pink
Issued: Spring 1958 - fall 1959
Pun: "Come on kid, make up your mind!"

Model No.	U.S. $	Can. $	U.K. £
D-394	55.00	110.00	95.00

Note: Model D-394 should be attached to a bisque branch.

Weakling (The) or Toothless

Model No.: D-401
Designer: Nell Bortells
Height: 2 1/8", 5.39 cm
Colour: Golden brown body
Issued: Spring 1958 - fall 1958
Pun: "Once I was a 97 pound weakling."

Model No.	U.S. $	Can. $	U.K. £
D-401	65.00	130.00	115.00

Well Built Hickock

Model No.: D-427
Designer: Nell Bortells
Height: 1 ¾", 4.44 cm
Colour: See Introduction
Issued: Spring 1959 - fall 1959
Pun: "Diet? All it takes is willpower."

Model No.	U.S. $	Can. $	U.K. £
D-427	55.00	110.00	95.00

Yogi

Model No.: D-426
Designer: Nell Bortells
Height: 1 ¾", 4.44 cm
Colour: Unknown
Issued: Spring 1959 - fall 1959
Pun: Unknown

Model No.	U.S. $	Can. $	U.K. £
D-426	55.00	110.00	95.00

MINIATURE SERIES

Miniatures have been Hagen-Renaker's bread and butter for over 50 years. Other lines have come and gone, but the miniatures remain.

Early miniatures were much larger than later pieces.

This early duck, skunk and swan are about 2" high.

In the past, some miniatures were matte, and some have been seen in both matte and gloss. In the early 1960s, many pieces (for example, Lord Bug and Lady Bug) were released in matte, bright-coloured, cold paint, Auerspurse colours. Hagen-Renaker decided that these pieces, while very attractive, lacked the presence of the glossy pieces and discontinued the use of this colour technique. All miniatures are glossy now.

Stamp, sticker or paper identification is usually limited to all or part of *Hagen-Renaker* stamped on the base of early miniatures; small oval black and gold *California* stickers on larger miniatures such as horses or on bases, or the paper cards to which many miniatures were glued.

Some very interesting stickers and decals were added to the original Hagen-Renaker models to make them into souvenirs. For example, the cocker spaniel's sticker reads *Wind Cave, Natl Park, SD*; the palomino horse is labelled **Coulee Dam** and the boxer's sticker reads *Souvenir of Bassett, Nebr.* Who knew that a collection of miniatures could prove to be a travelogue?

Miniatures have been marketed in various ways. As previously mentioned, a retailer could order miniatures on cards (pre-priced or not priced) or without cards. At one time, the card and animal could be inserted into a clear plastic hanger to put on a wire spinner. Predating that was the pictured three-sided paper hanger/display shown

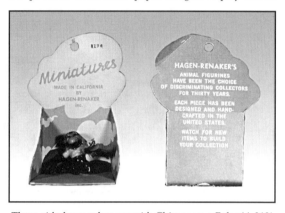

Three-sided paper hanger with Chimpanzee Baby *(A-313)*

below. Miniatures were also sold in boxed sets of tiny tableaus such as the skink and atomizer and the squirrel on a branch. The models were glued on a card and inserted into a small plastic box.

While miniatures have been sold from the factory attached to pieces of rustic wood, many retailers have no doubt attached miniatures to various things as they wished.

Miniatures have also been sold as part of music boxes assembled at the Hagen-Renaker factory in San Marcos for a Las Vegas company. In 1 1/2 years, 25,000 music boxes were assembled.

Miniature duck painted as a Mallard (A-218)

Ceramic advertising sign
Hagen-Renaker, Inc., 50 Years of Excellence 1945 - 1995

BIRDS

BLUEBIRDS

Bluebird
Style One, First Version

Model No.:	A-064
Designer:	Martha Armstrong
Height:	7/16", 1.1 cm
Colour:	Blue, black eyes and beak
Issued:	Fall 1965 - fall 1976
Varieties:	Disney model 5099 (Bluebird)

Model No.	U.S. $	Can. $	U.K. £
A-064	5.00	10.00	8.50

Bluebird
Style One, Second Version

Model No.:	A-985
Designer:	Helen Perrin Farnlund
Height:	½", 1.3 cm
Colour:	Blue and black
Issued:	Fall 1976 - spring 1981

Model No.	U.S. $	Can. $	U.K. £
A-985	5.00	10.00	8.50

Bluebird
Style Two

Model No.:	A-889
Designer:	Maureen Love
Height:	1 3/8", 3.5 cm
Colour:	Blue, white breast, wire legs
Issued:	Spring 1988

Model No.	U.S. $	Can. $	U.K. £
A-889	7.00	14.00	12.00

Note: Model A-889 was also used to make Crow, page 146.

Bluebird
Style Three

Model No.:	A-2028
Designer:	Maureen Love
Height:	1 ½", 3.8 cm
Colour:	Blue, red breast, wire legs
Issued:	Fall 1988 - spring 1989

Model No.	U.S. $	Can. $	U.K. £
A-2028	7.00	14.00	12.00

BUDGERIGAR

Budgie (In hoop)

Model No.:	A-2030
Designer:	Maureen Love
Height:	2½", 6.3 cm
Colour:	Turquoise; brown and white patterned back
Issued:	Fall 1988 - spring 1991

Model No.	U.S. $	Can. $	U.K. £
A-2030	16.00	32.00	28.00

Note: See Stoneware section, Budgies (2030), page 453.

BUZZARD

Buzzard

Model No.:	A-3286
Designer:	Robert McGuinness
Size:	2 3/8" x 4 ½", 6.0 x 11.9 cm
Colour:	Brown with black markings, white head
Issued:	Fall 1998 to the present

Model No.	U.S. $	Can. $	U.K. £
3286	5 .00	10.00	8.50

CARDINAL

Cardinal

Model No.:	A-3289
Designer:	Maureen Love
Height:	1¾", 4.4 cm
Colour:	Red bird, brown twig
Issued:	Fall 1998 to the present

Model No.	U.S. $	Can. $	U.K. £
3289	5.00	10.00	8.50

Note: See also Stoneware Series, page 454.

COCKATOO

Cockatoo (On ring)

Model No.:	A-897
Designer:	Maureen Love
Height:	1 7/8", 4.8 cm
Colour:	1. White with green leaf hanger
	2. White without leaf hanger
Issued:	Fall 1987 - fall 1988

Description	U.S. $	Can. $	U.K. £
1. With leaf hanger	20.00	40.00	35.00
2. Without leaf hanger	18.00	35.00	30.00

CHICKADEES

Chickadee Baby

Model No.:	A-287
Designer:	Robyn Sikking
Height:	5/8", 1.6 cm
Colour:	See below
Issued:	Spring 1956 - fall 1968 (17 seasons)

Colourways	U.S. $	Can. $	U.K. £
1. Blue	5.00	10.00	8.50
2. White, black shading	5.00	10.00	8.50

Chickadee Mama

Model No.:	A-288
Designer:	Robyn Sikking
Height:	1 ¼", 3.2 cm
Colour:	1. Grey bisque, wire legs
	2. Red-brown and white, wire legs
Issued:	Spring 1956 (10 seasons)

Model No.	U.S. $	Can. $	U.K. £
A-288	10.00	20.00	17.00

CHICKS

Chick, big feet

Model No.:	A-78
Designer:	Helen Perrin Farnlund
Height:	5/8", 1.6 cm
Colour:	Yellow
Issued:	1956

Model No.	U.S.$	Can.$	U.K.£
A-78	5.00	10.00	8.50

Chick, big head

Model No.:	A-447
Designer:	Helen Perrin Farnlund
Height:	3/8", 0.9 cm
Colour:	1. Yellow
	2. Yellow; Auerspurse (1960)
Issued:	Fall 1960 - fall 1983

Colourways	U.S.$	Can.$	U.K.£
1. Yellow	3.00	6.00	5.00
2. Yellow/Auerspurse	7.00	14.00	12.00

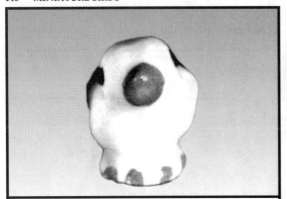

Chick, feet under body
Model No.:   A-37
Designer: Helen Perrin Farnlund
Height: ¾", 1.9 cm
Colour: 1. Black
               2. Yellow, bill open
Issued: 1949 - spring 1952

Colourways	U.S.$	Can.$	U.K.£
1. Black	3.00	6.00	5.00
2. Yellow	3.00	6.00	5.00

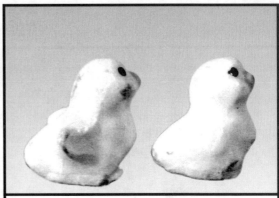

Chick, smallest
Model No.:   A-375
Designer: Helen Perrin Farnlund
Height: ¼", 0.6 cm
Colour: Yellow
Issued: 1970 - 1975

Model No.	U.S.$	Can.$	U.K.£
A-375	3.00	6.00	5.00

Note: This was made intermittently for nine seasons during the 1970s. Some models have moulded upturned wings.

Chick, wings up
Model No.:   A-193
Designer: Helen Perrin Farnlund
Height: 5/8", 1.6 cm
Colour: Yellow
Issued: c.1950, c.1980

Model No.	U.S.$	Can.$	U.K.£
A-193	3.00	6.00	5.00

Note: Model A-193 was made for four seasons in the 1950s and nine in the 1980s.

CROWS

Crow
Model No.:   A-889
Designer: Maureen Love
Height: 1 1/8", 2.8 cm
Colour: Black bird, wire legs, brown base
Issued: Fall 1987

Model No.	U.S. $	Can. $	U.K. £
A-889	10.00	20.00	17.00

Note: Model A-889 was also used to make Bluebird, Style Two, page 143.

Crow Baby

Model No.:   A-59
Designer: Helen Perrin Farnlund
Height: ½", 1.27 cm
Colour: Black, yellow bill
Issued: Fall 1959 - spring 1976

Model No.	U.S. $	Can. $	U.K. £
A-59	5.00	10.00	8.50

Crow Mama

Model No.:   A-58
Designer: Helen Perrin Farnlund
Height: 1", 2.5 cm
Colour: Black, yellow bill
Issued: Fall 1959 - spring 1976

Model No.	U.S. $	Can. $	U.K. £
A-58	8.00	16.00	14.00

Note: These form a set with Crow's Nest (A-393), page 391.

DOVES

Mr. Dove

Model No.:   A-895
Designer: Maureen Love
Height: 1", 2.5 cm
Colour: White
Issued: Spring 1987 - spring 1988

Model No.	U.S. $	Can. $	U.K. £
A-895	4.00	8.00	7.00

Note: This forms a pair with model A-896.
See also Specialties section, Doves in Bower (895), page 455.

Mrs. Dove

Model No.:   A-896
Designer: Maureen Love
Height: 7/8", 2.2 cm
Colour: White
Issued: Spring 1987 - spring 1988

Model No.	U.S. $	Can. $	U.K. £
A-896	4.00	8.00	7.00

Note: This forms a pair with model A-895.
See also Specialties section, Doves in Bower (895), page 455.

DUCKS

Duck Baby
Style One

Model No.:	A-8
Designer:	Maxine Renaker
Height:	1 ¼", 3.2 cm
Colour:	Pale yellow
Issued:	1948 - 1949

Model No.	U.S.$	Can.$	U.K.£
A-8	4.00	8.00	7.00

Note: This forms a pair with Duck Mama, Style One (A-9).

Duck Baby
Style Two

Model No.:	A-440
Designer:	Helen Perrin Farnlund
Height:	½", 1.3 cm
Colour:	See below
Issued:	Fall 1960 - fall 1961

Colourways	U.S.$	Can.$	U.K.£
1. Yellow	5.00	10.00	8.50
2. Yellow/Auerspurse	7.00	14.00	12.00

Duck Mama
Style One

Model No.:	A-9
Designer:	Maxine Renaker
Height:	2", 5.0 cm
Colour:	White
Issued:	1948 - 1949

Model No.	U.S.$	Can.$	U.K.£
A-9	8.00	16.00	14.00

Note: This forms a pair with Duck Baby, Style One (A-8).

Duck Mama
Style Two

Model No.:	A-443
Designer:	Helen Perrin Farnlund
Height:	1 3/8", 3.5 cm
Colour:	See below
Issued:	Fall 1960 - fall 1961, fall 1969

Colourways	U.S.$	Can.$	U.K.£
1. White	15.00	30.00	25.00
2. White/Auerspurse	15.00	30.00	25.00

Note: This model forms a pair with Duck Papa (A-441) page 149. It was reissued in 1969 as Sister Goose.

Duck Mama, swimming
Model No.:   A-364
Designer: Helen Perrin Farnlund
Height: 5/8", 1.6 cm
Colour: White
Issued: Spring 1958 - fall 1978

Model No.	U.S.$	Can.$	U.K.£
A-364/26	2.00	4.00	3.50

Note: Model A-364/26 was made intermittently for 29 seasons.

Duck Papa
Model No.:   A-441
Designer: Helen Perrin Farnlund
Height: 1 ½", 3.8 cm
Colour: 1. White
                2. White; Auerspurse
Issued: Fall 1960 - fall 1961

Colourways	U.S.$	Can.$	U.K.£
1. White	15.00	30.00	25.00
2. White / Auerspurse	15.00	30.00	25.00

Note: This forms a pair with Duck Mama, Style Two (A-443), page 136.

Duck, seated
Model No.:   A-319
Designer: Helen Perrin Farnlund
Height: 1 ¼", 3.2 cm
Colour: 1. Mallard
                2. White
Issued: Spring 1957 - fall 1996

Colourways	U.S.$	Can.$	U.K.£
1. Mallard	15.00	30.00	25.00
2. White	2.00	4.00	3.50

Note: Model A-319 was also used to make Duck Papa (3019), page 152, and Mallard Drake, page 165.

Duckling, seated
Model No.:   A-382
Designer: Helen Perrin Farnlund
Height: 2/3", 1.7 cm
Colour: Yellow
Issued: Spring 1958 - spring 1962

Model No.	U.S.$	Can.$	U.K.£
A-382	4.00	8.00	7.00

Note: Model A-382 was made for seven seasons.

Duckling, standing, big feet

Model No.:   A-273
Designer: Helen Perrin Farnlund
Height: ¾", 1.9 cm
Colour: Yellow
Issued: c.1955 - c.1975 (7 seasons)

Model No.	U.S.$	Can.$	U.K.£
A-273	3.00	6.00	5.00

Note: Model A-273 was also used to make Gosling, Style One, page 154.

Duckling, stooping

Model No.:   A-864
Designer: Helen Perrin Farnlund
Height: ¾", 1.9 cm
Colour: Yellow
Issued: Fall 1985 - fall 1986

Model No.	U.S.$	Can.$	U.K.£
A-864	3.00	6.00	5.00

Duckling, swimming

Model No.:   A-365
Designer: Helen Perrin Farnlund
Height: ½", 1.3 cm
Colour: Yellow
Issued: c.1978 - c.1995

Model No.	U.S.$	Can.$	U.K.£
A-365/27	2.00	4.00	3.50

Note: Model A-365 was made intermittently for 29 seasons.

Duckling, wings out

Model No.:   A-866
Designer: Helen Perrin Farnlund
Height: ¾", 1.9 cm
Colour: Yellow
Issued: Fall 1985 - spring 1988

Model No.	U.S.$	Can.$	U.K.£
A-866	4.00	8.00	7.00

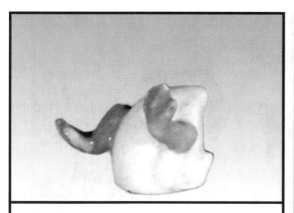

Half Duck

Model No.:	A-220
Designer:	Tom Masterson
Height:	½", 1.3 cm
Colour:	Yellow
Issued:	Spring 1954 (54 seasons)

Model No.	U.S.$	Can.$	U.K.£
A-220	2.00	4.00	3.50

Long-billed Duck Baby

Model No.:	A-219
Designer:	Tom Masterson
Height:	¾", 1.9 cm
Colour:	Yellow
Issued:	Spring 1954 (54 seasons)

Model No.	U.S.$	Can.$	U.K.£
A-219	2.00	4.00	3.50

Note: This forms a pair with Long-billed Duck Mama (A-218).

Long-billed Duck Mama

Model No.:	A-218
Designer:	Tom Masterson
Height:	1 ¼", 3.2 cm
Colour:	1. Mallard
	2. White
Issued:	Spring 1954 (54 seasons)

Colourways	U.S.$	Can.$	U.K.£
1. Mallard	15.00	30.00	25.00
2. White	2.00	4.00	3.50

Note: This forms a pair with Long-billed Duck Baby (A-219).

Duck Family on Duck Pond

Duck Mama

Model No.:	A-3018
Designer:	Helen Perrin Farnlund
Height:	5/8", 1.6 cm
Colour:	White, yellow beak
Issued:	1991 - spring 1996

Model No.	U.S.$	Can.$	U.K.£
A-3018	3.00	6.00	5.00

Duck Papa

Model No.:	A-3019
Designer:	Helen Perrin Farnlund
Height:	1 ¼", 1.1 cm
Colour:	White, yellow beak
Issued:	1991 - fall 1996

Model No.	U.S.$	Can.$	U.K.£
A-3019	3.00	6.00	5.00

Duckling, head turned

Model No.:	A-3020
Designer:	Helen Perrin Farnlund
Height:	7/16", 1.1 cm
Colour:	Yellow
Issued:	1991 - fall 1996

Model No.	U.S.$	Can.$	U.K.£
A-3020	2.00	4.00	3.50

Duckling, head up

Model No.:	A-3021
Designer:	Helen Perrin Farnlund
Height:	3/8", 0.9 cm
Colour:	Yellow
Issued:	1991 - spring 1993

Model No.	U.S.$	Can.$	U.K.£
A-3021	2.00	4.00	3.50

Duck Pond

Model No.:	A-3022
Designer:	Helen Perrin Farnlund
Size:	3 5/8" x 2 7/8", 9.2 x 7.3 cm
Colour:	Blue with black rocks
Issued:	1991 - fall 1992

Model No.	U.S.$	Can. $	U.K.£
A-3022	4.00	8.00	7.00

Note: Model A-3019 was also used to make Duck, seated (A-319), page 149, and Mallard Drake, Style Two, page 165.

EAGLES

Eagle

Model No.:	A-835	
Designer:	Helen Perrin Farnlund	
Height:	2", 5.0 cm	
Colour:	Brown and white	
Issued:	Fall 1983 - fall 1984	

Model No.	U.S. $	Can. $	U.K. £
A-835	12.00	24.00	20.00

Note: Pair with Eaglet (A-836).

Model No.:	A-836	
Designer:	Helen Perrin Farnlund	
Height:	1", 2.5 cm	
Colour:	Grey	
Issued:	Fall 1983 - fall 1984	

Model No.	U.S. $	Can. $	U.K. £
A-836	5.00	10.00	8.50

Note: This forms a pair with Eagle (A-835).

FINCH

GEESE

Finch

Model No.:	A-984	
Designer:	Helen Perrin Farnlund	
Height:	¼", 0.6 mm	
Colour:	Yellow	
Issued:	Fall 1976 - spring 1981	

Model No.	U.S. $	Can. $	U.K. £
A-984	5.00	10.00	8.50

Canada Goose

Model No.:	A-3033	
Designer:	Maureen Love	
Height:	2 1/8", 5.4cm	
Colour:	Grey with black markings	
Issued:	Fall 1991 - spring 1993	

Model No.	U.S.$	Can.$	U.K.£
A-3033	7.00	14.00	12.00

Canada Goose, seated

Model No.:	A-884
Designer:	Helen Perrin Farnlund
Height:	15/16", 2.4 cm
Colour:	Brown body and wings, black head and neck, white chin
Issued:	Spring 1987 - spring 1988

Model No.	U.S.$	Can.$	U.K.£
A-884	6.00	12.00	10.00

Canada Goose, taking off

Model No.:	A-883
Designer:	Helen Perrin Farnlund
Size:	1" x 2 7/8", 2.5 x 7.3 cm
Colour:	Brown body and wings, black head and neck, white chin
Issued:	Spring 1987 - spring 1988

Model No.	U.S.$	Can.$	U.K.£
A-883	6.00	12.00	10.00

Father Goose

Model No.:	A-269
Designer:	Helen Perrin Farnlund
Height:	2 ¼", 5.7 cm
Colour:	White goose with brown markings, tan boots, beige hat with a blue flower attached by a wire
Issued:	Fall 1955 - spring 1979
Varieties:	Also called Mother Goose

Description	U.S.$	Can.$	U.K.£
1. Monrovia	10.00	20.00	17.00
2. San Dimas	8.00	16.00	14.00

Note: Other colours of boots are known.

Gosling
Style One

Model No.:	A-273
Designer:	Helen Perrin Farnlund
Height:	7/8", 2.2 cm
Colour:	1. Yellow gosling, blue hat
	2. Yellow gosling, white hat, red ribbon
Issued:	Fall 1955 - fall 1989 (47 seasons)

Description	U.S.$	Can.$	U.K.£
1. Monrovia	4.00	8.00	7.00
2. San Dimas	3.00	6.00	5.00

Note: Model A-273 was also used to make Duckling, standing, big feet, page 150.

**Gosling
Style Two**
Model No.:   A-318
Designer: Helen Perrin Farnlund
Height: 5/8", 1.6 cm
Colour: Yellow with brown highlights
Issued: 1957, 1969

Model No.	U.S.$	Can.$	U.K.£
A-318	8.00	16.00	14.00

Note: This is also called Duckling.

Goose Family

Brother Goose
Model No.:   A-2058
Designer: Helen Perrin Farnlund
Height: 1", 2.5 cm
Colour: Yellow, blue hat
Issued: Fall 1989 - spring 1994

Model No.	U.S.$	Can.$	U.K.£
A-2058	3.00	6.00	5.00

Sister Goose
Model No.:   A-2059
Designer: Helen Perrin Farnlund
Height: 7/8", 2.2 cm
Colour: Yellow, white cap, lavender ribbon, bow
Issued: Fall 1989 to the present

Model No.	U.S.$	Can.$	U.K.£
A-2059	3.50	7.00	6.00

**Mother Goose
Style Two (Bonnet and shawl)**
Model No.:   A-2057
Designer: Helen Perrin Farnlund
Height: 2", 5.0 cm
Colour: 1. White, blue shawl and bonnet
              2. White, green shawl and bonnet
              3. White, lavender shawl and bonnet
              4. White, red shawl and bonnet
Issued: Spring 1990 - fall 1992, fall 1990 - fall 1991,
              fall 1989 to the present

Colourways	U.S.$	Can.$	U.K.£
1. Blue shawl (1990-92)	10.00	20.00	17.00
2. Green shawl (1990-91)	12.00	24.00	20.00
3. Lavender shawl (current)	5.00	10.00	8.50
4. Red shawl (1990-91)	12.00	24.00	20.00

Note: The colourway with a green/red shawl is also called Christmas Goose.

Grey Goose Family

Ma Goose

Model No.:	A-3116
Designer:	Robert McGuinness
Height:	1 2/3", 4.2 cm
Colour:	Grey with black markings, orange beak and feet
Issued:	Fall 1993 - fall 1996

Model No.	U.S.$	Can.$	U.K.£
A-3116	7.00	14.00	12.00

Gosling, head up

Model No.:	A-3117
Designer:	Robert McGuinness
Height:	1 ½", 3.8 cm
Colour:	Grey with black markings on wings
Issued:	Fall 1993 - spring 1995

Model No.	U.S.$	Can.$	U.K.£
A-3117	5.00	10.00	8.50

Gosling, head down

Model No.:	A-3118
Designer:	Robert McGuinness
Height:	1", 2.5 cm
Colour:	Grey with black markings on wings
Issued:	Fall 1993 - spring 1995

Model No.	U.S.$	Can.$	U.K.£
A-3118	5.00	10.00	8.50

Mother Goose
Style One (Blue hat)

Model No.:	A-381
Designer:	Helen Perrin Farnlund
Height:	1 ¾", 4.4 cm
Colour:	White goose, brown beak and feet, blue hat
Issued:	Spring 1958 - spring 1971

Description	U.S.$	Can.$	U.K.£
1. Monrovia	10.00	20.00	17.00
2. San Dimas	8.00	16.00	14.00

HAWK

HENS AND ROOSTERS

Hawk
Model No.:   A-3060
Designer: Maureen Love
Height: 2 ¼", 5.7 cm
Colour: Brown body, white neck
Issued: Spring 1992 - spring 1994

Model No.	U.S. $	Can. $	U.K. £
A-3060	8.00	16.00	14.00

Angular Hen
Model No.:   A-2040
Designer: Shi Yi Chen
Height: 1 ¼", 3.2 cm
Colour: White
Issued: Spring 1989 - spring 1995

Model No.	U.S.$	Can.$	U.K.£
A-2040	5.00	10.00	8.50

Note: This forms a pair with Angular Rooster (A-2039).

Angular Rooster
Model No.:   A-2039
Designer: Shi Yi Chen
Height: 2 ½", 6.4 cm
Colour: White
Issued: Spring 1989 - spring 1997

Model No.	U.S.$	Can.$	U.K.£
A-2039	5.00	10.00	8.50

Note: This forms a pair with Angular Hen (A-2040).

Bantie Hen
Style One (Head down, pecking)
Model No.:   A-33
Designer: Helen Perrin Farnlund
Height: 1 ½", 3.8 cm
Colour: See below
Issued: 1949 - 1950

Description	U.S.$	Can.$	U.K.£
1. Yellow/brown/green	7.00	14.00	12.00
2. Yellow/red/green	7.00	14.00	12.00

Note: Set with Bantie Rooster, style one, (A-24) page 158.

Bantie Hen
Style Two (With triangle tail)

Model No.:	A-91
Designer:	Helen Perrin Farnlund
Height:	1 1/8", 2.8 cm
Colour:	Yellow; brown and red markings
Issued:	Fall 1953 - spring 1955

Description	U.S.$	Can.$	U.K.£
Style two	5.00	10.00	8.50

Note: This forms a pair with Bantie Rooster, Style Two (A-92), page 159.

Bantie Hen
Style Three (Head up, small comb)

Model No.:	A-93
Designer:	Maureen Love
Height:	1 ½", 3.8 cm
Colour:	1. Brown with green highlights; gloss
	2. Yellow with green highlights; matte
Issued:	1956 - unknown

Colourways	U.S.$	Can.$	U.K.£
1. Brown	10.00	20.00	17.00
2. Yellow	15.00	30.00	25.00

Note: This forms a pair with Bantie Rooster, Style Three (A-94), page 159.

Bantie Hen
Style Four (Head up, large comb)

Model No.:	A-3242
Designer:	Maureen Love
Height:	1 5/8", 4.1 cm
Colour:	Black body, yellow neck, red comb
Issued:	Spring 1997 to the present

Description	U.S.$	Can.$	U.K.£
Style four	3.50	7.00	6.00

Note: This forms a pair with Bantie Rooster, Style Four (A-3241), page 159.

Bantie Rooster
Style One

Model No.:	A-24
Designer:	Helen Perrin Farnlund
Height:	1 7/8", 4.8 cm
Colour:	See below
Issued:	1949 - 1950

Colourways	U.S.$	Can.$	U.K.£
1. White/brown/green	7.00	14.00	12.00
2. Yellow	7.00	14.00	12.00

Note: This forms a pair with Bantie Hen, Style One (A-33), page 157.

Bantie Rooster
Style Two (Triangle tail)

Model No.:	A-92
Designer:	Helen Perrin Farnlund
Height:	1 ½", 3.8 cm
Colour:	1. Brown and white
	2. Grey and white
	3. Yellow; brown and red markings
Issued:	Fall 1953 - spring 1955

Model No.	U.S.$	Can.$	U.K.£
A-92	5.00	10.00	8.50

Note: This forms a pair with Bantie Hen, Style Two (A-91), page 158.

Bantie Rooster
Style Three (Long neck)

Model No.:	A-94
Designer:	Maureen Love
Height:	2 1/8", 5.4 cm
Colour:	1. Brown with green highlights; gloss
	2. Yellow with green highlights; matte
Issued:	1956 - unknown

Colourways	U.S.$	Can.$	U.K.£
1. Brown	10.00	20.00	17.00
2. Yellow	15.00	30.00	25.00

Note: This forms a pair with Bantie Hen, Style Three (A-93), page 158.

Bantie Rooster
Style Four

Model No.:	A-3241
Designer:	Maureen Love
Height:	2 1/8", 5.4 cm
Colour:	Black body, yellow neck, red comb
Issued:	Spring 1997 to the present

Model No.	U.S.$	Can.$	U.K.£
A-3241	4.00	8.00	6.50

Note: This forms a pair with Bantie Hen, Style Four (A-3242), page 158.

Photograph not
available
at press time

Classic Hen
Style One

Model No.:	A-285
Designer:	Helen Perrin Farnlund
Height:	Unknown
Colour:	Unknown
Issued:	Fall 1964 - spring 1973

Model No.	U.S.$	Can.$	U.K.£
A-285	15.00	30.00	25.00

Photograph not
available
at press time

Classic Hen
Style Two

Model No.:	A-342
Designer:	Martha Armstrong
Height:	Unknown
Colour:	Unknown
Issued:	Fall 1964 - spring 1973

Model No.	U.S.$	Can.$	U.K.£
A-342	15.00	30.00	25.00

Photograph not
available
at press time

Classic Rooster
Style One

Model No.:	A-286
Designer:	Helen Perrin Farnlund
Height:	Unknown
Colour:	Unknown
Issued:	Fall 1964 - spring 1973

Model No.	U.S.$	Can.$	U.K.£
A-286	15.00	30.00	25.00

Classic Rooster
Style Two

Model No.:	A-343
Designer:	Martha Armstrong
Height:	2 3/8", 6.0 cm
Colour:	White with grey shading
Issued:	Fall 1964 - spring 1973

Model No.	U.S.$	Can.$	U.K.£
A-343	15.00	30.00	25.00

Photograph not
available
at press time

Hen, feathered feet
Style One

Model No.:	A-68
Designer:	Helen Perrin Farnlund
Height:	Unknown
Colour:	See below
Issued:	1950

Colourways	U.S.$	Can.$	U.K.£
1. Brown	8.00	16.00	14.00
2. White	8.00	16.00	14.00
3. Yellow	8.00	16.00	14.00

Note: This forms a pair with Rooster, feathered feet, Style One (A-67), page 162.

Photograph not
available
at press time

Hen, feathered feet
Style Two
Model No.:   A-446
Designer: Helen Perrin Farnlund
Height: Unknown
Colour: White
Issued: Fall 1960 - fall 1961

Model No.	U.S.$	Can.$	U.K.£
A-446	18.00	36.00	30.00

Note: This forms a pair with Rooster, feathered feet,
Style Two (A-445,) page 162.

Leghorn Chick
Model No.:   A-3164
Designer: Robert McGuinness
Height: ½", 1.3 cm
Colour: Yellow
Issued: Spring 1994 - fall 1996

Model No.	U.S.$	Can.$	U.K.£
A-3164	3.00	6.00	5.00

Note: This forms a set with Leghorn Rooster (A-3159)
and Leghorn Hen (A-3160).

Leghorn Hen
Model No.:   A-3160
Designer: Robert McGuinness
Height: 1 ¾", 4.4 cm
Colour: Brown and white, red comb
Issued: Fall 1994 to the present

Model No.	U.S.$	Can.$	U.K.£
A-3160	3.50	7.00	6.00

Note: This forms a set with Leghorn Rooster (A-3159)
and Leghorn Chick (A-3164).

Leghorn Rooster
Model No.:   A-3159
Designer: Robert McGuinness
Height: 1 ½", 3.8 cm
Colour: Black and white, red comb
Issued: Fall 1994 to the present

Model No.	U.S.$	Can.$	U.K.£
A-3159	4.50	9.00	8.00

Note: This forms a set with Leghorn Hen (A-3160) and
Leghorn Chick (A-3164).

Rooster, feathered feet
Style One

Model No.:	A-67
Designer:	Helen Perrin Farnlund
Height:	1 7/8", 4.8 cm
Colour:	See below
Issued:	1950

Colourways	U.S.$	Can.$	U.K.£
1. Brown	8.00	16.00	14.00
2. White	8.00	16.00	14.00
3. Yellow	8.00	16.00	14.00

Note: This forms a pair with Hen, feathered feet, Style One (A-68), page 160.

Rooster, feathered feet
Style Two

Model No.:	A-445
Designer:	Helen Perrin Farnlund
Height:	2 1/8", 5.4 cm
Colour:	White; green, blue and brown markings, red comb
Issued:	Fall 1960 - Fall 1961

Model No.	U.S.$	Can.$	U.K.£
A-445	18.00	36.00	30.00

Note: Pair with Hen, feathered feet, Style Two (A-446), page 149. Auerspurse colourway issued fall 1960.

Squatty Hen
First Version (With chick)

Model No.:	A-373
Designer:	Helen Perrin Farnlund
Height:	1", 2.5 cm
Colour:	White hen, yellow chicks
Issued:	Spring 1958

Description	U.S.$	Can.$	U.K.£
First version	15.00	30.00	25.00

Squatty Hen
Second Version (Without chick)

Model No.:	A-373
Designer:	Helen Perrin Farnlund
Height:	1", 2.5 cm
Colour:	1. Brown
	2. White
Issued:	Fall 1976 - fall 1987

Colourways	U.S.$	Can.$	U.K.£
1. Brown	15.00	30.00	25.00
2. White	15.00	30.00	25.00

Note: Model A-373 was made for a total of 25 seasons. Pair with Squatty Rooster (A-374), page 163.

Squatty Rooster

Model No.:	A-374
Designer:	Helen Perrin Farnlund
Height:	1 ¼", 3.2 cm
Colour:	1. Brown
	2. White
Issued:	Spring 1958 - spring 1971

Colourways	U.S.$	Can.$	U.K.£
1. Brown	10.00	20.00	17.00
2. White	6.00	12.00	10.00

Note: This forms a pair with Squatty Hen (A-373), page 162.

Tiny Hen

Model No.:	A-040
Designer:	Helen Perrin Farnlund
Height:	7/8", 2.2 cm
Colour:	White, green shading, red comb; gloss
Issued:	Fall 1962 - fall 1963

Model No.	U.S.$	Can.$	U.K.£
A-040	8.00	16.00	14.00

Note: This forms a pair with Tiny Rooster (A-041).

Tiny Rooster

Model No.:	A-041
Designer:	Helen Perrin Farnlund
Height:	1 1/8", 2.8
Colour:	White, green shading, red comb; gloss
Issued:	Fall 1962 - fall 1963

Model No.	U.S.$	Can.$	U.K.£
A-041	8.00	16.00	14.00

Note: This forms a pair with Tiny Hen (A-040).

HUMMINGBIRDS

Hummingbird
Style One, First Version

Model No.: A-811
Designer: Helen Perrin Farnlund
Height: 1 1/8", 2.8 cm
Colour: Green wings, white breast, wire bill
Issued: 1982

Description	U.S. $	Can. $	U.K. £
First version	12.00	24.00	20.00

Fuchsia

Model No.: A-812
Designer: Helen Perrin Farnlund
Height: 1 ¼", 3.1 cm
Colour: 1. Pink
        2. Pink and purple
Issued: 1982

Colourways	U.S. $	Can. $	U.K. £
1. Pink	12.00	24.00	20.00
2. Pink/purple			

Note: Fuchsia has a hole in the side for insertion of the bird's wire beak. Fuchsia has a wire extending from the stem for suspension; it is missing from this illustration.

Hummingbird
Style One, Second Version

Model No.: A-811
Designer: Helen Perrin Farnlund
Height: 1 1/8", 2.8 cm
Colour: Green back and wings, white belly, red throat and head
Issued: Spring 1988 - spring 1990

Description	U.S. $	Can. $	U.K. £
Second version	8.00	16.00	14.00

Note: A wire for suspension is attached to the bird.

Hummingbird
Style Two

Model No.: A-3178
Designer: Robert McGuinness
Height: 2 1/8", 5.4 cm
Colour: Red head, pink and lavender wings, white flowers
Issued: Fall 1995 to the present

Model No.	U.S. $	Can. $	U.K. £
A-3178	10.00	20.00	17.00

LARK

Lark

Model No.:	A-983
Designer:	Helen Perrin Farnlund
Height:	3/8", 0.9 mm
Colour:	Yellow
Issued:	Fall 1976 - spring 1981

Model No.	U.S. $	Can. $	U.K. £
A-983	5.00	10.00	8.50

MACAW

Macaw

Model No.:	A-2007
Designer:	Maureen Love
Height:	3 ¼", 8.3 cm
Colour:	Blue back, yellow chest and tail feathers
Issued:	Spring 1988 - spring 1990

Model No.	U.S. $	Can. $	U.K. £
A-2007	15.00	30.00	25.00

MALLARD DUCKS

Mallard Drake
Style One (Wings out, head to left)

Model No.:	A-134
Designer:	Helen Perrin Farnlund
Height:	2 ½", 6.4 cm
Colour:	Green, light and dark brown, white; gloss
Issued:	Spring 1951 - fall 1952

Description	U.S.$	Can.$	U.K.£
Style one	18.00	36.00	30.00

Mallard Drake
Style Two (Seated)

Model No.:	A-319
Designer:	Helen Perrin Farnlund
Height:	1 ¼", 3.2 cm
Colour:	Green head, brown body
Issued:	Spring 1957

Description	U.S.$	Can.$	U.K.£
Style two	20.00	40.00	35.00

Note: See also Duck, seated, page 149 and Duck Papa, page 152.

Mallard Drake
Style Three (Wings out, head forward)
Model No.: A-862
Designer: Maureen Love
Height: 2 ¾", 7.0 cm
Colour: Brown, black and white
Issued: Fall 1985 - spring 1997

Description	U.S.$	Can.$	U.K.£
Style three	12.00	24.00	20.00

Mallard Duck, mouth closed
Model No.: A-135
Designer: Helen Perrin Farnlund
Height: 1 ¾", 4.4 cm
Colour: 1. Golden brown with dark brown markings; matte
2. Pale brown with dark brown markings; matte
Issued: Spring 1951 - fall 1952

Colourways	U.S.$	Can.$	U.K.£
1. Golden brown	15.00	30.00	25.00
2. Pale brown	15.00	30.00	25.00

Mallard Duck, mouth open
Model No.: A-863
Designer: Helen Perrin Farnlund
Height: 1 ½", 3.8 cm
Colour: 1. Brown, black wing bars
2. Dark brown, blue wing bars
3. Light brown, blue wing bars
Issued: Fall 1985 - spring 1989

Colourways	U.S.$	Can.$	U.K.£
1. Brown/black	12.00	24.00	20.00
2. Dark brown/blue	12.00	24.00	20.00
3. Light brown/blue	12.00	24.00	20.00

Mallard Duckling
Model No.: A-137
Designer: Helen Perrin Farnlund
Height: 1 1/8", 2.8 cm
Colour: Yellow, orange beak and feet
Issued: Spring 1951 - spring 1953

Model No.	U.S.$	Can.$	U.K.£
A-137	5.00	10.00	8.50

Note: The size may vary slightly.

Mallard Duck Family

Mallard Papa

Model No.:	A-3281
Designer:	Maureen Love
Height:	1 9/16", 4.0 cm
Colour:	Dark brown, green head, red breast
Issued:	Fall 1998 to the present

Model No.	U.S.$	Can.$	U.K.£
A-3281	2.00	4.00	3.50

Mallard Mama

Model No.:	A-3282
Designer:	Maureen Love
Height:	1 3/8", 3.5 cm
Colour:	Red-brown
Issued:	Fall 1998 to the present

Model No.	U.S.$	Can.$	U.K.£
A-3282	4.00	8.00	7.00

Mallard Duckling

Model No.:	A-3283
Designer:	Maureen Love
Height:	¾", 1.9 cm
Colour:	Dark brown and yellow
Issued:	Fall 1998 to the present

Model No.	U.S.$	Can.$	U.K.£
A-3283	4.00	8.00	7.00

ORIOLES

Oriole
Style One (Tail down)

Model No.:	A-063
Designer:	Martha Armstrong
Height:	9/16", 0.8 cm
Colour:	Red, black eyes and beak
Issued:	Fall 1965 - fall 1976
Varieties:	Disney model 5098 (Cardinal)

Description	U.S. $	Can. $	U.K. £
Style one	5.00	10.00	8.50

Oriole
Style Two (Tail up)

Model No.:	A-982
Designer:	Helen Perrin Farnlund
Height:	¼", 0.6 cm
Colour:	Orange and black
Issued:	Fall 1976 - spring 1981

Description	U.S. $	Can. $	U.K. £
Style two	5.00	10.00	8.50

Note: Pair with Birdbath (A-986), page 386.

OSTRICHES

Ostrich Baby and Mama

Model No.:	Baby — A-44
	Mama — A-43
Designer:	Helen Perrin Farnlund
Height:	Baby — 1", 2.5 cm
	Mama — 2 ½", 6.4 cm
Colour:	1. Black; brown head, neck and legs; white tail
	2. Lavender; pink neck, head and legs
Issued:	Fall 1959 - spring 1987

Description	U.S. $	Can. $	U.K. £
1. Baby — black	6.00	12.00	10.00
2. Baby — lavender	15.00	30.00	25.00
3. Mama — black	10.00	20.00	17.00
4. Mama — lavender	25.00	50.00	45.00

Ostrich Egg

Model No.:	A-43A
Designer:	Helen Perrin Farnlund
Height:	½", 1.3 cm
Colour:	White
Issued:	Spring 1959, spring 1960, spring 1980 - fall 1982

Model No.	U.S. $	Can. $	U.K. £
A-43A	6.00	12.00	10.00

OWLS

Barn Owl
Style One (Standing)
Model No.: A-421
Designer: Helen Perrin Farnlund
Height: 1", 2.5 cm
Colour: See below
Issued: c.1965, c.1975

Colourways	U.S. $	Can. $	U.K. £
1. Brown	6.00	12.00	10.00
2. Grey	6.00	12.00	10.00

Note: Model A-421 was made for 25 seasons.

Barn Owl
Style Two (On stump)
Model No.: A-3196
Designer: Maureen Love
Height: 1 7/8", 4.8 cm
Colour: Light brown body, white face and breast, brown stump
Issued: Fall 1996 to the present

Model No.	U.S. $	Can. $	U.K. £
A-3196	5.00	10.00	8.50

Barn Owl Baby
Model No.: A-422
Designer: Helen Perrin Farnlund
Height: 5/8", 1.6 cm
Colour: See below
Issued: c.1965, c.1975

Colourways	U.S. $	Can. $	U.K. £
1. Brown	4.00	8.00	7.00
2. Grey	4.00	8.00	7.00

Note: Model A-422 was made for 25 seasons.

Owl on Branch
Style One (Large branch)
Model No.: A-3129
Designer: Edith Carrion
Height: 1 7/8", 4.8 cm
Colour: Golden brown
Issued: Fall 1993 - fall 1995

Model No.	U.S. $	Can. $	U.K. £
A-3129	5.00	10.00	8.50

Owl on Branch
Style Two (Small branch)
Model No.:	A-3199
Designer:	Robert McGuinness
Height:	1 7/8", 4.8 cm
Colour:	Brown, white breast
Issued:	Spring 1996 to the present

Model No.	U.S. $	Can. $	U.K. £
A-3199	6.00	12.00	10.00

Owl Mama (A-155), Owl Papa (A-154), Owlet (A-156)

Owl Family

The owls, designed by Tom Masterson, were issued in fall 1951 and produced for more than 30 years. Earlier models were brown with white markings and later models, buff with dark brown markings; size and colour variations occur. These owls were glued onto a base for display.

Owl Mama
Model No.:	A-155
Height:	1 ¼", 3.2 cm

Colourways	U.S. $	Can. $	U.K. £
1. Brown	5.00	10.00	8.50
2. Buff	8.00	16.00	14.00

Owl Papa
Model No.:	A-154
Height:	1 ½", 3.8 cm

Colourways	U.S. $	Can. $	U.K. £
1. Brown	5.00	10.00	8.50
2. Buff	8.00	16.00	14.00

Owlet
Model No.:	A-156
Height:	7/8", 2.2 cm

Colourways	U.S. $	Can. $	U.K. £
1. Brown	3.00	6.00	5.00
2. Buff	5.00	10.00	8.50

Professor Owl
First Variation (Black mortarboard)
Model No.: A-421
Designer: Helen Perrin Farnlund
Height: 1 1/8", 2.8 cm
Colour: Grey
Issued: Spring 1960 - fall 1961

Description	U.S. $	Can. $	U.K. £
First version	15.00	30.00	25.00

Note: For information on the Book (A-421A); see page 387.

Professor Owl
Second Variation (Beige mortarboard)
Model No.: A-846
Designer: Helen Perrin Farnlund
Height: 1 1/8", 2.8 cm
Colour: Brown
Issued: Fall 1984 - fall 1988

Description	U.S. $	Can. $	U.K. £
Second version	7.00	14.00	12.00

Snowy Owl Baby
Model No.: A-352
Designer: Martha Armstrong
Height: ¾", 1.9 cm
Colour: White
Issued: c.1957 - c.1972

Description	U.S. $	Can. $	U.K. £
1. Monrovia	5.00	10.00	8.50
2. San Dimas	4.00	8.00	7.00

Snowy Owl Mama
Model No.: A-351
Designer: Martha Armstrong
Height: 1 3/8", 3.5 cm
Colour: White
Issued: c.1957 - c.1972

Description	U.S. $	Can. $	U.K. £
1. Monrovia	10.00	20.00	17.00
2. San Dimas	7.00	14.00	12.00

Note: Models A-351 and A-352 were made for 29 seasons in the late 1950s and early 1970s.

Wise Old Owl

Model No.: A-883
Designer: Helen Perrin Farnlund
Height: 1 ¾", 4.4 cm
Colour: Brown and white owl with yellow eyes
Issued: Fall 1984 - spring 1988

Model No.	U.S. $	Can. $	U.K. £
A-883	8.00	16.00	14.00

Note: This forms a pair with Tree (A-834), page 395.

PARROTS

Parrot Baby With Nest

Model No.: A-870
Designer: Helen Perrin Farnlund
Height: 1 1/16", 2.7 cm
Colour: Light green
Issued: Fall 1973

Model No.	U.S. $	Can. $	U.K. £
A-870	10.00	20.00	17.00

Parrot Baby

Model No.: A-492/871
Designer: Helen Perrin Farnlund
Height: ¾", 1.9 cm
Colour: 1. Green; Auerspurse
        2. Green; gloss
Issued: Spring 1961,
        spring 1986 - 1987

Description	U.S. $	Can. $	U.K. £
1. Auerspurse	10.00	20.00	17.00
2. Gloss	7.00	14.00	12.00

Parrot Mama

Model No.: A-492/870
Designer: Helen Perrin Farnlund
Height: 1 ¼", 3.2 cm
Colour: 1. Green; Auerspurse
        2. Green; gloss
Issued: Spring 1961,
        spring 1986 - spring 1988

Description	U.S. $	Can. $	U.K. £
1. Auerspurse	18.00	36.00	30.00
2. Gloss	10.00	20.00	17.00

PELICANS

Production on models A-101 and A-102 began in fall 1959 and resumed from fall 1976 to fall 1987.

Pelican

Model No.:	A-101
Designer:	Helen Perrin Farnlund
Height:	1 ¼", 3.1 cm
Colour:	1. Grey with orange bill
	2. White with yellow bill
Issued:	See above

Colourways	U.S. $	Can. $	U.K. £
1. Grey/orange	7.00	14.00	12.00
2. White/yellow	7.00	14.00	12.00

Pelican Baby

Model No.:	A-102
Designer:	Helen Perrin Farnlund
Height:	1", 2.5 cm
Colour:	1. Grey with orange bill
	2. White with yellow bill
Issued:	See above

Colourways	U.S. $	Can. $	U.K. £
1. Grey/orange	4.00	8.00	7.00
2. White/yellow	4.00	8.00	7.00

Pelican, flying

Model No.:	A-810
Designer:	Maureen Love
Width:	4", 10.1 cm
Colour:	Light and dark brown
Issued:	1982

Model No.	U.S. $	Can. $	U.K. £
A-810	15.00	30.00	25.00

Note: A wire is attached to the pelican's tail for posing.

Pelican on Piling

Model No.:	A-3265
Designer:	Robert McGuinness
Height:	2 3/8", 6.0 cm
Colour:	Brown body and wings, white head and neck, yellow crest
Issued:	Fall 1998 to the present

Model No.	U.S. $	Can. $	U.K. £
A-3265	7.00	14.00	12.00

PEREGRINE FALCONS

Peregrine Falcon

Model No.:	A-2075
Designer:	Maureen Love
Height:	1 5/8", 4.1 cm
Colour:	Grey, white and black body; yellow head and feet
Issued:	Spring 1990 - fall 1993

Model No.	U.S. $	Can. $	U.K. £
A-2075	10.00	20.00	17.00

Peregrine Falcon Baby

Model No.:	A-3012
Designer:	Shi Yi Chen
Height:	7/8", 2.2 cm
Colour:	Grey and yellow
Issued:	Spring 1991

Model No.	U.S. $	Can. $	U.K. £
A-3012	7.00	14.00	12.00

PENGUINS

Penguin Baby
Style One (Beak open, yellow feet)

Model No.:	A-26
Designer:	Maxine Renaker (possibly)
Height:	1", 2.5 cm
Colour:	Black and white body, dark yellow beak and feet
Issued:	1949

Model No.	U.S. $	Can. $	U.K. £
A-26	5.00	10.00	8.50

Penguin Mama
Style One (Yellow feet)

Model No.:	A-25
Designer:	Maxine Renaker (possibly)
Height:	2 ¼", 5.7 cm
Colour:	Black and white body, dark yellow beak and feet
Issued:	1949

Model No.	U.S. $	Can. $	U.K. £
A-25	10.00	20.00	17.00

Emperor Penguin

Model No.:	A-2018		
Designer:	Shi Yi Chen		
Height:	1 15/16", 5.4 cm		
Colour:	Black and white body, orange chest		
Issued:	Fall 1988 to the present		

Model No.	U.S. $	Can. $	U.K. £
A-2018	5.00	10.00	8.50

Penguin Baby
Style Two (Right wing raised)

Model No.:	A-232
Designer:	D. Haas
Height:	1", 2.5 cm
Colour:	See below
Issued:	Fall 1954 - spring 1955
	Fall 1971 to the present

Colourways	U.S. $	Can. $	U.K. £
1. Black/white	3.00	6.00	5.00
2. Purple /pink	10.00	20.00	17.00

Note: The issue date for the purple/pink colourway is unknown.

Penguin Mama
Style Two (White feet)

Model No.:	A-230
Designer:	D. Haas
Height:	1 ¾", 4.4 cm
Colour:	See below
Issued:	Fall 1954 - spring 1955
	1971 to the present

Colourways	U.S. $	Can. $	U.K. £
1. Black/white	4.00	8.00	7.00
2. Purple/pink	20.00	40.00	35.00

Note: The issue date for the purple/pink colourway is unknown.

Penguin Papa With Hat

Model No.:	A-231
Designer:	D. Haas
Height:	2", 5.1 cm
Colour:	Black and white body, black hat, dark yellow bill and feet
Issued:	Fall 1954 - spring 1955
	1971 to the present

Model No.	U.S. $	Can. $	U.K. £
A-231	4.00	8.00	7.00

Penguin, skating
Style One (Bent over)

Model No.:	A-3240
Designer:	Helen Perrin Farnlund
Height:	1 1/8", 2.8 cm
Colour:	Black and white body, yellow beak, brown feet, silver skates
Issued:	Spring 1997 - spring 1998

Description	U.S. $	Can. $	U.K. £
Style one	6.00	12.00	10.00

Penguin, skating
Style Two (Upright)

Model No.:	A-3264
Designer:	Helen Perrin Farnlund
Height:	2", 5.1 cm
Colour:	Black and white body, dark yellow beak, silver skates, blue and yellow hat and scarf
Issued:	Spring 1998 to the present

Description	U.S. $	Can. $	U.K. £
Style two	7.00	14.00	12.00

Penguin, sliding

Model No.:	A-882
Designer:	Helen Perrin Farnlund
Height:	1", 2.5 cm
Colour:	Black and white body, dark yellow bill
Issued:	Spring 1987 - spring 1994

Model No.	U.S. $	Can. $	U.K. £
A-882	4.00	8.00	7.00

PUFFIN

Puffin

Model No.:	A-894
Designer:	Helen Perrin Farnlund
Height:	1 3/8", 3.5 cm
Colour:	Black and white body, yellow and black bill, yellow feet
Issued:	Fall 1987 - fall 1988

Model No.	U.S. $	Can. $	U.K. £
A-894	15.00	30.00	25.00

QUAIL

Quail Baby
First Version (Metal feather)
Model No.: A-322
Designer: Martha Armstrong
Height: ½", 1.3 cm
Colour: Light brown body with black and white markings, black head, metal feather
Issued: Spring 1957

Model No.	U.S. $	Can. $	U.K. £
A-322	15.00	30.00	25.00

Quail Papa/Quail Mama
First Version (Metal feather)
Model No.: A-321
Designer: Martha Armstrong
Height: 1", 2.5 cm
Colour: Light brown body, white markings, black and white head, wire legs, metal feather
Issued: Spring 1957

Model No.	U.S. $	Can. $	U.K. £
A-321	20.00	40.00	35.00

Quail Papa /Quail Mama
Second Version (With moulded feather)
Model No.: A-321
Designer: Martha Armstrong
Height: 1", 2.5 cm
Colour: Brown head and body, blue breast, black feather
Issued: 1972, spring 1986 - spring 1988

Description	U.S. $	Can. $	U.K. £
Second version	10.00	20.00	17.00

Quail Baby
Second Version (Without feather)
Model No.: A-322
Designer: Martha Armstrong
Height: ½", 1.3 cm
Colour: 1. Black head, brown and white body, white breast
2. Brown head and body, blue breast
Issued: 1972, spring 1986 - fall 1987

Description	U.S. $	Can. $	U.K. £
Second version	7.00	14.00	12.00

ROBINS

Robin Baby

Model No.:	A-168
Designer:	Tom Masterson
Height:	5/8", 1.6 cm
Colour:	Light brown breast, white body, black head
Issued:	Spring 1952, fall 1957, fall 1965 - spring 1979

Description	U.S. $	Can. $	U.K. £
1. Monrovia	5.00	10.00	8.50
2. San Dimas	4.00	8.00	7.00

Robin Mama

Model No.:	A-167
Designer:	Tom Masterson
Height:	1 ¼", 3.2 cm
Colour:	Light and dark brown
Issued:	Spring 1952, fall 1957, fall 1965 - spring 1979

Description	U.S. $	Can. $	U.K. £
1. Monrovia	8.00	16.00	14.00
2. San Dimas	5.00	10.00	8.50

SEAGULLS

Seagull, flying

Model No.: A-989
Designer: Maureen Love
Width: 2", 5.1 cm
Colour: White, grey, orange bill
Issued: Fall 1976 - fall 1982

Model No.	U.S. $	Can. $	U.K. £
A-989	10.00	20.00	17.00

Seagull, landing

Model No.: A-988
Designer: Maureen Love
Height: 7/8", 2.2 cm
Colour: White, grey, orange bill
Issued: Fall 1976 - fall 1982

Model No.	U.S. $	Can. $	U.K. £
A-988	7.00	14.00	12.00

Seagull, swimming

Model No.: A-987
Designer: Maureen Love
Height: 5/8", 1.6 cm
Colour: White, grey, orange bill
Issued: Fall 1976 - spring 1978

Model No.	U.S. $	Can. $	U.K. £
A-987	7.00	14.00	12.00

Seagull Cove

Model No.: A-995
Designer: Maureen Love
Size: 6" x 4 ½", 15.0 x 11.9 cm
Colour: Pale yellow, pale blue and grey
Issued: Fall 1976 - fall 1977

Description	U.S. $	Can. $	U.K. £
1. Cove	20.00	40.00	35.00
2. Complete set	30.00	60.00	50.00

SWANS

Swan Family On Swan Lake

Swan Lake with Cygnets (C-3, C-5, C-1, C-6, C-4 and C-2) and Swan, Style Two, (A-380)

Swan, Style One, Defined wings, raised

Swan, Style Two, Wings flat to body

Swan
Style One (Defined wings, raised)

Model No.: A-380
Designer: Helen Perrin Farnlund
Height: 1 1/8", 2.8 cm
Colour: White
Issued: Spring 1958, fall 1970, fall 1971

Model No.	U.S. $	Can. $	U.K. £
A-380	15.00	30.00	25.00

Swan
Style Two (Wings flat to body)

Model No.: A-380
Designer: Helen Perrin Farnlund
Height: 1 1/8", 2.8 cm
Colour: White
Issued: Fall 1976 - spring 1990

Model No.	U.S. $	Can. $	U.K. £
A-380	6.00	12.00	10.00

Cygnet
First Version (Head up, forward)

Model No.: C-1
Designer: Helen Perrin Farnlund
Height: 7/16", 0.4 cm
Colour: Grey and black, orange beak
Issued: Fall 1976 - fall 1978

Model No.	U.S. $	Can. $	U.K. £
C-1	4.00	8.00	7.00

Cygnet
Fourth Version (Head up, right)

Model No.: C-4
Designer: Helen Perrin Farnlund
Height: 7/16", 0.4 cm
Colour: Grey and black, orange beak
Issued: Fall 1976 - spring 1978

Model No.	U.S. $	Can. $	U.K. £
C-4	4.00	8.00	7.00

Cygnet
Second Version (Head up, left)

Model No.: C-2
Designer: Helen Perrin Farnlund
Height: 7/16", 0.4 cm
Colour: Grey and black, orange beak
Issued: Fall 1976 - spring 1978

Model No.	U.S. $	Can. $	U.K. £
C-2	4.00	8.00	7.00

Cygnet
Fifth Version (Beak open)

Model No.: C-5
Designer: Helen Perrin Farnlund
Height: 7/16", 0.4 cm
Colour: Grey and black, orange beak
Issued: Fall 1976 - spring 1978

Model No.	U.S. $	Can. $	U.K. £
C-5	4.00	8.00	7.00

Cygnet
Third Version (Sleeping)

Model No.: C-3
Designer: Helen Perrin Farnlund
Height: 7/16", 0.4 cm
Colour: Grey and black, orange beak
Issued: Fall 1976 - spring 1978

Model No.	U.S. $	Can. $	U.K. £
C-3	4.00	8.00	7.00

Cygnet
Sixth Version (Drinking)

Model No.: C-6
Designer: Helen Perrin Farnlund
Height: 5/16", 0.8 cm
Colour: Grey and black, orange beak
Issued: Fall 1976 - spring 1978

Model No.	U.S. $	Can. $	U.K. £
C-6	4.00	8.00	7.00

Swan Lake

Model No.: A-380A
Designer: Helen Perrin Farnlund
Length: 5", 12.7 cm
Colour: Tan and blue
Issued: Fall 1976 - fall 1977

Description	U.S. $	Can. $	U.K. £
1 Swan Lake	20.00	40.00	35.00
2. Complete set	30.00	60.00	50.00

Note: Only models C-5 and C-6 were available singly.

Swan Mama

Model No.:	A-66	
Designer:	Helen Perrin Farnlund	
Height:	1 ¾", 4.4 cm	
Colour:	White	
Issued:	1950	

Model No.	U.S. $	Can. $	U.K. £
A-66	15.00	30.00	25.00

Cygnet, standing

Model No.:	A-64	
Designer:	Helen Perrin Farnlund	
Height:	1 1/8", 2.8 cm	
Colour:	Yellow	
Issued:	1950	

Model No.	U.S. $	Can. $	U.K. £
A-64	8.00	16.00	14.00

Cygnet, swimming

Model No.:	A-65	
Designer:	Helen Perrin Farnlund	
Height:	7/8", 2.2 cm	
Colour:	Yellow	
Issued:	1950	

Model No.	U.S. $	Can. $	U.K. £
A-65	8.00	16.00	14.00

TOUCAN

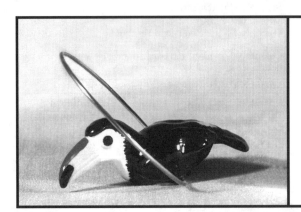

Toucan

Model No.:	A-899	
Designer:	Maureen Love	
Height:	2", 5.1 cm	
Colour:	Black body; white face; red, orange and black beak	
Issued:	1988	

Model No.	U.S. $	Can. $	U.K. £
A-899	15.00	30.00	25.00

Note: See also Specialties section, Toucan (899), page 460.

TWEETIE BIRDS

Papa (A-106), Baby (A-105), Mama (A-107)

Tweetie Bird Family
Style One

Tweetie Bird Baby
Style One

Model No.:	A-105
Designer:	Helen Perrin Farnlund
Height:	1", 2.5 cm
Colour:	1. Blue
	2. Pale yellow, black dot eyes, wire legs
Issued:	Spring 1950 - Fall 1951, fall 1967

Colourways	U.S. $	Can. $	U.K. £
1. Blue	5.00	10.00	8.50
2. Yellow	5.00	10.00	8.50

Tweetie Bird Mama
Style One

Model No.:	A-107
Designer:	Helen Perrin Farnlund
Height:	¾", 1.9 cm
Colour:	1. Blue
	2. Pale yellow, black wings and tail feathers, wire legs
Issued:	Spring 1950 - fall 1951, fall 1967

Colourways	U.S. $	Can. $	U.K. £
1. Blue	8.00	16.00	14.00
2. Yellow	8.00	16.00	14.00

Tweetie Bird Papa
Style One

Model No.:	A-106
Designer:	Helen Perrin Farnlund
Height:	1 ¾", 4.4 cm
Colour:	1. Blue
	2. Pale yellow, black wings and tail feathers, wire legs
Issued:	Spring 1950 - fall 1951, fall 1967

Colourways	U.S. $	Can. $	U.K. £
1. Blue	10.00	20.00	17.00
2. Yellow	10.00	20.00	17.00

Mama (A-482), Papa (A-481), Sister (A-484), Brother (A-483)

Tweetie Bird Family
Style Two

These birds were available in the following colourways: blue, brown, green, orange and yellow, with blue being the most common colour..

Tweetie Bird Mama
Style Two

Model No.: A-482
Designer: Helen Perrin Farnlund
Height: 7/8", 2.2 cm
Issued: 1961, 1966 - 1988

Colourways	U.S. $	Can. $	U.K. £
1. Blue	6.00	12.00	10.00
2. Other colourways	10.00	20.00	17.00

Tweetie Bird Papa
Style Two

Model No.: A-481
Designer: Helen Perrin Farnlund
Height: 1 1/8", 2.8 cm
Issued: 1961, 1966 - 1988

Colourways	U.S. $	Can. $	U.K. £
1. Blue	6.00	12.00	10.00
2. Other colourways	10.00	20.00	17.00

Tweetie Bird Sister

Model No.: A-484
Designer: Helen Perrin Farnlund
Height: 7/8", 2.2 cm
Issued: 1961, 1966 - 1988

Colourways	U.S. $	Can. $	U.K. £
1. Blue	6.00	12.00	10.00
2. Other colourways	10.00	20.00	17.00

Tweetie Bird Brother

Model No.: A-483
Designer: Helen Perrin Farnlund
Height: 7/8", 2.2 cm
Issued: 1961, 1966 - 1968

Colourways	U.S. $	Can. $	U.K. £
1. Blue	10.00	20.00	17.00
2. Other colourways	10.00	20.00	17.00

Baby Bird

Model No.: A-495
Designer: Helen Perrin Farnlund
Height: ½", 1.3 cm
Issued: 1961, 1966 - 1988

Colourways	U.S. $	Can. $	U.K. £
1. Blue	5.00	10.00	8.50
2. Other colourways	9.00	18.00	15.00

WOOD DUCK

Wood Duck
Model No.: A-3443
Designer: Maureen Love
Height: 1 ¾", 4.4 cm
Colour: Black, brown and white
Issued: Fall 1997 to the present

Model No.	U.S.$	Can.$	U.K.£
A-3443	5.50	11.00	9.50

Note: This duck is a modification of the Stoneware Mallard (2036), page 457.

WOODPECKERS

Woodpecker Baby
Model No.: A-223A
Designer: Tom Masterson
Height: ¾", 1.9 cm
Colour: White body shaded with black, red stripe on head, wire legs
Issued: 1954

Model No.	U.S. $	Can. $	U.K. £
A-223A	15.00	30.00	25.00

Woodpecker Baby in Nest
Model No.: A-223B
Designer: Tom Masterson
Height: 1", 2.5 cm
Colour: White body shaded with black, red stripe on head, brown nest
Issued: Fall 1973

Model No.	U.S. $	Can. $	U.K. £
A-223B	15.00	30.00	25.00

Woodpecker Mama
Model No.: A-222
Designer: Tom Masterson
Height: 2 ½", 6.4 cm
Colour: White body shaded with black, red stripe on head, wire legs
Issued: 1954

Model No.	U.S. $	Can. $	U.K. £
A-222	25.00	50.00	45.00

Penguin Mama, Style Two (A-230); Penguin Baby, Style Two (A-232)

BUTTERFLIES AND MOTHS

INDEX TO MINIATURE
BUTTERFLIES AND MOTHS

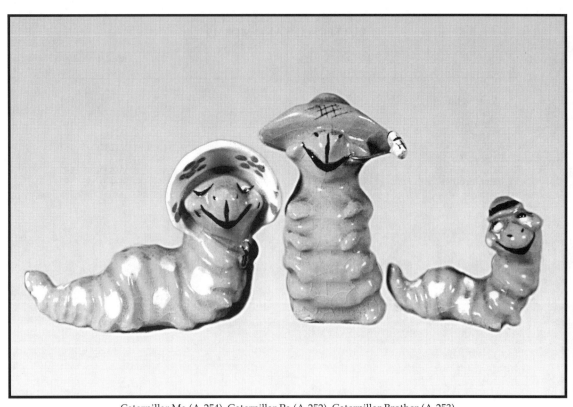

Caterpillar Ma (A-254), Caterpillar Pa (A-252), Caterpillar Brother (A-253)

BUTTERFLIES

Monarch Butterfly, large

Model No.:	A-99
Designer:	Helen Perrin Farnlund
Size:	2 ¾" x 1 ¾", 7.0 x 4.4 cm
Colour:	Orange and black with white markings; metal antenna and legs
Issued:	Spring 1950, spring 1951

Model No.	U.S.$	Can.$	U.K.£
A-99	20.00	40.00	35.00

Monarch Butterfly, medium

Model No.:	A-113
Designer:	Helen Perrin Farnlund
Size:	1 ¾" x 1 ½", 4.4 x 3.8 cm
Colour:	Orange and black with white markings; metal antenna and legs
Issued:	Spring 1950, spring 1951, fall 1967

Model No.	U.S.$	Can.$	U.K.£
A-113	20.00	40.00	35.00

Monarch Butterfly, small

Model No.:	A-115
Designer:	Helen Perrin Farnlund
Size:	1 ¼" x 5/8", 3.1 x 1.59 cm
Colour:	Orange and black with white markings; metal antenna and legs
Issued:	Spring 1950, spring 1951

Model No.	U.S.$	Can.$	U.K.£
A-115	15.00	30.00	25.00

CATERPILLARS

Caterpillar Mama/Papa

Model No.:	A-100
Designer:	Helen Perrin Farnlund
Height:	1", 2.54 cm
Colour:	Green; black and white eyes
Issued:	Spring 1950 - c.1970
Varieties:	Also called Worm Mama/Papa

Description	U.S.$	Can.$	U.K.£
1. Monrovia	9.00	18.00	15.00
2. San Dimas	7.00	14.00	12.00

Caterpillar Baby

Model No.:	A-119
Designer:	Helen Perrin Farnlund
Height:	5/8", 1.58 cm
Colour:	Green; black and white eyes
Issued:	Spring 1950 - fall 1954
Varieties:	Also called Worm Baby

Model No.	U.S.$	Can.$	U.K.£
A-119	6.00	12.00	10.00

Note: Early models show teeth, the whites of the eyes and eyebrows.
Other colourways exist. Mama was made for nineteen seasons from spring 1950 to the early 1970s.

Caterpillar Baby and Mama

Model No.:	1. Baby — A-38
	2. Mama — A-37
Designer:	Helen Perrin Farnlund
Length:	1. Baby ¾", 1.9 cm
	2. Mama 1 ¼", 3.1 cm
Colour:	Brown with green spots
Issued:	c.1960 - c.1970

Description	U.S.$	Can.$	U.K.£
1. Baby	3.00	6.00	5.00
2. Mama	6.00	12.00	10.00

Caterpillar Baby/Brother

Model No.:	A-253
Designer:	Nell Bortells
Height:	¾", 1.9 cm
Colour:	Pale green; lavender beanie
Issued:	Spring 1955 - fall 1982

Description	U.S.$	Can.$	U.K.£
1. Monrovia	8.00	16.00	14.00
2. San Dimas	3.00	6.00	5.00

Caterpillar Sister

Model No.:	A-254
Designer:	Nell Bortells
Height:	¾", 1.90 cm
Colour:	Pale green; red bow; white teeth
Issued:	Fall 1969 - fall 1975

Description	U.S.$	Can.$	U.K.£
1. Monrovia	8.00	16.00	14.00
2. San Dimas	3.00	6.00	5.00

Caterpillar Pa

Model No.:	A-252
Designer:	Nell Bortells
Height:	1 ¼", 3.1 cm
Colour:	Green; black hat
Issued:	Spring 1955 - spring 1988

Description	U.S.$	Can.$	U.K.£
1. Monrovia	10.00	20.00	17.00
2. San Dimas	5.00	10.00	8.50

Caterpillar Ma

Model No.:	A-254
Designer:	Nell Bortells
Height:	1", 2.54 cm
Colour:	Green; blue bonnet with black ties
Issued:	Spring 1955 - fall 1971

Description	U.S.$	Can.$	U.K.£
1. Monrovia	10.00	20.00	17.00
2. San Dimas	5.00	10.00	8.50

Note: Early models of A-253 had a propeller.

MOTHS

Moth, large

Model No.:	A-489
Designer:	Helen Perrin Farnlund
Size:	2 ¾" x 1 ¾", 7.0 x 4.4 cm
Colour:	1. Blue; wire antenna and legs
	2. Orange; wire antenna and legs
Issued:	Spring 1961 - fall 1961

Colourways	U.S.$	Can.$	U.K.£
1. Blue	20.00	40.00	35.00
2. Orange	20.00	40.00	35.00

Moth, small

Model No.:	A-490
Designer:	Helen Perrin Farnlund
Size:	1 ¼" x 5/8", 3.2 x 1.6 cm
Colour:	1. Blue; wire antenna and legs
	2. Orange; wire antenna and legs
Issued:	Spring 1961 - fall 1961

Colourways	U.S.$	Can.$	U.K.£
1. Blue	15.00	30.00	25.00
2. Orange	15.00	30.00	25.00

MINIATURE CATS

INDEX TO
MINIATURE CATS

ABYSSINNIAN

ALLEY CATS

Abyssinnian

Model No.:	A-2004
Designer:	Shi Yi Chen
Height:	1 3/8", 3.5 cm
Colour:	Tan, brown shading
Issued:	Spring 1989 - spring 1990

Model No.	U.S.$	Can.$	U.K.£
A-2004	6.00	12.00	10.00

Alley Cat

Model No.:	A-464
Designer:	Helen Perrin Farnlund
Height:	¾", 1.9 cm
Colour:	1. Black, white chest
	2. Grey, white chest
Issued:	Fall 1959 - spring 1976

Colourways	U.S.$	Can.$	U.K.£
1. Black/white	10.00	20.00	17.00
2. Grey/white	5.00	10.00	8.50

Alley Kitten
First Version (Thicker, less definition)

Model No.:	A-005
Designer:	Helen Perrin Farnlund
Height:	5/8", 1.6 cm
Colour:	See below
Issued:	Fall 1961 - spring 1962,
	spring 1968 - spring 1969

Colourways	U.S.$	Can.$	U.K.£
1. Cream	10.00	20.00	17.00
2. Grey-black	10.00	20.00	17.00

Alley Kitten
Second Version (Thinner, more defined)

Model No.:	A-005
Designer:	Helen Perrin Farnlund
Height:	7/8", 2.2 cm
Colour:	Grey tabby, green eyes
Issued:	Fall 1981 - spring 1987

Model No.	U.S.$	Can.$	U.K.£
A-005	4.00	8.00	7.00

Note: Model A-005 was made intermittently for 18 seasons. Other colourways exist.

ASSORTED CATS AND KITTENS

Basketball Cat
Model No.:   A-2046
Designer: Maureen Love
Height: 3 ½″, 8.9 cm
Colour: White cat, black and brown markings,
                blue or green ball, ceramic or Plexiglas
                base
Issued: Spring 1989 - fall 1989

Description	U.S.$	Can.$	U.K.£
1. Ceramic base	8.00	16.00	14.00
2. Plexiglas base	8.00	16.00	14.00

Note: Earlier issues had a Plexiglas base.

Cat, crouching
Model No.:   A-3079
Designer: Robert McGuinness
Height: 11/16″, 1.7 cm
Colour: Grey
Issued: Fall 1992 to the present

Model No.	U.S.$	Can.$	U.K.£
A-3079	3.00	6.00	5.00

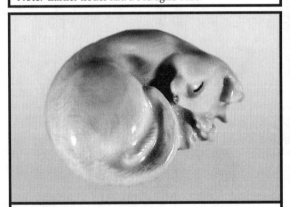

Cat, curled
Model No.:   A-3123
Designer: Robert McGuinness
Height: ½″, 1.3 cm
Colour: White
Issued: Fall 1993 to the present

Model No.	U.S.$	Can.$	U.K.£
A-3123	2.50	5.00	4.00

Cat, sleeping
Model No.:   A-3131
Designer: Robert McGuinness
Height: 7/8″, 2.2 cm
Colour: Grey
Issued: Fall 1994 to the present

Model No.	U.S.$	Can.$	U.K.£
A-3131	3.00	6.00	5.00

Cat, walking

Model No.:	A-3078
Designer:	Robert McGuinness
Height:	2 1/16", 5.2 cm
Colour:	Grey cat
Issued:	Fall 1992 to the present

Model No.	U.S.$	Can.$	U.K.£
A-3078	3.00	6.00	5.00

Cat With Ball

Model No.:	A-2047
Designer:	Maureen Love
Length:	2 ½", 6.4 cm
Colour:	White; black and brown markings; blue or green ball
Issued:	Spring 1989 - fall 1989

Colourways	U.S.$	Can.$	U.K.£
1. Blue ball	8.00	16.00	14.00
2. Green ball	8.00	16.00	14.00

Dancing Cats 'Jitterbug' or 'Swing'

Model No.:	A-2003
Designer:	Laurilyn Burson and Maureen Love
Height:	2 ½", 6.4 cm
Colour:	White; black and brown markings
Issued:	1. 'Jitterbug' — spring 1988 - fall 1989
Reissued:	2. 'Swing' — Fall 1998 to the present

Description	U.S.$	Can.$	U.K.£
1. 'Jitterbug'	10.00	20.00	17.00
2. 'Swing'	8.00	16.00	14.00

Note: Earlier issues had a black Plexiglas or ceramic base; later issues had a taupe base.

Dancing Cats 'Two Step' or 'Romantic'

Model No.:	A-2002
Designer:	Maureen Love and Laurilyn Burson
Height:	2 ½", 6.4 cm
Colour:	White; black and brown markings
Issued:	1. 'Two Step' — Spring 1988 - fall 1989
Reissued:	2. 'Romantic' — Fall 1998 to the present

Description	U.S.$	Can.$	U.K.£
1. 'Two-Step'	10.00	20.00	17.00
2. 'Romantic'	8.00	16.00	14.00

Note: Earlier issues had a black Plexiglas or ceramic base; later issues had a taupe base.

Fluffy Cat, Papa
First Version (Tail out)

Model No.:	A-353
Designer:	Martha Armstrong
Height:	1 ¾", 4.4 cm
Colour:	White
Issued:	Fall 1957 - spring 1958

Description	U.S.$	Can.$	U.K.£
First version	30.00	60.00	50.00

Fluffy Cat, Papa
Second Version (Tail to body)

Model No.:	A-353
Designer:	Martha Armstrong
Height:	1 ¾", 4.4 cm
Colour:	White
Issued:	Spring 1969

Description	U.S.$	Can.$	U.K.£
Second version	15.00	30.00	25.00

Fluffy Cat, Papa
Third Version (On pillow)

Model No.:	A-353
Designer:	Martha Armstrong
Height:	2 1/16", 5.2 cm
Colour:	White cat, blue pillow
Issued:	Fall 1968

Description	U.S.$	Can.$	U.K.£
Third version	30.00	60.00	50.00

Fluffy Cat, seated

Model No.:	A-208
Designer:	Helen Perrin Farnlund
Height:	1 ½", 3.8 cm
Colour:	1. Grey
	2. Orange
	3. White
Issued:	Fall 1953 - fall 1956

Colourways	U.S.$	Can.$	U.K.£
1. Grey	10.00	20.00	17.00
2. Orange	10.00	20.00	17.00
3. White	10.00	20.00	17.00

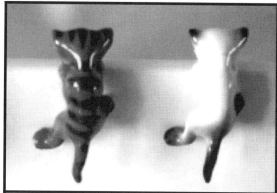

Happy Cat

Model No.:	A-39
Designer:	Helen Perrin Farnlund
Height:	1 ¾", 4.4 cm
Colour:	Yellow, white chest and tail tip, blue bow
Issued:	Fall 1962, fall 1982 - spring 1984

Description	U.S.$	Can.$	U.K.£
1. Monrovia	15.00	30.00	25.00
2. San Dimas	12.00	24.00	20.00

Kitten, climbing

Model No.:	A-377
Designer:	Helen Perrin Farnlund
Height:	1 3/8", 35 cm
Colour:	1. Dark orange, black stripes
	2. Light orange, darker orange stripes
	3. Siamese
Issued:	Fall 1958 - spring 1988

Colourways	U.S.$	Can.$	U.K.£
1. Dark orange	15.00	30.00	25.00
2. Light orange	10.00	20.00	17.00
3. Siamese	5.00	10.00	8.50

Note: Model A-377 was made for 59 seasons.

Kitten in Armchair

Model No.:	1. Kitten — A-997
	2. Armchair — A-998
Designer:	Helen Perrin Farnlund
Height:	1. Kitten — ½", 1.3 cm
	2. Armchair — 1 ½", 3.8 cm
Colour:	White kitten, blue and white chair
Issued:	Spring 1976 - spring 1979

Description	U.S.$	Can.$	U.K.£
1. Kitten	5.00	10.00	8.50
2. Armchair	10.00	20.00	17.00

Note: These models were sold separately.

Kitten on Piano Bench

Model No.:	A-3125-1
Designer:	Helen Perrin Farnlund
Height:	1. Bench — 1", 2.5 cm
	2. Bench/kitten — 2 5/16", 5.8 cm
Colour:	1. Bench — Brown bench, purple seat
	2. Kitten — Grey
Issued:	1. Bench — Fall 1993 - spring 1995
	2. Bench/kitten — Fall 1993 to the present

Description	U.S.$	Can.$	U.K.£
1. Bench	5.00	10.00	8.50
2. Bench/kitten	7.00	14.00	12.00

Note: This forms a set with Piano (A-3124), page 392.

Kitten, playing, tail up

Model No.:	A-75
Designer:	Helen Perrin Farnlund
Height:	1″, 2.5 cm
Colour:	White, green eyes
Issued:	1950

Model No.	U.S.$	Can.$	U.K.£
A-75	14.00	28.00	24.00

Kitten, stalking

Model No.:	A-56
Designer:	Helen Perrin Farnlund
Height:	1 ½″, 3.8 cm
Colour:	Grey
Issued:	Fall 1959 - spring 1960

Model No.	U.S.$	Can.$	U.K.£
A-56	8.00	16.00	14.00

Note: This forms a set with A-54, 55 57 and Milk Bottle (A-55). Model A-56 was reworked to make Siamese Kitten, stalking (A-868), page 211.

Little Kitten Found Mittens
Style One (Kitten holds mittens in right paw)

Model No.:	A-301
Designer:	Helen Perrin Farnlund
Height:	1 7/8″, 4.8 cm
Colour:	1. Grey cat with purple shirt
	2. Orange cat with green shirt
Issued:	Fall 1956, spring 1967

Colourways	U.S.$	Can.$	U.K.£
1. Grey/purple (1967)	15.00	30.00	25.00
2. Orange/green (1956)	18.00	36.00	30.00

Note: This forms a set with A-300, page 200; A-302, page 201; and A-875, page 213.

Little Kitten Lost Mittens

Model No.:	A-300/857
Designer:	Helen Perrin Farnlund
Height:	1 3/8″, 3.5 cm
Colour:	See below
Issued:	Fall 1956, spring 1967,
	spring 1985 to the present

Colourways	U.S.$	Can.$	U.K.£
1. Grey (1967)	15.00	30.00	25.00
2. Orange (1956)	18.00	36.00	30.00
3. Siamese	3.50	7.00	6.00

Note: This forms a set with A-301, page 200; A-302, page 201; and A-875, page 213.

Little Kitten With Pie

Model No.:	A-302
Designer:	Helen Perrin Farnlund
Height:	1 ¾", 4.4 cm
Colour:	1. Grey cat with purple shirt
	2. Orange cat with green shirt
Issued:	Fall 1956, spring 1967

Colourways	U.S.$	Can.$	U.K.£
1. Grey/purple (1967)	15.00	30.00	25.00
2. Orange/green (1956)	18.00	36.00	30.00

Note: Model A-302 was revised to make Kitten Who Found Mittens (A-875); see page 213.

Papa Cat

Model No.:	A-54/454
Designer:	Helen Perrin Farnlund
Height:	2 ¼", 5.7 cm
Colour:	See below
Issued:	Fall 1959 - spring 1960
	fall 1982 to the present

Colourways	U.S.$	Can.$	U.K.£
1. Black/white	8.00	16.00	14.00
2. Grey	15.00	30.00	25.00
3. Grey-black	3.00	6.00	5.00

Note: Set with Cats A-55, 56, 57 and milk bottle (A-53).

PERSIAN CATS AND KITTENS

Persian Cat

Model No.:	A-019
Designer:	Helen Perrin Farnlund
Height:	1 ½", 3.8 cm
Colour:	White, brown points, blue eyes; gloss or matte
Issued:	Spring 1962 - fall 1997

Description	U.S.$	Can.$	U.K.£
1. Gloss	10.00	20.00	17.00
2. Matte	10.00	20.00	17.00

Persian Kitten

Model No.:	A-018
Designer:	Helen Perrin Farnlund
Height:	5/8", 1.6 cm
Colour:	White, brown points, blue eyes; gloss or matte
Issued:	Spring 1962 to the present

Description	U.S.$	Can.$	U.K.£
1. Gloss	2.00	4.00	3.50
2. Matte	2.00	4.00	3.50

Note: Model A-019 was made intermittently for over twenty years between 1962 and 1997, and model A-018 has been made intermittenttly since 1962.

Persian Cat, licking paw

Model No.:	None
Designer:	Helen Perrin Farnlund
Height:	1 ½", 3.8 cm
Colour:	White
Issued:	Unknown

Description	U.S.$	Can.$	U.K.£
Persian Cat	Possibly not put into production		

Persian Cat, Mama

Model No.:	A-385
Designer:	Helen Perrin Farnlund
Height:	1 7/8", 4.8 cm
Colour:	Grey, white chest and tail tips, green eyes
Issued:	Fall 1959 - spring 1960

Model No.	U.S.$	Can.$	U.K.£
A-385	20.00	40.00	35.00

Note: This forms a set with kittens A-386 and A-396, page 203, and Milk Bowl (A-383), page 390.

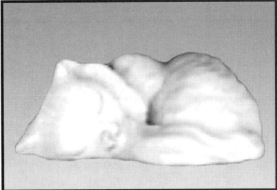

Persian Cat, reclining

Model No.:	A-207
Designer:	Helen Perrin Farnlund
Height:	1 ¼", 3.1 cm
Colour:	See below
Issued:	c.1950 - c.1970, fall 1989 to the present

Colourways	U.S.$	Can.$	U.K.£
1. Grey	10.00	20.00	17.00
2. Orange	10.00	20.00	17.00
3. White	10.00	20.00	17.00

Note: Grey and orange colourways were made for 12 seasons in the 1950s and 1970s. The white colourway was reissued in fall 1989 and is still current.

Persian Cat, sleeping

Model No.:	A-86
Designer:	Helen Perrin Farnlund
Height:	1", 2.5 cm
Colour:	1. Grey
	2. White
Issued:	Spring 1950 - fall 1971

Colourways	U.S.$	Can.$	U.K.£
1. Grey	10.00	20.00	17.00
2. White	10.00	20.00	17.00

Note: Model A-86 was made intermittently for six seasons between 1950 and 1971.

Persian Kitten, playing

Model No.:	A-386
Designer:	Helen Perrin Farnlund
Height:	1", 2.5 cm
Colour:	Grey, white chest and tail tips, green eyes
Issued:	Fall 1959 - spring 1960, fall 1982 (9 seasons)

Model No.	U.S.$	Can.$	U.K.£
A-386	4.00	8.00	7.00

Note: This forms a set with kittens A-385, page 202 and A-396, and Milk Bowl (A-383), page 390

Persian Kitten, standing

Model No.:	A-396
Designer:	Helen Perrin Farnlund
Height:	1", 2.5 cm
Colour:	Grey, white chest and tail tips, green eyes
Issued:	Fall 1959, spring 1960, fall 1982

Model No.	U.S.$	Can.$	U.K.£
A-396	8.00	16.00	14.00

Note: This forms a set with kittens A-385, page 202 and A-386, and Milk Bowl (A-383), page 390

SCOTTISH FOLD CATS

Scottish Fold Kitten

Model No.:	A-2043
Designer:	Shi Yi Chen
Height:	7/8", 2.2 cm
Colour:	1. Grey
	2. White with brown spots
Issued:	Spring 1989 - spring 1990

Colourways	U.S.$	Can.$	U.K.£
1. Grey	4.00	8.00	7.00
2. White	4.00	8.00	7.00

Scottish Fold Tabby

Model No.:	A-2042
Designer:	Shi Yi Chen
Height:	5/8", 1.6 cm
Colour:	1. Grey
	2. White with brown spots
Issued:	Spring 1989 - spring 1990

Colourways	U.S.$	Can.$	U.K.£
1. Grey	5.00	10.00	8.50
2. White	5.00	10.00	8.50

Scottish Fold Tom

Model No.:	A-2041
Designer:	Shi Yi Chen
Height:	1 ¼", 3.1 cm
Colour:	1. Grey
	2. White with brown spots
Issued:	Spring 1989 - spring 1990

Colourways	U.S.$	Can.$	U.K.£
1. Grey	5.00	10.00	8.50
2. White	5.00	10.00	8.50

SIAMESE CATS AND KITTENS

Siamese Cat, boxing

Model No.:	A-227
Designer:	Helen Perrin Farnlund
Height:	2", 5.0 cm
Colour:	Siamese; gloss or matte
Issued:	c.1950, c.1970

Model No.	U.S.$	Can.$	U.K.£
A-227	15.00	30.00	25.00

Note: Model A-227 was issued for six seasons — two in the 1950s and four in the 1970s.

Siamese Cat, climbing
Style One

Model No.:	A-265
Designer:	Maureen Love
Size:	1 1/8" x 3 ¾", 2.8 x 9.5 cm
Colour:	Siamese
Issued:	1955

Model No.	U.S.$	Can.$	U.K.£
A-265	20.00	40.00	35.00

Note: A wire was attached to the right front foot for placement.

Siamese Cat, climbing
Style Two, Version One (Tail down)
Model No.:   A-376
Designer: Helen Perrin Farnlund
Height: 2 ½", 6.4 cm
Colour: 1. Siamese
    2. Other colourways
Issued: Fall 1958 - spring 1992

Colourways	U.S.$	Can.$	U.K.£
1. Siamese	5.00	10.00	8.50
2. Other colourways	15.00	30.00	25.00

Siamese Cat, climbing
Style Two, Version Two (Tail up)
Model No.:   A-3228
Designer: Robert McGuinness
Height: 2", 5.0 cm
Colour: Siamese
Issued: Fall 1996 - spring 1998

Model No.	U.S.$	Can.$	U.K.£
A-3228	5.00	10.00	8.50

Siamese Cat, creeping
Model No.:   A-175
Designer: Helen Perrin Farnlund
Height: 1 ¼", 3.1 cm
Colour: Siamese
Issued: Fall 1955 - fall 1977

Model No.	U.S.$	Can.$	U.K.£
A-175	25.00	50.00	45.00

Note: Model A-175 was made for six seasons.

Siamese Cat, fishing
Model No.:   A-178
Designer: Tom Masterson
Length: 2 5/8", 6.6 cm
Colour: Siamese cat, orange fish; gloss
Issued: 1952, spring 1968

Model No.	U.S.$	Can.$	U.K.£
A-178	25.00	50.00	45.00

Note: The Monrovia fish has more detail and decoration than the San Dimas fish does.

Siamese Cat, lying

Model No.:	A-326
Designer:	Don Winton
Height:	1 1/8″, 2.8 cm
Colour:	1. Black
	2. Siamese
Issued:	Spring 1957 - spring 1993

Colourways	U.S.$	Can.$	U.K.£
1. Black	6.00	12.00	10.00
2. Siamese	5.00	10.00	8.50

Note: Model A-326 was made intermittently for 45 seasons between 1957 and 1993. The black colourway was available in the 1990s.

Siamese Cat, seated
Style One

Model No.:	A-2
Designer:	Helen Perrin Farnlund
Height:	1 ½″, 3.8 cm
Colour:	1. Siamese, blue eyes
	2. White with black spots
Issued:	1949 - 1952

Colourways	U.S.$	Can.$	U.K.£
1. Siamese	10.00	20.00	17.00
2. White/black	10.00	20.00	17.00

Siamese Cat, seated
Style Two

Model No.:	A-260
Designer:	Maureen Love
Height:	2 ¼″, 5.7 cm
Colour:	Siamese, blue eyes; gloss
Issued:	Spring 1955 - fall 1974

Model No.	U.S.$	Can.$	U.K.£
A-260	10.00	20.00	17.00

Note: Model A-260 was made for 16 seasons. The model illustrated has been attached to a base for display.

Siamese Cat, seated
Style Three ('Bowling Pin Cat')

Model No.:	A-324
Designer:	Don Winton
Height:	2 ½″, 6.4 cm
Colour:	See below
Issued:	Spring 1957 - spring 1993

Colourways	U.S.$	Can.$	U.K.£
1. Black	5.00	10.00	8.50
2. Siamese	7.00	14.00	12.00

Note: Model A-324 was made intermittently for 32 seasons between 1957 and 1993. The black colourway was available during the 1990s.

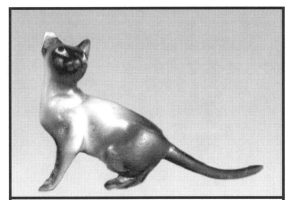

Siamese Cat, standing, tail out

Model No.:	A-325
Designer:	Don Winton
Height:	2″, 5.0 cm
Colour:	Siamese, blue eyes: gloss or matte
Issued:	Spring 1957 - spring 1978

Description	U.S.$	Can.$	U.K.£
1. Gloss	12.00	24.00	20.00
2. Matt	18.00	36.00	30.00

Note: Model A-325 was made intermittently for 20 seasons between 1957 and 1978.

Siamese Cat, walking
Style One, Version One (Long legs)

Model No.:	A-73
Designer:	Helen Perrin Farnlund
Height:	1 ¼″, 3.1 cm
Colour:	1. Orange tabby
	2. Siamese
Issued:	Spring 1950 - fall 1953

Colourways	U.S.$	Can.$	U.K.£
1. Orange tabby	10.00	20.00	17.00
2. Siamese	10.00	20.00	17.00

Siamese Cat, walking
Style One, Version Two (Short legs)

Model No.:	A-454
Designer:	Helen Perrin Farnlund
Height:	1 ¼″, 3.1 cm
Colour:	Siamese, blue eyes
Issued:	Fall 1963 - spring 1971

Model No.	U.S.$	Can.$	U.K.£
A-454	8.00	16.00	14.00

Siamese Cat, walking
Style Two

Model No.:	A-007/002
Designer:	Helen Perrin Farnlund
Height:	1 3/8″, 3.5 cm
Colour:	Siamese
Issued:	Fall 1961 to the present

Model No.	U.S.$	Can.$	U.K.£
A-007/002	3.00	6.00	5.00

Note: This model, also known as Tom Cat and Mama Cat, has been made intermittently for 67 seasons since 1961.

Siamese Kitten, boxing

Model No.:	A-008
Designer:	Helen Perrin Farnlund
Height:	¾", 1.9 cm
Colour:	Siamese
Issued:	Spring 1958 to the present

Model No.	U.S.$	Can.$	U.K.£
A-008	2.00	4.00	3.50

Siamese Kitten, creeping
Style One (Head turned to left)

Model No.:	A-262
Designer:	Maureen Love
Height:	1 ½", 3.8 cm
Colour:	Siamese
Issued:	Spring 1955

Model No.	U.S.$	Can.$	U.K.£
A-262	15.00	30.00	25.00

Siamese Kitten, creeping
Style Two (Head forward)

Model No.:	A-262
Designer:	Maureen Love
Height:	1 ½", 3.8 cm
Colour:	Siamese, black eyes; gloss
Issued:	c.1955 - fall 1976

Model No.	U.S.$	Can.$	U.K.£
A-262	15.00	30.00	25.00

Note: Model A-262 was made intermittently for six
seasons between 1955 and 1976.

Siamese Kitten 'Curious Kitty'

Model No.:	A-55/869
Designer:	Helen Perrin Farnlund
Height:	1 ¼", 3.1 cm
Colour:	See below
Issued:	Fall 1959
Reissued:	Spring 1986 to the present

Colourways	U.S.$	Can.$	U.K.£
1. Grey (1959)	10.00	20.00	17.00
2. Siamese (current)	3.00	6.00	5.00

Note: This forms a set with A-54, 56, 57 and Milk Bottle
(A-55).

Siamese Kitten, drinking

Model No.:	A-369
Designer:	Helen Perrin Farnlund
Height:	7/16″, 1.1 cm
Colour:	1. Calico
	2. Orange
	3. Siamese
Issued:	Spring 1959 to the present

Colourways	U.S.$	Can.$	U.K.£
1. Calico	10.00	20.00	17.00
2. Orange	10.00	20.00	17.00
3. Siamese	2.00	4.00	3.50

Siamese Kitten, head turned

Model No.:	A-19
Designer:	Helen Perrin Farnlund
Height:	1″, 2.5 cm
Colour:	1. Siamese, blue eyes
	2. White with black spots
Issued:	1949 - 1951

Colourways	U.S.$	Can.$	U.K.£
1. Siamese	10.00	20.00	17.00
2. White/black	10.00	20.00	17.00

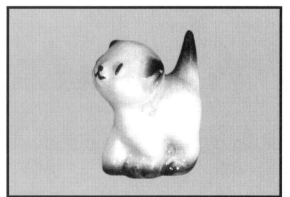

Siamese Kitten, nose up

Model No.:	A-74
Designer:	Helen Perrin Farnlund
Height:	1″, 2.5 cm
Colour:	1. Orange tabby
	2. Siamese, blue eyes
Issued:	1950 - 1952

Colourways	U.S.$	Can.$	U.K.£
1. Orange tabby	10.00	20.00	17.00
2. Siamese	10.00	20.00	17.00

Siamese Kitten, on hind legs

Model No.:	A-181
Designer:	Tom Masterson
Height:	1 ½″, 3.8 cm
Colour:	Siamese, black eyes; gloss or matte
Issued:	Fall 1952 - fall 1976

Description	U.S.$	Can.$	U.K.£
1. Gloss	15.00	30.00	25.00
2. Matte	15.00	30.00	25.00

Note: Model A-181 was made intermittently for 29 seasons between 1952 and 1976.

Siamese Kitten, playful, paw down

Model No.: A-437
Designer: Helen Perrin Farnlund
Height: 7/8″, 2.2 cm
Colour: 1. Grey, green eyes
2. Siamese, blue eyes
Issued: Fall 1960 - fall 1988

Colourways	U.S.$	Can.$	U.K.£
1. Grey	6.00	12.00	10.00
2. Siamese	6.00	12.00	10.00

Note: Model A-437 was made intermittently for seven seasons between 1960 and 1988.

Siamese Kitten, playful, paw up

Model No.: A-436
Designer: Helen Perrin Farnlund
Height: 7/8″, 2.2 cm
Colour: See below
Issued: Fall 1960 - 1988

Colourways	U.S.$	Can.$	U.K.£
1. Black	2.50	5.00	4.00
2. Black/white	6.00	12.00	10.00
3. Grey	6.00	12.00	10.00
4. Siamese	6.00	12.00	10.00

Note: Model A-436 was made for 20 seasons. The Siamese colourway is a more stocky model.

Siamese Kitten, roughneck

Model No.: A-299
Designer: Helen Perrin Farnlund
Height: 1 ¼″, 3.1 cm
Colour: Siamese; gloss or matte
Issued: Fall 1956 - spring 1959

Description	U.S.$	Can.$	U.K.£
1. Gloss	15.00	30.00	25.00
2. Matte	10.00	20.00	17.00

Siamese Kitten, running

Model No.: A-57
Designer: Helen Perrin Farnlund
Height: 1″, 2.5 cm
Colour: 1. Grey
2. Siamese
Issued: Fall 1959 - spring 1960

Colourways	U.S.$	Can.$	U.K.£
1. Grey	8.00	16.00	14.00
2. Siamese	4.00	8.00	7.00

Note: The release dates of the Siamese colourway are unknown. The grey colourway forms a set with A-54, 55, 56 and Milk Bottle (A-55).

Siamese Kitten, seated, Style One

Model No.:	A-368
Designer:	Helen Perrin Farnlund
Height:	5/8", 1.6 cm
Colour:	1. Calico
	2. Orange
	3. Siamese
Issued:	Spring 1959 to the present

Colourways	U.S.$	Can.$	U.K.£
1. Calico	10.00	20.00	17.00
2. Orange	10.00	20.00	17.00
3. Siamese	2.00	4.00	3.50

Siamese Kitten, seated
Style Two

Model No.:	A-3045
Designer:	Robert McGuinness
Height:	7/8", 2.2 cm
Colour:	1. Orange tabby
	2. Siamese
Issued:	Fall 1991 to the present

Colourways	U.S.$	Can.$	U.K.£
1. Orange tabby	3.50	7.00	5.00
2. Siamese (current)	2.50	5.00	4.00

Siamese Kitten, stalking

Model No.:	A-868
Designer:	Helen Perrin Farnlund
Height:	1 1/16", 2.7 cm
Colour:	Siamese
Issued:	Spring 1986 to the present

Model No.	U.S.$	Can.$	U.K.£
A-868	2.50	5.00	4.00

Siamese Kitten, standing, facing left

Model No.:	A-3044
Designer:	Robert McGuinness
Height:	1", 2.5 cm
Colour:	1. Orange tabby
	2. Siamese
Issued:	Fall 1991 to the present

Colourways	U.S.$	Can.$	U.K.£
1. Orange tabby	3.50	7.00	6.00
2. Siamese (current)	2.50	5.00	4.00

Note: Model A-56 (Kitten, stalking), page 200, was revised to produce model A-868.

Siamese Kitten, standing, facing right
Model No.:   A-3043
Designer: Robert McGuinness
Height: 1″, 2.5 cm
Colour: 1. Orange tabby
              2. Siamese
Issued: Fall 1991 - fall 1993

Colourways	U.S.$	Can.$	U.K.£
1. Orange tabby	4.00	8.00	7.00
2. Siamese	4.00	8.00	7.00

Siamese Kitten, walking
First Version (Thicker, less detail)
Model No.:   A-004
Designer: Helen Perrin Farnlund
Height: ¾″, 1.9 cm
Colour: Cream Siamese, light brown points
Issued: Fall 1961

Model No.	U.S.$	Can.$	U.K.£
A-004	20.00	40.00	35.00

Siamese Kitten, walking
Second Version (Thinner, defined detail)
Model No.:   A-004
Designer: Helen Perrin Farnlund
Height: 11/16″, 1.7 cm
Colour: Siamese, dark brown points
Issued: Fall 1961 to the present

Model No.	U.S.$	Can.$	U.K.£
A-004	2.00	4.00	3.00

Siamese Kitten and Grocery Bag
Model No.:   A-3088/A-3087
Designer: Robert McGuinness
Height: 1. Grocery bag — 7/8″, 2.2 cm
              2. Kitten — ¾″, 1.9 cm
Colour: 1. Grocery bag — Brown
              2. Kitten — Siamese
Issued: Fall 1992 - fall 1994

Description	U.S.$	Can.$	U.K.£
Set	12.00	24.00	20.00

Siamese Kitten and Yarn (On back)

Model No.:	A-3010
Designer:	Robert McGuinness
Height:	5/8″, 1.6 cm
Colour:	Siamese, blue yarn
Issued:	Spring 1991 to the present

Model No.	U.S.$	Can.$	U.K.£
A-3010	2.50	5.00	4.00

Siamese Kitten and Yarn (Standing)

Model No.:	A-261
Designer:	Maureen Love
Height:	1 ½″, 3.8 cm
Colour:	Siamese kitten, blue yarn
Issued:	c.1950

Model No.	U.S.$	Can.$	U.K.£
A-261	15.00	30.00	25.00

Note: Model A-261 was made intermittently for six seasons during the 1950s.

Siamese 'Kitten Who Found His Mittens'

Model No.:	A-875
Designer:	Helen Perrin Farnlund
Height:	1 ¾″, 4.4 cm
Colour:	Siamese with light blue sweater and dark blue mittens
Issued:	Spring 1987 - fall 1988

Model No.	U.S.$	Can.$	U.K.£
A-875	8.00	16.00	14.00

Note: Model A-875 was revised from model A-302, see page 201. Model A-875 forms a set with A-301, page 200; A-300, page 200; and A-302, page 201.

Siamese Kitten With Scratching Post

Model No.:	A-3089
Designer:	Robert McGuinness
Height:	1 5/8″, 4.1 cm
Colour:	Siamese kitten, blue base and post
Issued:	Spring 1993 to the present

Model No.	U.S.$	Can.$	U.K.£
A-3089	3.50	7.00	6.00

Siamese Mama Cat, crouching
Style One (Facing right)
Model No.:   A-439
Designer: Helen Perrin Farnlund
Height: 1", 2.5 cm
Colour: 1. Calico
          2. Siamese
Issued: c.1960 - c.1965,
          fall 1973 - fall 1974

Colourways	U.S.$	Can.$	U.K.£
1. Calico	10.00	20.00	17.00
2. Siamese	5.00	10.00	8.50

Siamese Mama Cat, crouching
Style Two (Facing left)
Model No.:   A-3042
Designer: Robert McGuinness
Height: 1 3/8", 3.5 cm
Colour: 1. Orange tabby
          2. Siamese
Issued: Fall 1991 - fall 1993

Colourways	U.S.$	Can.$	U.K.£
1. Orange tabby	5.00	10.00	8.50
2. Siamese	5.00	10.00	8.50

Siamese Mama Cat, seated
Model No.:   A-438
Designer: Helen Perrin Farnlund
Height: 1 ½", 3.8 cm
Colour: 1. Siamese
          2. Other colourways
Issued: Fall 1960 to the present

Colourways	U.S.$	Can.$	U.K.£
1. Siamese	3.00	6.00	5.00
2. Other colourways	10.00	20.00	17.00

Siamese Mama Cat, sucking thumb
Model No.:   A-367
Designer: Helen Perrin Farnlund
Height: 1 ¼", 3.1 cm
Colour: See below
Issued: Spring 1958 - fall 1979

Colourways	U.S.$	Can.$	U.K.£
1. Grey tabby	10.00	20.00	17.00
2. Orange tabby	15.00	30.00	25.00
3. Siamese	5.00	10.00	8.50

Note: This cat was also called Alley Cat and Mama Cat.
The model illustrated has been attached to a base
for display.

Siamese Papa Cat, looking up
Model No.:   A-3046
Designer: Robert McGuinness
Height: 1 3/8", 3.5 cm
Colour: 1. Orange tabby
              2. Siamese
Issued: Fall 1991 to the present

Colourways	U.S.$	Can.$	U.K.£
1. Orange tabby	5.00	10.00	8.50
2. Siamese (current)	5.00	10.00	8.50

Siamese Papa Cat, stalking
Model No.:   A-955
Designer: Helen Perrin Farnlund
Height: 1 1/8", 2.8 cm
Colour: 1. Orange with black stripes
              2. Siamese
Issued: Fall 1961 - spring 1993

Colourways	U.S.$	Can.$	U.K.£
1. Orange/black	10.00	20.00	17.00
2. Siamese	5.00	10.00	8.50

Note: Model A-955 was made intermittently for 28 seasons between 1961 and 1993.

Siamese Cat, facing right
Model No.:   A-49
Designer: Don Winton
Height: 1 ¾", 4.4 cm
Colour: Light brown, black points
Issued: 1964 - 1971

Colourways	U.S.$	Can.$	U.K.£
A-49	15.00	30.00	25.00

Note: See also Disney model 5009 (Si™) page 500.

Siamese Cat, facing left
Model No.:   A-50
Designer: Don Winton
Height: 1 11/16", 4.3 cm
Colour: Light brown, black points
Issued: 1964 - 1971

Colourways	U.S.$	Can.$	U.K.£
A-50	15.00	30.00	25.00

Note: See also Disney model 5010 (Am™), page 497.

Miniature cats in orange tabby colourways
Kitten, climbing (A-377); Cat, climbing (A-376);
Kitten drinking (A-369); Kitten, seated (A-368);
Mama Cat, sucking thumb (A-367)

MINIATURE DOGS

INDEX TO
MINIATURE DOGS

AFGHAN HOUND

Afghan Hound

Model No.:	A-3063
Designer:	Robert McGuinness
Height:	2 3/8", 6.0 cm
Colour:	Cream with brown shading
Issued:	Spring 1992 - spring 1993

Model No.	U.S.$	Can.$	U.K.£
A-3063	8.00	16.00	14.00

AUSTRALIAN SHEPHERD

Australian Shepherd

Model No.:	A-2052
Designer:	Maureen Love
Height:	1 ¾", 4.4 cm
Colour:	Grey and red-brown
Issued:	Spring 1989 - spring 1990

Model No.	U.S.$	Can.$	U.K.£
A-2052	8.00	16.00	14.00

BASSET HOUNDS

Basset Hound Mama
Style One (Facing right)

Model No.:	A-954
Designer:	Maxine Renaker
Height:	1", 2.5 cm
Colour:	White, brown and black
Issued:	Spring 1978 - fall 1988

Model No.	U.S.$	Can.$	U.K.£
A-954	4.00	8.00	7.00

Basset Hound Mama
Style Two (Facing left)

Model No.:	A-3154
Designer:	Robert McGuinness
Height:	1 7/8", 4.8 cm
Colour:	Brown and black; white face, feet and tip of tail
Issued:	Fall 1994 to the present

Model No.	U.S.$	Can.$	U.K.£
A-3154	5.00	10.00	8.50

Basset Hound Papa
Model No.:   A-959
Designer: Maxine Renaker
Height: 1 ¼", 3.3 cm
Colour: White, brown and black
Issued: Spring 1978 - fall 1995

Model No.	U.S.$	Can.$	U.K.£
A-959	4.00	8.00	7.00

Basset Hound Puppy, lying
Model No.:   A-3155
Designer: Robert McGuinness
Height: ½", 1.3 cm
Colour: Brown and black; white face, feet
                 and tip of tail
Issued: Fall 1994 to the present

Model No.	U.S.$	Can.$	U.K.£
A-3155	3.50	7.00	6.00

Basset Hound Puppy, running
Model No.:   A-953
Designer: Maxine Renaker
Height: ¾", 1.9 cm
Colour: White, brown and black
Issued: Spring 1978 - fall 1988

Model No.	U.S.$	Can.$	U.K.£
A-953	4.00	8.00	7.00

Basset Hound Puppy, seated
Model No.:   A-3190
Designer: Robert McGuinness
Height: 1", 2.5 cm
Colour: Dark brown and tan; white nose,
                 chest, feet and tip of tail
Issued: Fall 1995 to the present

Model No.	U.S.$	Can.$	U.K.£
A-3190	3.50	7.00	6.00

BICHON FRISE

BORDER COLLIE

Bichon Frise

Model No.:	A-3272	
Designer:	Robert McGuinness	
Height:	1 3/8", 3.5 cm	
Colour:	White	
Issued:	Spring 1998 to the present	

Model No.	U.S.$	Can.$	U.K.£
A-3272	4.50	9.00	8.00

Border Collie

Model No.:	A-3208	
Designer:	Maureen Love	
Height:	1 3/8", 3.5 cm	
Colour:	Black and white	
Issued:	Spring 1996 - spring 1998	

Model No.	U.S.$	Can.$	U.K.£
A-3208	6.00	12.00	10.00

Note: This forms a pair with Piglet, walking (A-3207), page 260.

BLOODHOUNDS

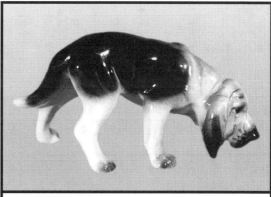

Bloodhound, seated

Model No.:	A-77/854	
Designer:	Don Winton	
Height:	1 5/8", 4.1 cm	
Colour:	Brown, dark brown ears, white muzzle	
Issued:	c.1960, c.1980	

Model No.	U.S.$	Can.$	U.K.£
A-77/854	8.00	16.00	14.00

Note: Model A-77/854 was made for 8 seasons c.1960, c.1980. See Disney model 5013 (Trusty™), page 501

Bloodhound, standing

Model No.:	A-2062	
Designer:	Maureen Love	
Height:	1 3/8", 3.5 cm	
Colour:	Black and tan	
Issued:	Fall 1989 - fall 1992	

Model No.	U.S.$	Can.$	U.K.£
A-2062	13.00	26.00	23.00

BOSTON TERRIER

Boston Terrier Puppy, begging

Model No.: A-225
Designer: Tom Masterson
Height: 7/8", 2.2 cm
Colour: Black and white
Issued: 1954 - 1955, spring 1959,
fall 1971 - spring 1972

Model No.	U.S.$	Can.$	U.K.£
A-225	8.00	16.00	14.00

Boston Terrier Puppy, seated

Model No.: A-224
Designer: Tom Masterson
Height: 7/8", 2.2 cm
Colour: Black and white
Issued: Spring 1954 - Spring 1986

Model No.	U.S.$	Can.$	U.K.£
A-224	4.00	8.00	7.00

Boston Terrier Mama

Model No.: A-176
Designer: Tom Masterson
Height: 1 ½", 3.8 cm
Colour: Black and white
Issued: Spring 1954 to the present

Model No.	U.S.$	Can.$	U.K.£
A-176	3.50	7.00	6.00

Note: Model A-176 has been made intermittently for 53 seasons since 1954 and model A-225 was produced for 33 seasons.

In the spring of 1972, these models were decorated in brown and called French Bulldogs. This variation would be valued at $15.00 each.

Boston Terrier Puppy, standing

Model No.: A-1760
Designer: Maureen Love
Height: 5/8", 1.6 cm
Colour: Black and white
Issued: Fall 1994 to the present

Model No.	U.S.$	Can.$	U.K.£
A-1760	2.25	4.50	4.00

BOXERS

Boxer, standing

Model No.:	A-141
Designer:	Tom Masterson
Height:	2″, 5.1 cm
Colour:	Light or dark tan
Issued:	Fall 1951 - spring 1952

Model No.	U.S.$	Can.$	U.K.£
A-141	20.00	40.00	35.00

Boxer, ledge stander

Model No.:	A-139
Designer:	Tom Masterson
Height:	1 ¾″, 4.4 cm
Colour:	Light or dark tan
Issued:	Fall 1951 - spring 1952

Model No.	U.S.$	Can.$	U.K.£
A-139	20.00	40.00	35.00

Boxer Mama

Model No.:	A-283
Designer:	Tom Masterson
Height:	2″, 5.1 cm
Colour:	Tan; gloss or matte
Issued:	Spring 1956 - fall 1976

Description	U.S.$	Can.$	U.K.£
1. Gloss	7.00	14.00	12.00
2. Matte	12.00	24.00	20.00

Note: Model A-283 was made for 29 seasons. Earlier models had a matte finish.

Boxer Puppy

Model No.:	A-284
Designer:	Tom Masterson
Height:	1″, 2.5 cm
Colour:	Tan; gloss or matte
Issued:	Spring 1956 - fall 1976

Colourways	U.S.$	Can.$	U.K.£
1. Tan	5.00	10.00	8.50
2. Tan, taped ears	12.00	24.00	20.00

Note: Models A-284 was made for 29 seasons. Earlier models had taped ears.

BULLDOG

Bulldog
Style One

Model No.:	A-855	
Designer:	Don Winton	
Height:	1 ¼", 3.2 cm	
Colour:	See below	
Issued:	Spring 1985 - spring 1988	

Colourways	U.S.$	Can.$	U.K.£
1. Red-brown, tan face	10.00	20.00	17.00
2. Red-brown, white face	10.00	20.00	17.00

Note: See Disney model 5058 (Bull™), page 497.

Bulldog
Style Two

Model No.:	A-2087	
Designer:	Maureen Love	
Height:	1 ½", 3.8 cm	
Colour:	White	
Issued:	Fall 1990 to the present	

Model No.	U.S.$	Can.$	U.K.£
A-2087	4.00	8.00	7.00

CHIHUAHUAS

Chihuahua

Model No.:	A-078	
Designer:	Don Winton	
Height:	1 ½", 3.8 cm	
Colour:	Tan	
Issued:	Fall 1966 - fall 1967	

Model No.	U.S.$	Can.$	U.K.£
A-078	15.00	30.00	25.00

Note: See Disney model 5006 (Pedro™), page 499.

Chihuahua, Mama

Model No.:	A-337	
Designer:	Tom Masterson	
Height:	1", 2.5 cm	
Colour:	Golden brown	
Issued:	c. 1958 - c.1978	

Model No.	U.S.$	Can.$	U.K.£
A-337	10.00	20.00	17.00

Note: Model A-337 was made for 20 seasons. Earlier models had detailed eyes.

Chihuahua, facing right
Model No.: A-035
Designer: Helen Perrin Farnlund
Height: 1", 2.5 cm
Colour: Red-brown, white chest
Issued: Fall 1962 to the present

Model No.	U.S.$	Can.$	U.K.£
A-035	4.00	8.00	7.00

Chihuahua Puppy, walking
Model No.: A-036
Designer: Helen Perrin Farnlund
Height: 7/8", 2.2 cm
Colour: Red-brown, white chest
Issued: Fall 1962 - fall 1988

Model No.	U.S.$	Can.$	U.K.£
A-036	6.00	12.00	10.00

Chihuahua, facing left
Model No.: A-247
Designer: Tom Masterson
Height: 1 5/8", 4.1 cm
Colour: Red-brown, white chest
Issued: Spring 1954 - fall 1972

Description	U.S.$	Can.$	U.K.£
1. Monrovia	20.00	40.00	35.00
2. San Dimas	15.00	30.00	25.00

Chihuahua Puppy, begging
Model No.: A-338
Designer: Tom Masterson
Height: 7/8", 2.2 cm
Colour: Golden brown
Issued: c.1958 - c.1978

Description	U.S.$	Can.$	U.K.£
1. Monrovia	5.00	10.00	8.50
2. San Dimas	5.00	10.00	8.50

Note: Model A-035 was made for 27 seasons; model A-036, 9 seasons; model A-247, 10 seasons; and model A-338, 20 seasons. Earlier models of A-338 had detailed eyes.

Chihuahua, seated
Model No.: Unknown
Designer: Tom Masterson
Height: 1 7/8", 4.8 cm
Colour: Golden brown, white chest
Issued: Fall 1954 - spring 1955

Description	U.S.$	Can.$	U.K.£
Chihuahua	20.00	40.00	35.00

COCKER SPANIELS

Cocker Spaniel With Newspaper
Model No.:   A-255
Designer: Maureen Love
Height: 1 ¾", 4.4 cm
Colour: Golden brown
Issued: Spring 1956 - fall 1957

Model No.	U.S.$	Can.$	U.K.£
A-255	25.00	50.00	45.00

Cocker Spaniel Juvenile
Model No.:   A-257/339
Designer: Maureen Love
Height: 1 ¼", 3.2 cm
Colour: 1. Black
             2. Golden brown
Issued: Spring 1955 - spring 1958

Colourways	U.S.$	Can.$	U.K.£
1. Black	14.00	28.00	24.00
2. Golden brown	10.00	20.00	17.00

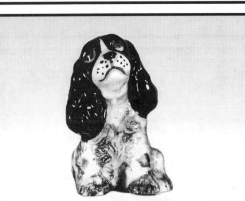

Cocker Spaniel 'Butch'
Model No.:   A-320
Designer: Albert Staehl
Redesigner: Don Winton
Height: 1 9/16", 4.0 cm
Colour: Black and white
Issued: 1957

Model No.	U.S.$	Can.$	U.K.£
A-320	50.00	100.00	85.00

Note: See page 428 for the Pedigree model of 'Butch'.

Cocker Spaniel, seated

Model No.:	A-205
Designer:	Helen Perrin Farnlund
Height:	1 ½", 3.8 cm
Colour:	See below
Issued:	Fall 1953 - fall 1972

Colourways	U.S.$	Can.$	U.K.£
1. Black and white	10.00	20.00	17.00
2. Brown and white	10.00	20.00	17.00
3. Tan	10.00	20.00	17.00

Note: Model A-205 was made intermittently for eight seasons between 1953 and 1972.

Cocker Spaniel, standing

Model No.:	A-98
Designer:	Helen Perrin Farnlund
Height:	1 3/8", 3.5 cm
Colour:	1. Black and white
	2. Brown and white
	3. Tan
Issued:	Spring 1950 - spring 1954

Colourways	U.S.$	Can.$	U.K.£
1. Black/white	8.00	16.00	14.00
2. Brown/white	8.00	16.00	14.00
3. Tan	8.00	16.00	14.00

Cocker Spaniel, walking

Model No.:	A-028
Designer:	Helen Perrin Farnlund
Height:	1 3/8", 3.5 cm
Colour:	Golden brown
Issued:	Fall 1962 to the present

Model No.	U.S.$	Can.$	U.K.£
A-028	4.00	8.00	7.00

Note: Model A-028 has been in production for 40 seasons.

Cocker Spaniel Puppy, seated

Model No.:	A-97
Designer:	Helen Perrin Farnlund
Height:	7/8", 2.2 cm
Colour:	1. Black and white
	2. Brown and white
	3. Tan
Issued:	Spring 1950 - spring 1954

Colourways	U.S.$	Can.$	U.K.£
1. Black/white	7.00	14.00	12.00
2. Brown/white	7.00	14.00	12.00
3. Tan	7.00	14.00	12.00

Puppy, paws out (A-93); Mama (A-90); Puppy, playing (A-91); Puppy, on hind legs (A-92)

Cocker Spaniel, Mama

Model No.:	A-90
Designer:	Don Winton
Height:	1 ¼", 3.2 cm
Colour:	1. Pale brown, darker brown ears and feet
	2. White with black spots
Issued:	Spring 1971 to the present

Colourways	U.S.$	Can.$	U.K.£
1. Pale brown	4.00	8.00	7.00
2. White	13.00	26.00	23.00

Note: See also Disney model 5001 (Lady™), page 498.

Cocker Spaniel Puppy, playing

Model No.:	A-91
Designer:	Don Winton
Height:	5/8", 1.6 cm
Colour:	Pale brown, darker brown ears and feet
Issued:	Spring 1971 to the present

Model No.	U.S.$	Can.$	U.K.£
A-91	2.00	4.00	3.50

Note: See also Disney model 5005 (Fluffy™), page 498.

Cocker Spaniel Puppy, on hind legs, paws together

Model No.:	A-92
Designer:	Don Winton
Height:	1", 2.5 cm
Colour:	Pale brown, darker brown ears and feet
Issued:	Spring 1971 to the present

Model No.	U.S.$	Can.$	U.K.£
A-92	2.00	4.00	3.50

Note: See also Disney model 5003 (Ruffles™), page 499.

Cocker Spaniel Puppy, on hind legs, paws out

Model No.:	A-93
Designer:	Don Winton
Height:	1", 2.5 cm
Colour:	Pale brown, darker brown ears and feet
Issued:	Spring 1986 - fall 1987

Model No.	U.S.$	Can.$	U.K.£
A-93	6.00	12.00	10.00

Note: See also Disney model 5002 (Scooter™), page 500.

Cocker Spaniel Puppy, running
Model No.:   A-029/340
Designer: Helen Perrin Farnlund
Height: 7/8", 2.2 cm
Colour: 1. Black and white
            2. Golden brown
Issued: Fall 1962 - spring 1964

Colourways	U.S.$	Can.$	U.K.£
1. Black/white	12.00	24.00	20.00
2. Golden brown	12.00	24.00	20.00

COLLIES

Collie
Style One (Standing, head forward)
Model No.:   A-359
Designer: Tom Masterson
Height: 1 ½", 3.8 cm
Colour: Red-brown; dark brown shading; white
            nose, neck, feet and tip of tail; gloss, matte
Issued: Fall 1957 - fall 1996

Description	U.S.$	Can.$	U.K.£
1. Gloss	4.00	8.00	7.00
2. Matte	18.00	36.00	30.00

Note: Model A-359 was made intermittently for over
45 seasons between 1957 and 1996.

Collie
Style Two (Standing, head upturned)
Model No.:   A-3237
Designer: Robert McGuinness
Height: 1 5/8", 4.1 cm
Colour: Chestnut; white chest, tail tip and nose
Issued: Spring 1997 to the present

Model No.	U.S.$	Can.$	U.K.£
A-3237	4.00	8.00	7.00

DACHSHUND

Dachshund 'Schnapsie'
Model No.:   A-78
Designer: Helen Perrin Farnlund
Height: 1 ½", 3.8 cm
Colour: Red-brown
Issued: Spring 1950 - fall 1951

Model No.	U.S.$	Can.$	U.K.£
A-78	12.00	24.00	20.00

Dachshund 'Schnapsie, Jr.'
Model No.:   A-81
Designer: Helen Perrin Farnlund
Height: 7/8", 2.2 cm
Colour: Red-brown
Issued: Spring 1950 - fall 1951

Model No.	U.S.$	Can.$	U.K.£
A-81	8.00	16.00	14.00

Dachshund, standing, facing right
Model No.:   A-74
Designer: Don Winton
Height: 1 ¼", 3.2 cm
Colour: Tan, black ears and nose
Issued: Fall 1966 - fall 1968

Model No.	U.S.$	Can.$	U.K.£
A-74	15.00	30.00	25.00

Note: See Disney model 5011 (Dachsie™), page 498.

Dachshund Puppy, seated, paw up
Model No.:   A-3204
Designer: Robert McGuinness
Height: 7/8", 2.2 cm
Colour: Red-brown
Issued: Spring 1996 to the present

Model No.	U.S.$	Can.$	U.K.£
A-3204	2.50	5.00	4.00

Dachshund Puppy, seated

Model No.:	A-348
Designer:	Helen Perrin Farnlund
Height:	7/8", 2.2 cm
Colour:	Red-brown
Issued:	Fall 1957 - spring 1992

Model No.	U.S.$	Can.$	U.K.£
A-348	4.00	8.00	7.00

Dachshund, standing, facing left

Model No.:	A-347
Designer:	Helen Perrin Farnlund
Height:	1 ¼", 3.2 cm
Colour:	Red-brown
Issued:	Fall 1957 to the present

Model No.	U.S.$	Can.$	U.K.£
A-347	3.50	7.00	6.00

Note: Model A-347 has been made for over 30 years.

DALMATIANS

Puppy, crouching (A-456); Mama (A-497); Puppy, standing (A-498); 'Muttsey' (A-455)

Dalmatian, Mama

Model No.:	A-497
Designer:	Helen Perrin Farnlund
Height:	2", 5.1 cm
Colour:	1. Black, brown and white
	2. White, black spots
Issued:	Fall 1961 to the present

Colourways	U.S.$	Can.$	U.K.£
1. Black/brown/white	18.00	36.00	30.00
2. White/black	4.00	8.00	7.00

Dalmatian 'Muttsey', paw up

Model No.:	A-455
Designer:	Tom Masterson
Height:	1 ½", 3.8 cm
Colour:	1. Black, brown and white
	2. White, black spots
Issued:	Spring 1959 - spring 1986

Colourways	U.S.$	Can.$	U.K.£
1 Black/brown/white	10.00	20.00	17.00
2. White/black	8.00	16.00	14.00

Dalmatian Puppy, crouching

Model No.:	A-456
Designer:	Tom Masterson
Height:	1 ¼", 3.1 cm
Colour:	1. Black, brown and white
	2. White, black spots
Issued:	Spring 1959 - Spring 1986

Colourways	U.S.$	Can.$	U.K.£
1. Black/brown/white	10.00	20.00	17.00
2. White/black	8.00	16.00	14.00

Dalmatian Puppy, standing

Model No.:	A-498
Designer:	Helen Perrin Farnlund
Height:	1 ½", 3.8 cm
Colour:	1. Black, brown and white
	2. White, brown spots
Issued:	Fall 1961 - unknown

Colourways	U.S.$	Can.$	U.K.£
1. Black/brown/white	15.00	30.00	25.00
2. White/black	3.00	6.00	5.00

Note: Models A-497 and A-498 were made for over 50 seasons.

DOBERMANS

Doberman, Adult

Model No.:	A-827
Designer:	Helen Perrin Farnlund
Height:	2 ¼", 5.7 cm
Colour:	Black; tan nose, legs and inner ears
Issued:	Spring 1983 to the present

Model No.	U.S.$	Can.$	U.K.£
A-827	4.00	8.00	7.00

Doberman, Puppy

Model No.:	A-828
Designer:	Helen Perrin Farnlund
Height:	1", 2.5 cm
Colour:	Black; tan nose, legs and inner ears
Issued:	Spring 1983 - fall 1986

Model No.	U.S.$	Can.$	U.K.£
A-828	8.00	16.00	14.00

Note: Model A-827 has been been in production for over 15 years.

GERMAN SHEPHERDS

German Shepherd, standing

Model No.:	A-825
Designer:	Maureen Love
Height:	2", 5.0 cm
Colour:	Black and light tan
Issued:	Spring 1983 to the present

Model No.	U.S.$	Can.$	U.K.£
A-825	4.00	8.00	7.00

German Shepherd and Frisbee

Model No.:	A-2073
Designer:	Maureen Love
Height:	2 ½", 6.4 cm
Colour:	Black and grey-tan dog, light blue Frisbee, cream base
Issued:	Spring 1990 to the present

Model No.	U.S.$	Can.$	U.K.£
A-2073	7.00	14.00	12.00

German Shepherd Puppy
Model No.: A-826
Designer: Maureen Love
Height: 1", 2.5 cm
Colour: Black and light tan
Issued: Spring 1983 - spring 1986

Model No.	U.S.$	Can.$	U.K.£
A-826	7.00	14.00	12.00

GOLDEN RETRIEVERS

Golden Retriever
Model No.: A-3188
Designer: Maureen Love
Height: 2 1/8", 5.4 cm
Colour: Golden
Issued: Fall 1995 to the present

Model No.	U.S.$	Can.$	U.K.£
A-3188	5.00	10.00	8.50

Golden Retriever Puppy
Model No.: A-3205
Designer: Robert McGuinness
Height: 1", 2.5 cm
Colour: Golden
Issued: Spring 1996 to the present

Model No.	U.S.$	Can.$	U.K.£
A-3205	2.50	5.00	4.00

GREAT DANE

Great Dane
Model No.: A-3056
Designer: Robert McGuinness
Height: 2 ¾", 7.0 cm
Colour: Tan
Issued: Spring 1992 to the present

Model No.	U.S.$	Can.$	U.K.£
A-3056	6.00	12.00	10.00

HUSKY

Husky
Model No.: A-890
Designer: Maureen Love
Height: 2", 5.0 cm
Colour: Grey
Issued: Spring 1988 to the present

Model No.	U.S.$	Can.$	U.K.£
A-890	4.50	9.00	8.00

IRISH SETTER

Irish Setter
Model No.: A-3055
Designer: Robert McGuinness
Height: 2", 5.1 cm
Colour: Red-brown
Issued: Spring 1992 - spring 1996

Model No.	U.S.$	Can.$	U.K.£
A-3055	7.00	14.00	12.00

JACK RUSSELL TERRIER

Jack Russell Terrier
Model No.: A-3255
Designer: Maureen Love
Height: 1 17/18", 4.9 cm
Colour: White, brown patches, black tail and ears
Issued: Fall 1997 to the present

Model No.	U.S.$	Can.$	U.K.£
A-3255	4.50	9.00	8.00

LABRADOR RETRIEVER

Labrador Retriever

Model No.:	A-888
Designer:	Maureen Love
Height:	2", 5.0 cm
Colour:	See below
Issued:	Fall 1987 to the present

Colourways	U.S.$	Can.$	U.K.£
1. Black	4.50	9.00	8.00
2. Golden	4.50	9.00	8.00

Labrador Retriever Puppy

Model No.:	A-3888
Designer:	Maureen Love
Height:	1 1/6", 3.0 cm
Colour:	See below
Issued:	Fall 1994 to the present

Colourways	U.S.$	Can.$	U.K.£
1. Black	2.00	4.00	3.50
2. Golden	2.00	4.00	3.50

LHASA APSOS

Lhasa Apso, facing left

Model No.:	A-816
Designer:	Helen Perrin Farnlund
Height:	1", 2.5 cm
Colour:	Light tan, brown shading
Issued:	Fall 1982 - spring 1987

Model No.	U.S.$	Can.$	U.K.£
A-816	9.00	18.00	15.00

Lhasa Apso, facing right

Model No.:	A-3146
Designer:	Robert McGuinness
Height:	1 ½", 3.8 cm
Colour:	Light tan, red-brown shading
Issued:	Spring 1994 - spring 1996

Model No.	U.S.$	Can.$	U.K.£
A-3146	7.00	14.00	12.00

OLD ENGLISH SHEEPDOG

Lhasa Apso Puppy
Model No.: A-817
Designer: Helen Perrin Farnlund
Height: ½", 1.3 cm
Colour: Light tan, brown shading
Issued: Fall 1982 - spring 1987

Model No.	U.S.$	Can.$	U.K.£
A-817	5.00	10.00	8.50

Old English Sheepdog
Model No.: A-3122
Designer: Robert McGuinness
Height: 5/8", 1.6 cm
Colour: White and grey
Issued: Fall 1993 - fall 1995

Model No.	U.S.$	Can.$	U.K.£
A-3122	6.00	12.00	10.00

PEKINESE

Pekinese, seated
Model No.: A-3013
Designer: Shi Yi Chen
Height: 1 1/8", 2.8 cm
Colour: Light tan with brown shading
Issued: Spring 1991 - spring 1993

Model No.	U.S.$	Can.$	U.K.£
A-3013	7.00	14.00	12.00

Pekinese, standing, facing left
Model No.: A-076
Designer: Don Winton
Height: 1 5/8", 4.1 cm
Colour: Orange
Issued: Fall 1966 - fall 1967

Model No.	U.S.$	Can.$	U.K.£
A-076	30.00	60.00	50.00

Note: See Disney model 5079 (Peg™), page 499.

Pekinese, standing, facing right

Model No.:	A-33
Designer:	Helen Perrin Farnlund
Height:	1", 2.5 cm
Colour:	1. Dark brown, white chest and tail; matte
	2. Light tan, red-brown; shading; gloss
Issued:	Fall 1962 - spring 1971

Description	U.S.$	Can.$	U.K.£
1. Dark brown; matte	15.00	30.00	25.00
2. Light tan; gloss	8.00	16.00	14.00

Pekinese Puppy, seated

Model No.:	A-34
Designer:	Helen Perrin Farnlund
Height:	½", 1.3 cm
Colour:	1. Dark brown, white chest and tail; matte
	2. Light tan, red-brown: shading; gloss
Issued:	Fall 1962 - fall 1970

Colourways	U.S.$	Can.$	U.K.£
1. Dark brown; matte	10.00	20.00	17.00
2. Light tan; gloss	8.00	16.00	14.00

Pekinese Puppy, standing

Model No.:	A-3014
Designer:	Shi Yi Chen
Height:	7/8", 2.2 cm
Colour:	Light tan with brown shading
Issued:	Spring 1991 - spring 1992

Model No.	U.S.$	Can.$	U.K.£
A-3014	5.00	10.00	8.50

POMERANIANS

Pomeranian, seated

Model No.:	A-2077
Designer:	Maureen Love
Height:	1 7/16", 3.6 cm
Colour:	Red-brown
Issued:	Spring 1990 - fall 1990

Model No.	U.S.$	Can.$	U.K.£
A-2077	8.00	16.00	14.00

Pomeranian, standing

Model No.:	A-3130
Designer:	Robert McGuinness
Height:	1 1/8", 2.8 cm
Colour:	Light tan, red-brown shading
Issued:	Fall 1993 to the present

Model No.	U.S.$	Can.$	U.K.£
A-3130	3.00	6.00	5.00

POODLES

Poodle
Style One

Model No.:	A-82
Designer:	Helen Perrin Farnlund
Height:	2", 5.1 cm
Colour:	White; gloss
Issued:	Spring 1950 - spring 1991

Model No.	U.S.$	Can.$	U.K.£
A-82	8.00	16.00	14.00

Note: Model A-82 was made for 23 seasons.

Poodle, Style Two

Model No.:	A-346
Designer:	Martha Armstrong
Height:	2", 5.1 cm
Colour:	See below
Issued:	Spring 1958 - fall 1979

Colourways	U.S.$	Can.$	U.K.£
1. Grey	8.00	16.00	14.00
2. Pink (1966)	10.00	20.00	17.00
3. White	8.00	16.00	14.00

Note: Model A-346 was made for 33 seasons.

Poodle
Style Three

Model No.:	A-3047
Designer:	Maureen Love
Height:	2 ¼", 5.7 cm
Colour:	Grey
Issued:	Fall 1991 - fall 1993

Model No.	U.S.$	Can.$	U.K.£
A-3047	8.00	16.00	14.00

Poodle Puppy 'Chubby'

Model No.:	A-83
Designer:	Helen Perrin Farnlund
Height:	1 1/8", 2.8 cm
Colour:	White; gloss
Issued:	1950, spring 1981 - spring 1987

Model No.	U.S.$	Can.$	U.K.£
A-83	5.00	10.00	8.50

Poodle Puppy 'Thin'

Model No.:	A-349
Designer:	Martha Armstrong
Height:	7/8", 2.22 cm
Colour:	See below
Issued:	Fall 1957 - fall 1979

Colourways	U.S.$	Can.$	U.K.£
1. Grey (1966)	8.00	16.00	14.00
2. Pink (1966)	10.00	20.00	17.00
3. White	8.00	16.00	14.00

Note: Model A-349 was produced for 21 seasons, mostly in the 1970s.

Toy Poodle

Model No.:	A-3230
Designer:	Robert McGuinness
Height:	1", 2.5 cm
Colour:	White
Issued:	Spring 1997 to the present

Model No.	U.S.$	Can.$	U.K.£
A-3230	3.00	6.00	5.00

ROTTWEILER

Rottweiler
Model No.: A-3138
Designer: Maureen Love
Height: 1 ¾", 4.4 cm
Colour: Black, tan legs and chest
Issued: Fall 1993 to the present

Model No.	U.S.$	Can.$	U.K.£
A-3138	6.00	12.00	10.00

SAINT BERNARD

Saint Bernard
Model No.: A-3064
Designer: Robert McGuinness
Height: 1 7/8", 4.8 cm
Colour: Golden brown; white shoulders, face and tail tip
Issued: Spring 1992 to the present

Model No.	U.S.$	Can.$	U.K.£
A-3064	5.50	11.00	9.50

Note: For Dog Dish (A-2008), see page 389.

SCHNAUZER

Schnauzer
Model No.: A-898
Designer: Maureen Love
Height: 2", 5.0 cm
Colour: Dark and light grey
Issued: Fall 1987 to the present

Model No.	U.S.$	Can.$	U.K.£
A-898	4.00	8.00	7.00

SCOTTISH TERRIER

Scottish Terrier
Model No.: A-075/856
Designer: Don Winton
Height: 1", 2.5 cm
Colour: Black
Issued: Fall 1966
Re-issued: Spring 1985 to the present

Model No.	U.S.$	Can.$	U.K.£
A-075/856	4.00	8.00	7.00

Note: See Disney model 5007 (Jock™), page 498.

SHAR PEI

Shar Pei

Model No.:	A-2022	
Designer:	Maureen Love	
Height:	1 3/8", 3.5 cm	
Colour:	Tan dog, blue balloon	
Issued:	Fall 1988 to the present	

Model No.	U.S.$	Can.$	U.K.£
A-2022	6.00	12.00	10.00

Shar Pei, Puppy

Model No.:	A-2023	
Designer:	Shi Yi Chen	
Height:	1 1/8", 2.9 cm	
Colour:	Tan	
Issued:	Fall 1988 - spring 1992	

Model No.	U.S.$	Can.$	U.K.£
A-2023	5.00	10.00	8.50

Note: The balloon is suspended by a coated wire.

SHIH TZU

Shih Tzu 'Mandy'

Model No.:	A-2076	
Designer:	Robert McGuinness	
Height:	1 ½", 3.8 cm	
Colour:	White and black, light blue bow	
Issued:	Spring 1990 to the present	

Model No.	U.S.$	Can.$	U.K.£
A-2076	4.00	8.00	7.00

SPRINGER SPANIELS

Springer Spaniel
Model No.:   A-3142
Designer: Robert McGuinness
Height: 2", 5.1 cm
Colour: Black and white
Issued: Spring 1994 to the present

Model No.	U.S.$	Can.$	U.K.£
A-3142	6.00	12.00	10.00

Springer Spaniel Puppy
Model No.:   A-3203
Designer: Robert McGuinness
Height: 1", 2.5 cm
Colour: Black and white
Issued: Spring 1996 to the present

Model No.	U.S.$	Can.$	U.K.£
A-3203	3.00	6.00	5.00

TERRIERS

Terrier
Model No.:   A-079/93
Designer: Don Winton
Height: 2 ¼", 5.7 cm
Colour: See below
Issued: Spring 1971 - spring 1992

Colourways	U.S.$	Can.$	U.K.£
1. Brown/black/white	18.00	36.00	30.00
2. Chestnut	14.00	28.00	24.00
3. Grey-brown/white	10.00	20.00	17.00
4. Red-brown/white	14.00	28.00	24.00

Note: Model A-078/93 was made for 20 seasons.
See Disney model 5008 (Tramp™), page 500.

Terrier Puppy
Model No.: A-94
Designer: Don Winton
Height: 1", 2.5 cm
Colour: Tan, red-brown shading
Issued: Spring 1971 - spring 1973

Model No.	U.S.$	Can.$	U.K.£
A-94	10.00	20.00	17.00

Note: See Disney model 5004 (Scamp™), page 500.

WEST HIGHLAND TERRIER

YORKSHIRE TERRIER

West Highland Terrier
Model No.: A-3135
Designer: Maureen Love
Height: 1 ¾", 4.4 cm
Colour: White
Issued: Fall 1993 to the present

Model No.	U.S.$	Can.$	U.K.£
A-3135	2.50	5.00	4.00

Yorkshire Terrier
Model No.: A-3177
Designer: Unknown
Height: 1 5/8", 4.1 cm
Colour: Brown, red-brown and tan, pale blue bow
Issued: Fall 1995 to the present

Model No.	U.S.$	Can.$	U.K.£
A-3177	3.00	6.00	5.00

MUTTS

Puppy, seated (A-12); Puppy, playing (A-16); Adult (A-31)

1949 Issue

Puppy, seated

Model No.:	A-12	
Designer:	Helen Perrin Farnlund	
Height:	1 ½″, 3.8 cm	
Colour:	White; black or brown markings	
Issued:	1949	

Model No.	U.S.$	Can.$	U.K.£
A-12	8.00	16.00	14.00

Adult, standing

Model No.:	A-31	
Designer:	Helen Perrin Farnlund	
Height:	1 ½″, 3.8 cm	
Colour:	White; black or brown markings	
Issued:	1949	

Model No.	U.S.$	Can.$	U.K.£
A-31	8.00	16.00	14.00

Puppy, playing

Model No.:	A-16	
Designer:	Helen Perrin Farnlund	
Height:	¾″, 1.9 cm	
Colour:	White; black or brown markings	
Issued:	1949	

Model No.	U.S.$	Can.$	U.K.£
A-16	8.00	16.00	14.00

Adult, running

Model No.:	A-186
Designer:	Helen Perrin Farnlund
Height:	1 ¼″, 3.1 cm
Colour:	1. White, black spot on back
	2. White, brown and black
Issued:	Fall 1952 - fall 1968

Colourways	U.S.$	Can.$	U.K.£
1. White/black spot	15.00	30.00	25.00
2. White /brown/black	20.00	40.00	35.00

Note: Model A-186 was made intermittently for
     five seasons between 1952 and 1968.

Puppy, seated (A-434); Puppy, seated (A-664); Adult (A-499)

1960/1961 Issue

These models were designed by Helen Perrin Farnlund in a white, black and brown colourway.

Puppy, seated

Model No.:	A-499
Height:	1", 2.5 cm
Issued:	Fall 1961 - spring 1962

Model No.	U.S.$	Can.$	U.K.£
A-499	14.00	28.00	24.00

Adult, standing

Model No.:	A-432
Height:	1 ¾", 4.4 cm
Issued:	1960 to the present

Model No.	U.S.$	Can.$	U.K.£
A-432	3.00	6.00	5.00

Puppy, seated

Model No.:	A-434
Height:	7/8", 2.2 cm
Issued:	1960 to the present

Model No.	U.S.$	Can.$	U.K.£
A-434	2.00	4.00	3.50

Note: Models A-432 and A-434 have been made intermittently for 42 seasons since 1960.

Bad Puppy

Model No.:	A-3069
Designer:	Robert McGuinness
Height:	11/16", 1.7 cm
Colour:	Brown with white face and belly
Issued:	Fall 1992 - fall 1993

Model No.	U.S.$	Can.$	U.K.£
A-3069	5.00	10.00	8.50

Circus Dogs

These models, which were part of the 1955 Circus Set, were moulded in three sections (head, collar and body) and were available with hats, masks and a stand. Many colourways are possible.

Circus Dog, begging

Model No.:   A-279
Designer: Tom Masterson
Height: 2", 5.0 cm
Colour: White, black eyes and ears, cream and red collar
Issued: Fall 1955 - fall 1956
Series: Circus Collection

Model No.	U.S.$	Can.$	U.K.£
A-279	20.00	40.00	35.00

Circus Dog, seated

Model No.:   A-268
Designer: Tom Masterson
Height: 2", 5.0 cm
Colour: Cream dog, white ruff trimmed with red
Issued: Fall 1955 - fall 1956
Series: Circus Collection

Model No.	U.S.$	Can.$	U.K.£
A-268	20.00	40.00	35.00

Curbstone Setter, Mama

Model No.:   A-2063
Designer: Nell Bortells
Height: 1 1/8", 2.8 cm
Colour: White with red-brown spots and ears
Issued: Spring 1990 - fall 1991

Model No.	U.S.$	Can.$	U.K.£
A-2063	8.00	16.00	14.00

Curbstone Setter, Puppy

Model No.:   A-2064
Designer: Nell Bortells
Height: 1 1/8", 2.8 cm
Colour: White with red-brown spots and ears
Issued: Spring 1990 - fall 1991

Model No.	U.S.$	Can.$	U.K.£
A-2064	5.00	10.00	8.50

Good Puppy

Model No.:	A-3068
Designer:	Robert McGuinness
Height:	5/8", 1.6 cm
Colour:	Brown, white face and belly
Issued:	Fall 1992 - spring 1994

Model No.	U.S.$	Can.$	U.K.£
A-3068	5.00	10.00	8.50

Hound Dawgs

These dogs, designed by Helen Perrin Farnlund, were produced for over 30 years; the hydrant for over 20 years.

Hound Dawg Puppy, seated

Model No.:	A-4733
Height:	5/8", 1.58 cm
Colour:	See below
Issued:	Spring 1959 - fall 1984

Colourways	U.S.$	Can.$	U.K.£
1. Brown, black and white	7.00	14.00	12.00
2. Brown, black ears	5.00	10.00	8.50
3. Grey, black ears	7.00	14.00	12.00
4. Yellow, black ears	5.00	10.00	8.50

Hound Dawg Puppy, playing

Model No.:	A-474
Height:	3/8", 0.9 cm
Colour:	See below
Issued:	Spring 1959 - spring 1992

Colourways	U.S.$	Can.$	U.K.£
1. Brown, black and white	7.00	14.00	12.00
2. Brown, black ears	5.00	10.00	8.50
3. Grey, black ears	7.00	14.00	12.00
4. Yellow, black ears	5.00	10.00	8.50

Hound Dawg

Model No.:	A-463
Height:	1 3/8", 3.5 cm
Colour:	See below
Issued:	Spring 1959 - spring 1992

Colourways	U.S.$	Can.$	U.K.£
1. Brown, black and white	10.00	20.00	17.00
2. Brown, black ears	5.00	10.00	8.50
3. Grey, black ears	10.00	20.00	17.00
4. Yellow, black ears	5.00	10.00	8.50

Hydrant

Model No.:	A-444/464
Designer:	Helen Perrin Farnlund
Height:	1 ¼", 3.2 cm
Colour:	Red
Issued:	Spring 1959 - spring 1978

Model No.	U.S.$	Can. $	U.K.£
A-444/464	6.00	12.00	10.00

Papa Dog

Model No.:	A-496
Designer:	Helen Perrin Farnlund
Height:	2″, 5.1 cm
Colour:	Brown, black and white
Issued:	Fall 1961 - spring 1962

Model No.	U.S.$	Can.$	U.K.£
A-496	30.00	60.00	50.00

Puppy, lying

Model No.:	A-273
Designer:	Nell Bortells
Height:	½″, 1.3 cm
Colour:	White, black markings
Issued:	Fall 1956

Model No.	U.S.$	Can.$	U.K.£
A-273	15.00	30.00	25.00

Puppy, on hind legs

Model No.:	A-206
Designer:	Helen Perrin Farnlund
Height:	1 ¾″, 4.4 cm
Colour:	Red-brown, white underbelly
Issued:	Fall 1953

Model No.	U.S.$	Can.$	U.K.£
A-206	20.00	40.00	35.00

Puppy, scratching

Model No.:	A-2983
Designer:	Robert McGuinness
Height:	15/16″, 2.4 cm
Colour:	Brown, white nose and chest
Issued:	Fall 1990 to the present

Model No.	U.S.$	Can.$	U.K.£
A-2983	2.50	5.00	4.00

Puppy, seated

Model No.:	A-272
Designer:	Nell Bortells
Height:	1 ¼", 3.1 cm
Colour:	White, black markings
Issued:	Fall 1956

Model No.	U.S.$	Can.$	U.K.£
A-272	15.00	30.00	25.00

Puppy, seated, head turned

Model No.:	A-001
Designer:	Helen Perrin Farnlund
Height:	1", 2.5 cm
Colour:	Black, brown and white
Issued:	Fall 1961

Model No.	U.S.$	Can.$	U.K.£
A-001	20.00	40.00	35.00

Puppy, running

Model No.:	A-187
Designer:	Helen Perrin Farnlund
Height:	1", 2.5 cm
Colour:	1. Brown, white and black
	2. White with black spots
Issued:	Fall 1952 - fall 1968

Colourways	U.S.$	Can.$	U.K.£
1. Brown/white/black	12.00	24.00	20.00
2. White/black	12.00	24.00	20.00

Note: Model A-187 was made intermittently for five seasons between 1952 and 1968.

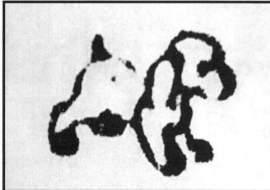

Puppy, standing

Model No.:	A-433
Designer:	Helen Perrin Farnlund
Height:	1". 2.5 cm
Colour:	Brown
Issued:	Spring 1960 (5 seasons)

Model No.	U.S.$	Can.$	U.K.£
A-433	20.00	40.00	35.00

FARM ANIMALS AND FARM CATTLE

INDEX TO FARM ANIMALS

Lamb, facing left (A-276A), black and white colourway (left) and
white and black colourway (centre); Ewe, facing left (A-275)

GOATS

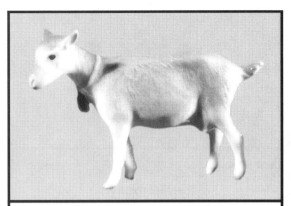

Doe

Model No.:	A-3119		
Designer:	Robert McGuinness		
Height:	1 ¾", 4.4 cm		
Colour:	Golden brown, pale yellow legs		
Issued:	Spring 1994 - fall 1997		

Model No.	U.S.$	Can.$	U.K.£
A-3119	6.00	12.00	10.00

Note: This forms a set with Kid, nursing (A-3120), and Kid, standing (A-3121), page 254.

Goat Mama

Model No.:	A-848		
Designer:	Helen Perrin Farnlund		
Height:	1 3/8", 3.5 cm		
Colour:	White		
Issued:	Fall 1984 - spring 1988		

Model No.	U.S.$	Can.$	U.K.£
A-848	10.00	20.00	17.00

Note: This forms a pair with Kid (A-849).

Goat Papa

Model No.:	A-237		
Designer:	Maureen Love		
Height:	2 ½", 6.4 cm		
Colour:	See below		
Issued:	Spring 1954 - spring 1956, spring 1969		

Colourways	U.S.$	Can.$	U.K.£
1. Brown, striped horns	25.00	50.00	45.00
2. Grey (1969)	15.00	30.00	25.00

Kid

Model No.:	A-849		
Designer:	Helen Perrin Farnlund		
Height:	¾", 1.9 cm		
Colour:	White		
Issued:	Fall 1984 - spring 1988		

Model No.	U.S.$	Can.$	U.K.£
A-849	8.00	16.00	14.00

Note: This forms a pair with Goat Mama (A-848).

Kid, butting

Model No.:	A-239
Designer:	Maureen Love
Height:	½", 1.3 cm
Colour:	1. Brown; white face; gloss
	2. Dark brown, light brown legs; gloss
Issued:	Spring 1954 - spring 1956, spring 1979

Colourways	U.S.$	Can.$	U.K.£
1. Brown	20.00	40.00	35.00
2. Dark brown	15.00	30.00	25.00

Kid, nursing

Model No.:	A-3120
Designer:	Robert McGuinness
Height:	5/8", 1.6 cm
Colour:	Golden brown, pale yellow legs
Issued:	Spring 1994 - fall 1995

Model No.	U.S.$	Can.$	U.K.£
A-3120	5.00	10.00	9.00

Note: This forms a set with Doe (A-3119), page 253, and Kid, standing (A-3121), page 254.

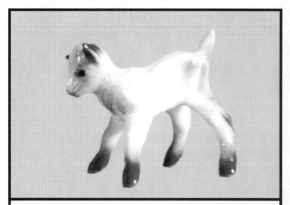

Kid, standing, head forward

Model No.:	A-238
Designer:	Maureen Love
Height:	½", 1.3 cm
Colour:	See below
Issued:	Spring 1954 - spring 1956, spring 1969, spring 1979

Colourways	U.S.$	Can.$	U.K.£
1. Brown/white; gloss	20.00	40.00	35.00
2. Dark brown; gloss (1979)	15.00	30.00	25.00
3. White; matte (1969)	20.00	40.00	35.00

Note: Dark brown models were issued in spring 1979.

Kid, standing, head up

Model No.:	A-3121
Designer:	Robert McGuinness
Height:	1", 2.5 cm
Colour:	Golden brown, pale yellow legs
Issued:	Spring 1994 - fall 1995

Model No.	U.S.$	Can.$	U.K.£
A-3121	5.00	10.00	9.00

Note: This forms a set with Doe (A-3119), page 253, and Kid, nursing (A-3120), page 254.

Nubian Doe

Model No.:	A-3149
Designer:	Helen Perrin Farnlund
Height:	1 3/8", 3.5 cm
Colour:	Grey
Issued:	Spring 1995 - spring 1998

Model No.	U.S.$	Can.$	U.K.£
A-3149	8.00	16.00	14.00

Note: This forms a pair with Nubian Kid (A-3150).

Nubian Kid

Model No.:	A-3150
Designer:	Helen Perrin Farnlund
Height:	1", 2.5 cm
Colour:	Grey
Issued:	Spring 1995 - fall 1996

Model No.	U.S.$	Can.$	U.K.£
A-3150	5.00	10.00	8.00

Note: This forms a pair with Nubian Doe (A-3149).

PIGS

Aerobic Pig, holding leg

Model No.:	A-3246
Designer:	Robert McGuinness
Height:	1 1/8", 2.8 cm
Colour:	White pig in pink outfit
Issued:	Fall 1997 to the present

Model No.	U.S.$	Can.$	U.K.£
A-3246	6.00	12.00	10.00

Aerobic Pig, leg up

Model No.:	A-3248
Designer:	Robert McGuinness
Height:	1 3/8", 3.5 cm
Colour:	White pig in pink outfit
Issued:	Fall 1997 to the present

Model No.	U.S.$	Can.$	U.K.£
A-3248	6.00	12.00	10.00

Aerobic Pig, seated, arms out

Model No.:	A-3247
Designer:	Robert McGuinness
Height:	1 ½", 3.8 cm
Colour:	White pig in pink outfit
Issued:	Fall 1997 to the present

Model No.	U.S.$	Can.$	U.K.£
A-3247	6.00	12.00	5.00

Pig, begging

Model No.:	A-165(b)
Designer:	Helen Perrin Farnlund
Height:	7/8", 2.2 cm
Colour:	Pink
Issued:	Fall 1974 - spring 1983
Varieties:	Also called Pig Brother

Model No.	U.S.$	Can.$	U.K.£
A-165b	5.00	10.00	8.50

Note: Model A-165(b) was originally used to make Piglet, begging, page 259.

Pig in a Poke

Model No.:	A-3109
Designer:	Edith Carrion
Height:	1 3/8", 3.5 cm
Colour:	White pig with black markings, brown sack
Issued:	Spring 1993 - fall 1994

Model No.	U.S.$	Can.$	U.K.£
A-3109	5.00	10.00	8.50

Pig Mama

Model No.:	A-18
Designer:	Helen Perrin Farnlund
Height:	1 ¼", 3.2 cm
Colour:	White with black markings
Issued:	1949

Model No.	U.S.$	Can.$	U.K.£
A-18	12.00	24.00	20.00

Note: This forms a pair with Piglet, standing (A-17), page 260.

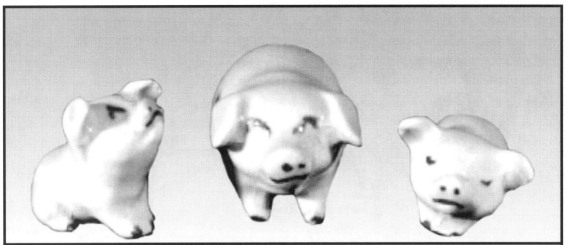

Piglet, seated (A-371)   Pig Mama (A-370)   Piglet, standing (A-372)

Pig Family - 1958

Piglet, seated

Model No.:	A-371	
Designer:	Helen Perrin Farnlund	
Height:	5/8", 1.6 cm	
Colour:	Peach with pink shading	
Issued:	1958	

Model No.	U.S.$	Can.$	U.K.£
A-371	5.00	10.00	8.50

Pig Mama

Model No.:	A-370	
Designer:	Helen Perrin Farnlund	
Height:	½", 1.3 cm	
Colour:	Peach with pink shading	
Issued:	1958, Spring 1974 - fall 1981	

Colourways	U.S.$	Can.$	U.K.£
1. Peach	15.00	30.00	25.00
2. Pink	10.00	20.00	17.00

Piglet, standing

Model No.:	A-372	
Designer:	Helen Perrin Farnlund	
Height:	½", 1.3 cm	
Colour:	1. Peach with pink shading	
	2. Pink	
Issued:	1958, 1983	

Model No.	U.S.$	Can.$	U.K.£
A-372	10.00	20.00	17.00

Note: In 1974 model A-370 was re-issued in a pink colouway.
The piglets were also re-issued in 1983, see page 258.

Pig Mama

Model No.:	A-166(a)	
Designer:	Tom Masterson	
Height:	1 ¼", 3.2 cm	
Colour:	Black and white	
Issued:	Spring 1952	

Model No.	U.S.$	Can.$	U.K.£
A-166a	15.00	30.00	25.00

Note: Model A-166(a) is also illustrated on page 59.

Pig Papa (A-2078); Piglet, seated (A-824/371); Piglet, standing (A-823/372); Pig Mama, nursing (A-822)

Pig Family

Pig Papa
Model No.: A-2078
Designer: Nell Bortells
Height: 2 ½", 6.4 cm
Colour: White with black markings
Issued: Spring 1990 to the present

Model No.	U.S.$	Can.$	U.K.£
A-2078	5.00	10.00	8.00

Pig Mama, nursing
Model No.: A-822
Designer: Nell Bortells
Height: 1", 2.5 cm
Colour: White with black markings
Issued: Spring 1983 to the present

Model No.	U.S.$	Can.$	U.K.£
A-822	4.00	10.00	8.00

Piglet, seated
Model No.: A-824/371
Designer: Helen Perrin Farnlund
Height: 5/8", 1.6 cm
Colour: White with black markings
Issued: Spring 1983 to the present

Model No.	U.S.$	Can.$	U.K.£
A-824/371	2.00	4.00	3.50

Piglet, standing
Model No.: A-823/372
Designer: Helen Perrin Farnlund
Height: ½", 1.3 cm
Colour: White with black markings
Issued: Spring 1983 to the present

Model No.	U.S.$	Can.$	U.K.£
A-823/372	2.00	4.00	3.50

Pig, seated, looking up
Model No.: A-166(b)
Designer: Helen Perrin Farnlund
Height: 1 ¼", 3.2 cm
Colour: Pink
Issued: Fall 1975 - spring 1983

Model No.	U.S.$	Can.$	U.K.£
A-166b	5.00	10.00	8.50

Pig, seated, right leg up
Model No.:   A-821
Designer: Helen Perrin Farnlund
Height: 1″, 2.5 cm
Colour: Pink
Issued: Spring 1983 - fall 1988

Model No.	U.S.$	Can.$	U.K.£
A-821	5.00	10.00	8.50

Pig, standing
Model No.:   A-847
Designer: Helen Perrin Farnlund
Height: 1 1/8″, 2.8 cm
Colour: Pink
Issued: Spring 1983 to the present

Model No.	U.S.$	Can.$	U.K.£
A-847	3.00	6.00	5.00

Note: Model A-847 has been in production for 30 seasons.

Pig, trotting
Model No.:   A-820
Designer: Helen Perrin Farnlund
Height: 1 1/8″, 2.8 cm
Colour: Pink
Issued: Spring 1983 - fall 1996

Model No.	U.S.$	Can.$	U.K.£
A-820	3.00	6.00	5.00

Note: Model A-820 has been in production for 30 seasons.

Piglet, begging
Model No.:   A-165(a)
Designer: Tom Masterson
Height: 1″, 2.5 cm
Colour: Pink with black markings
Issued: Spring 1952

Model No.	U.S.$	Can.$	U.K.£
A-165	12.00	24.00	20.00

Note: Model A-165(a) was revised to make Pig, begging; see page 256.

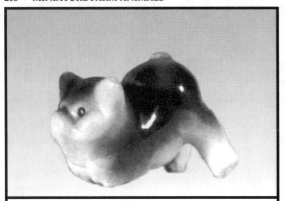

Piglet, kneeling

Model No.:	A-21
Designer:	Helen Perrin Farnlund
Height:	¾", 1.9 cm
Colour:	1. Pink with black or brown shading
	2. White with black markings
Issued:	1949

Colourways	U.S.$	Can.$	U.K.£
1. Pink/black	10.00	20.00	17.00
2. White/black	10.00	20.00	17.00

Piglet, standing

Model No.:	A-17
Designer:	Helen Perrin Farnlund
Height:	¾", 1.9 cm
Colour:	1. Pink with black markings
	2. White with black markings
Issued:	1949

Colourways	U.S.$	Can.$	U.K.£
1. Pink/black	9.00	18.00	15.00
2. White/black	9.00	18.00	15.00

Note: This forms a pair with Pig Mama (A-18), page 244.

Piglet, walking

Model No.:	A-3207
Designer:	Maureen Love
Height:	7/8", 2.2 cm
Colour:	White with pink markings
Issued:	Spring 1996 - spring 1998

Model No.	U.S.$	Can.$	U.K.£
A-3207	8.00	16.00	14.00

Note: This forms a pair with Border Collie (A-3208), page 221.

SHEEP

Early Lamb
First Version (Ears down)

Model No.:	A-35
Designer:	Helen Perrin Farnlund
Height:	1 5/8", 4.1 cm
Colour:	See below
Issued:	Spring 1949 - spring 1951
Varieties:	Also called Baby Black Sheep

Colourways	U.S.$	Can.$	U.K.£
1. Black	15.00	30.00	25.00
2. White	15.00	30.00	25.00

Early Lamb
Second Version (ear out)

Model No.:	A-35
Designer:	Helen Perrin Farnlund
Height:	1 5/8", 4.1 cm
Colour:	See below
Issued:	Spring 1949 - spring 1951

Colourways	U.S.$	Can.$	U.K.£
1. Black	15.00	30.00	25.00
2. White	15.00	30.00	25.00

Ewe, facing left

Model No.:	A-275
Designer:	Maureen Love
Height:	1 3/8", 3.5 cm
Colour:	1. White; gloss
	2. White; black nose, ears and feet; gloss or matte
Issued:	Fall 1955 - spring 1956, spring 1977 - fall 1995

Colourways	U.S.$	Can.$	U.K.£
1. White	8.00	16.00	14.00
2. White/black	15.00	30.00	25.00

Ewe, facing right

Model No.:	A-13
Designer:	Helen Perrin Farnlund
Height:	Unknown
Colour:	Unknown
Issued:	Spring 1949 - fall 1949

Model No.	U.S.$	Can.$	U.K.£
A-13		Rare	

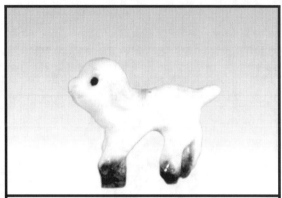

Lamb, facing left

Model No.:	A-276A
Designer:	Maureen Love
Height:	1″, 2.5 cm
Colour:	See below
Issued:	Fall 1955 - fall 1971

Description	U.S.$	Can.$	U.K.£
1. Black; gloss	10.00	20.00	17.00
2. Black/white; matte	15.00	30.00	23.00
3. White; gloss	10.00	20.00	17.00
4. White/black	15.00	30.00	23.00

Note: Model A-276A was made intermittently for eight seasons between 1955 and 1971.

Lamb, head foward

Model No.:	A-276B
Designer:	Maxine Renaker
Height:	7/8″, 2.2 cm
Colour:	White
Issued:	Spring 1975 to the present

Model No.	U.S.$	Can.$	U.K.£
A-276B	3.00	6.00	4.00

Lamb, head up

Model No.:	A-379
Designer:	Helen Perrin Farnlund
Height:	1 ¼″, 3.2 cm
Colour:	White, pink inner ears
Issued:	Spring 1958 - fall 1958

Model No.	U.S.$	Can.$	U.K.£
A-379	15.00	30.00	25.00

Lamb, head turned

Model No.:	A-378
Designer:	Helen Perrin Farnlund
Height:	1 ¼″, 3.2 cm
Colour:	White, pink inner ears
Issued:	Spring 1958 - fall 1958

Model No.	U.S.$	Can.$	U.K.£
A-378	15.00	30.00	25.00

FARM CATTLE

1949 - 1950 Cow and Calf

Calf, lying

Model No.:	A-60
Designer:	Helen Perrin Farnlund
Height:	1 ¼", 3.2 cm
Colour:	1. Black, spotted
	2. Brown, spotted
	3. Tan
Issued:	Spring 1949 - fall 1950

Colourways	U.S.$	Can.$	U.K.£
1. Black, spotted	10.00	20.00	17.00
2. Brown, spotted	10.00	20.00	17.00
3. Tan	10.00	20.00	17.00

Cow

Model No.:	A-63
Designer:	Helen Perrin Farnlund
Height:	2 5/8", 6.6 cm
Colour:	1. Black, spotted
	2. Brown, spotted
	3. Tan
Issued:	Spring 1949 - fall 1950

Colourways	U.S.$	Can.$	U.K.£
1. Black, spotted	20.00	40.00	35.00
2. Brown, spotted	20.00	40.00	35.00
3. Tan	20.00	40.00	35.00

Note: These moulds were also used by Walker-Renaker to make 'Holy Calf' and 'Holy Cow', page 566.

Calf, head turned to right

Model No.:	A-22
Designer:	Helen Perrin Farnlund
Height:	7/8", 2.2 cm
Colour:	1. Grey; Auerspurse
	2. Tan
Issued:	1962 - c.1970

Description	U.S.$	Can.$	U.K.£
1. Monrovia	15.00	30.00	26.00
2. San Dimas	7.00	14.00	12.00

Note: Model A-22 was made intermittently for eight seasons between 1962 and c.1970.

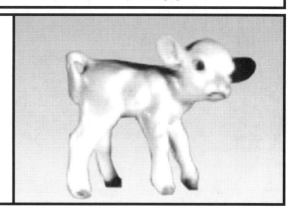

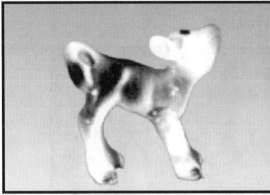

Calf, head up

Model No.:	A-211
Designer:	Helen Perrin Farnlund
Height:	1", 2.5 cm
Colour:	1. Black, spotted
	2. Tan
Issued:	Spring 1954 - c.1970

Description	U.S.$	Can.$	U.K.£
1. Monrovia	10.00	20.00	17.00
2. San Dimas	7.00	14.00	12.00

Note: Model A-211 was made intermittently for 27 seasons between 1954 and c.1970.

Cartoony Bull and Cow

Cartoony Bull

Model No.:	A-214
Designer:	Helen Perrin Farnlund
Height:	2", 5.1 cm
Colour:	1. Dark brown
	2. Light brown; matte
	3. Red-brown; gloss
	4. White
	5. White, black spots, gold horns
Issued:	Spring 1954 - c.1975

Colourways	U.S.$	Can.$	U.K.£
1. Dark brown	15.00	30.00	25.00
2. Light brown	12.00	24.00	20.00
3. Red-brown	12.00	24.00	20.00
4. White	15.00	30.00	25.00
5. White/black/gold horns	20.00	40.00	35.00

Cartoony Cow

Model No.:	A-210/23
Designer:	Helen Perrin Farnlund
Height:	1 ½", 3.8 cm
Colour:	1. Dark brown
	2. Light brown; matte
	3. Red-brown; gloss
	4. White
	5. White, black spots, gold horns
Issued:	Fall 1953 - c.1975

Colourways	U.S.$	Can.$	U.K.£
1. Dark brown	15.00	30.00	25.00
2. Light brown	12.00	24.00	20.00
3. Red-brown	12.00	24.00	20.00
4. White	15.00	30.00	25.00
5. White/black/gold horns	20.00	24.00	35.00

Note: Cartoony Bull was made for 27 seasons and Cartoony Cow, for 30 seasons. The red-brown colourway was issued c.1970. A variation of Cartoony Cow exists with the head forward and the tail curved higher.

Guernsey Cattle

Guernsey Bull

Model No.:	A-3200	
Designer:	Maureen Love	
Height:	1 ¾", 4.4 cm	
Colour:	White, red-brown markings	
Issued:	Spring 1996 - spring 1997	

Model No.	U.S.$	Can.$	U.K.£
A-3200	8.00	16.00	14.00

Guernsey Cow

Model No.:	A-3201	
Designer:	Maureen Love	
Height:	1 ½", 3.8 cm	
Colour:	White, red-brown markings	
Issued:	Spring 1996 to the present	

Model No.	U.S.$	Can.$	U.K.£
A-3201	8.00	16.00	14.00

Guernsey Calf

Model No.:	A-3202	
Designer:	Maureen Love	
Height:	7/8", 2.2 cm	
Colour:	White, red-brown markings	
Issued:	Spring 1996 - spring 1998	

Model No.	U.S.$	Can.$	U.K.£
A-3202	4.00	8.00	7.00

Note: Earlier models had brown horns; later models had black horns.

Hereford Bull

Model No.:	A-357	
Designer:	Maureen Love	
Height:	1 ½", 3.8 cm	
Colour:	Dark red-brown and white; gloss	
Issued:	Fall 1957, spring 1958, fall 1965	

Model No.	U.S.$	Can.$	U.K.£
A-357	30.00	60.00	50.00

Hereford Calf

Model No.:	A-291
Designer:	Maureen Love
Height:	1", 2.5 cm
Colour:	Dark red-brown and white; gloss
Issued:	Spring 1957, fall 1965

Model No.	U.S.$	Can.$	U.K.£
A-291	20.00	40.00	35.00

Note: Model A-291 was also used to make the Jersey Calf, page 267. The calf illustrated has a damaged tail.

Holstein Cattle

Holstein Bull

Model No.:	A-289A/292
Designer:	Maureen Love
Height:	1 7/8", 4.8 cm
Colour:	Black and white; gloss
Issued:	Spring 1988 to the present

Model No.	U.S.$	Can.$	U.K.£
A-289A/292	5.00	10.00	8.50

Holstein Calf

Model No.:	A-022
Designer:	Helen Perrin Farnlund
Height:	7/8", 2.2 cm
Colour:	Black and white; gloss
Issued:	Spring 1988 to the present

Model No.	U.S.$	Can.$	U.K.£
A-291	5.00	10.00	8.50

Holstein Cow

Model No.:	A-290A/293
Designer:	Maureen Love
Height:	1 ½", 3.8 cm
Colour:	Black and white; gloss
Issued:	Spring 1988 to the present

Model No.	U.S.$	Can.$	U.K.£
A-290A/293	5.00	10.00	8.50

Note: Models A-289 and A-290 were also used to make the Jersey Bull (horns removed) and Jersey Cow, page 267. Model A-291 in black and white is now offered with this set.

Holy Cow
Model No.:   A-813
Designer: Nell Bortells
Height: 2 ½", 6.4 cm
Colour: White; gold halo and hooves; yellow
             green, blue and red flowers on her side
Issued: Fall 1982 - spring 1986

Model No.	U.S.$	Can.$	U.K.£
A-813	13.00	26.00	23.00

Jersey Bull
Model No.:   A-289
Designer: Maureen Love
Height: 1 7/8", 4.7 cm
Colour: 1. Black, brown shading; matte
             2. Light brown; gloss
Issued: Spring 1956 - fall 1988

Colourways	U.S.$	Can.$	U.K.£
1. Black	30.00	60.00	50.00
2. Light brown	10.00	20.00	17.00

Note: Model A-289 was made for 13 seasons. It was also used to make the Holstein Bull, see page 266.

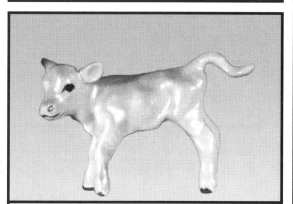

Jersey Calf
Model No.:   A-291
Designer: Maureen Love
Height: 1", 2.5 cm
Colour: 1. Light brown; gloss
             2. Pale brown; matte
Issued: Spring 1956 - fall 1988

Colourways	U.S.$	Can.$	U.K.£
1. Brown; gloss	12.00	24.00	20.00
2. Brown; matte	20.00	40.00	35.00

Note: Model A-291 was also used to make Hereford Calf, page 266, and was made for 13 seasons.

Jersey Cow
Model No.:   A-290
Designer: Maureen Love
Height: 1 ½", 3.8 cm
Colour: 1. Light brown; gloss
             2. Pale brown; matte
Issued: Spring 1956 - fall 1988

Colourways	U.S.$	Can.$	U.K.£
1. Brown; gloss	12.00	25.00	25.00
2. Brown; matte	20.00	40.00	35.00

Note: Model A-290 was made intermittently for 13 seasons between 1956 and 1988. It was also used to make the Holstein Cow, see page 266.

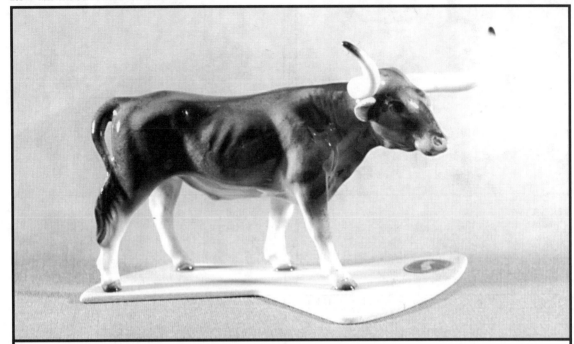

Longhorn Steer
Model No.:   A-3231
Designer: Maureen Love
Height: 2″, 5.1 cm
Colour: Light brown
Issued: Spring 1997 - fall 1998

Model No.	U.S.$	Can.$	U.K.£
A-3231	9.00	18.00	15.00

HORSES

Race tickets, similar to those issued with the Designer's Workshop Thoroughbred horses, were also issued with the earlier models of thoroughbred miniature horses.

The following moulds were leased by Breyer:

Name	Model No.	Name	Model No.
American Saddlebred, Style One	A-458	Thoroughbred Racehorse	
Arabian Foal	A-49	'Citation'	A-11
Arabian Mare	A-46	'Native Dancer'	A-12
Arabian Stallion, standing	A-47	'Seabiscuit'	A-10
Morgan Mare	A-388	'Silky Sullivan'	A-030
Morgan Stallion	A-389	'Swaps'	A-457
Percheron, tail down	A-459	Thoroughbred Foal	A-025
Quarter Horse Stallion	A-31	Thoroughbred Mare	A-024

INDEX TO MINIATURE HORSES

AMERICAN SADDLE BRED HORSES

American Saddle Bred, Style One

Model No.:	A-458
Designer:	Maureen Love
Height:	3", 7.6 cm
Colour:	1. Brown; matte
	2. White; matte
Issued:	Spring 1959 - fall 1963, spring 1967 - fall 1969

Colourways	U.S.$	Can.$	U.K.£
1. Brown	75.00	150.00	130.00
2. White	75.00	150.00	130.00

American Saddlebred, Style Two

Model No.:	A-2013
Designer:	Maureen Love
Height:	2 ¼", 5.7 cm
Colour:	Chestnut; gloss
Issued:	Fall 1988 to the present
Series:	Stamp Horses

Model No.	U.S.$	Can.$	U.K.£
A-2013	7.00	14.00	12.00

Note: Originally issued on a Plexiglas base, models now issued on a clay base. Model A-2013 is one of 4 designs issued to complement U.S. postal stamps.

APPALOOSAS

Appaloosa Mare and Foal (on base)

Model No.:	1. Mare — A-2011
	2. Foal — A-2010
Designer:	Maureen Love
Height:	1. Mare — 1 ½", 3.8 cm
	2. Foal — 2 ¼", 5.7 cm
Colour:	1. Mare — Chestnut snowflake
	2. Foal — Grey blanket
Issued:	Fall 1988 to the present

Description	U.S.$	Can.$	U.K.£
Mare and foal (on base)	9.00	18.00	15.00

Note: These models were originally issued on a black Plexiglas base and are now issued on a clay base.

ARABIANS

Arabian Foal, lying

Model No.: A-49
Designer: Maureen Love
Height: 1 ½", 3.8 cm
Colour: 1. Grey (Monrovia)
2. White (San Dimas)
Issued: Fall 1959 - fall 1965

Description	U.S.$	Can.$	U.K.£
1. Monrovia	40.00	80.00	70.00
2. San Dimas	30.00	60.00	50.00

Note: This forms a set with Arabian Mare (A-46), page 273, and Arabian Stallion (A-47), page 273.

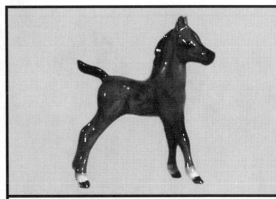

Arabian Foal, standing, tail pointing up

Model No.: A-298
Designer: Maureen Love
Height: 2", 5.1 cm
Colour: See below
Issued: Spring 1956 - spring 1959

Colourways	U.S.$	Can.$	U.K.£
1. Bay; gloss	40.00	80.00	70.00
2. Grey doeskin	30.00	60.00	50.00
3. Rose grey	30.00	60.00	50.00
4. White	30.00	60.00	50.00

Arabian Foal, standing, tail pointing straight

Model No.: A-48
Designer: Maureen Love
Height: 2", 5.1 cm
Colour: 1. Grey (Monrovia)
2. White (San Dimas)
Issued: Fall 1959 - spring 1973

Description	U.S.$	Can.$	U.K.£
1. Monrovia	35.00	70.00	60.00
2. San Dimas	30.00	60.00	50.00

Arabian Horse, prancing (Without base)

Model No.: A-297
Designer: Maureen Love
Height: 3 ¼", 8.3 cm
Colour: See below
Issued: Spring 1956 - fall 1959, spring 1973

Colourways	U.S.$	Can.$	U.K.£
1. Bay; gloss	100.00	200.00	175.00
2. Doeskin (San Dimas)	70.00	140.00	120.00
3. White (Monrovia)	70.00	140.00	120.00
4. White (San Dimas)	80.00	160.00	140.00

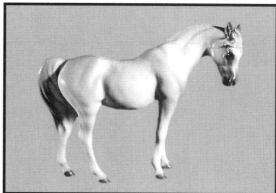

Arabian Horse, prancing
(With base)

Model No.:	A-2049
Designer:	Maureen Love
Height:	2 ½", 6.4 cm
Colour:	White; gloss
Issued:	Spring 1989 to the present

Model No.	U.S.$	Can.$	U.K.£
A-2049	6.00	12.00	10.00

Note: Originally issued on a black Plexiglas base, this is now issued on a tan ceramic base.

Arabian Mare

Model No.:	A-46
Designer:	Maureen Love
Height:	3", 7.6 cm
Colour:	1. Grey (Monrovia)
	2. White (San Dimas)
Issued:	Fall 1959 - spring 1969

Description	U.S.$	Can.$	U.K.£
1. Monrovia	65.00	130.00	115.00
2. San Dimas	55.00	110.00	95.00

Note: This forms a set with Arabian Stallion (A-47), and Arabian Foal (A-49), page 272.

Arabian Stallion, standing

Model No.:	A-47
Designer:	Maureen Love
Height:	3", 7.6 cm
Colour:	1. Grey; matte (Monrovia)
	2. White (San Dimas)
Issued:	Fall 1959 - fall 1972

Description	U.S.$	Can.$	U.K.£
1. Monrovia	55.00	110.00	95.00
2. San Dimas	45.00	90.00	80.00

Note: This forms a set with Arabian Mare (A-46), and Arabian Foal (A-49), page 272.

CIRCUS HORSES

Circus Pony, head down, with harness

Model No.:	A-267
Designer:	Maureen Love
Height:	1 ¾", 4.5 cm
Colour:	1. White; black mane and tail, gold harness, red plume
	2. White; blue or yellow harness, without plume
Issued:	Fall 1956 - spring 1957
	spring 1980- fall 1983

Colourways	U.S.$	Can.$	U.K.£
1. With plume	75.00	150.00	130.00
2. Without plume	25.00	50.00	40.00

Note: See also model A-315, page 292.

Circus Pony, head up, with plume

Model No.:	A-266
Designer:	Maureen Love
Height:	2 3/8", 6.0 cm
Colour:	White, black mane and tail, gold harness and hooves, red pipe-cleaner plume
Issued:	Fall 1955 - spring 1957

Model No.	U.S.$	Can.$	U.K.£
A-266	75.00	150.00	130.00

Note: See also model A-314, page 292.

Circus Pony, head up, without plume

Model No.:	A-266
Designer:	Maureen Love
Height:	2 3/8", 6.0 cm
Colour:	White; green, lavender, maroon or pink harness
Issued:	Spring 1980 - fall 1983

Model No.	U.S.$	Can.$	U.K.£
A-266	25.00	50.00	40.00

CLYDESDALES

Clydesdale Foal, on base

Model No.:	A-3156
Designer:	Maureen Love
Height:	2 13/16", 7.1 cm
Colour:	Bay, cream base
Issued:	Fall 1994 to the present

Model No.	U.S.$	Can.$	U.K.£
A-3156	8.00	16.00	14.00

Clydesdale Horse, on base

Model No.:	A-3127
Designer:	Maureen Love
Height:	2 3/8", 6.0 cm
Colour:	See below
Issued:	1. White — 1977 in a limited edition of 200
	2. Bay — Fall 1993 to the present

Colourways	U.S.$	Can.$	U.K.£
1. White, cream base	9.00	18.00	15.00
2. Bay, cream base	20.00	40.00	35.00

Note: The white colourway was issued for the Hagen-Renaker Collector's Club.

DRAFT HORSES

Draft Foal

Model No.:	A-62
Designer:	Helen Perrin Farnlund
Height:	2 1/8", 5.3 cm
Colour:	See below
Issued:	Spring 1949 - spring 1951

Colourways	U.S.$	Can.$	U.K.£
1. Chestnut	20.00	40.00	35.00
2. Palomino	20.00	40.00	35.00

Note: The size of this model may vary slightly.
Model A-62 forms a pair with Draft Horse (A-61).

Draft Horse, comical

Model No.:	A-61
Designer:	Helen Perrin Farnlund
Height:	3 ¼", 8.3 cm
Colour:	See below
Issued:	Spring 1949 - spring 1951

Colourways	U.S.$	Can.$	U.K.£
1. Chestnut	30.00	60.00	50.00
2. Palomino	30.00	60.00	50.00

Note: Earlier models had the pour hole in the feet; later models had it in the belly. Pair with model A-62.

Draft Horse, in harness

Model No.:	A-341
Designer:	Maureen Love
Height:	2 ¾", 7.0 cm
Colour:	1. Chestnut; gloss
	2. White; gloss
Issued:	1957, spring 1979 - fall 1985

Colourways	U.S.$	Can.$	U.K.£
1. Chestnut	20.00	40.00	35.00
2. White	80.00	160.00	140.00

Note: Model A-341 was revised to make model A-459 (Percheron), page 280.

HACKNEY

LIPIZZANER

Hackney

Model No.:	A-2085
Designer:	Maureen Love
Height:	2 ¾", 7.0 cm
Colour:	Bay, cream ceramic base
Issued:	Fall 1990 - spring 1994

Model No.	U.S.$	Can.$	U.K.£
A-2085	20.00	40.00	35.00

Lipizzaner

Model No.:	A-3169
Designer:	Maureen Love
Height:	3 ¼", 8.3 cm
Colour:	White
Issued:	Spring 1995 - spring 1997

Model No.	U.S.$	Can.$	U.K.£
A-3169	15.00	30.00	25.00

Note: The model is on the stand and base in a capriole position.

MORGAN HORSES

Morgan Foal, resting foot
Model No.: A-390
Designer: Maureen Love
Height: 2", 5.0 cm
Colour: 1. Chestnut (Monrovia)
2. Palomino (San Dimas)
Issued: Fall 1959 - fall 1973

Description	U.S.$	Can.$	U.K.£
1. Monrovia	35.00	70.00	60.00
2. San Dimas	30.00	60.00	50.00

Morgan Foal, scampering
Model No.: A-391
Designer: Maureen Love
Height: 2", 5.0 cm
Colour: 1. Chestnut (Monrovia)
2. Palomino (San Dimas)
Issued: Fall 1959 - fall 1967

Description	U.S.$	Can.$	U.K.£
1. Monrovia	50.00	100.00	85.00
2. San Dimas	50.00	100.00	85.00

Morgan Horse (On base)
Model No.: A-2009
Designer: Maureen Love
Height: 2 ½", 6.4 cm
Colour: Dark bay
Issued: Fall 1988 to the present
Series: Stamp Horses

Model No.	U.S.$	Can.$	U.K.£
A-2009	7.00	14.00	12.00

Note: Model A-2009 was originally issued on a black Plexiglas base; current models are on a clay base.

Morgan Mare
Model No.: A-388
Designer: Maureen Love
Height: 2 ¾", 7.0 cm
Colour: 1. Chestnut (Monrovia)
2. Palomino (San Dimas)
Issued: Fall 1959 - fall 1970

Description	U.S.$	Can.$	U.K.£
1. Monrovia	70.00	140.00	120.00
2. San Dimas	60.00	120.00	105.00

Morgan Stallion
Model No.:   A-389
Designer: Maureen Love
Height: 2 ¾", 7.0 cm
Colour: 1. Chestnut (Monrovia)
              2. Palomino (San Dimas)
Issued: Fall 1959 - fall 1973

Description	U.S.$	Can.$	U.K.£
1. Monrovia	65.00	130.00	115.00
2. San Dimas	55.00	110.00	95.00

MUSTANGS

Mustang, rearing, forelegs down
Model No.:   A-2051
Designer: Maureen Love
Height: 3 ½", 8.9 cm
Colour: 1. Cream, brown mane and legs
              2. Tan, brown mane and legs
Issued: Spring 1989 - fall 1993

Colourways	U.S.$	Can.$	U.K.£
1. Cream	20.00	40.00	35.00
2. Tan	12.00	24.00	20.00

Note: Earlier models of A-2051 were issued on a wooden base; later models were issued on a clay base. The cream colourway was issued in a limited edition of 200 in 1993 and released at the Model Horse Jamboree in Ontario, California.

Mustang, rearing, forelegs out

Model No.: A-2050
Designer: Maureen Love
Height: 3 13/16", 9.7 cm
Colour: Dark grey, black mane and legs
Issued: Spring 1989 - fall 1993

Model No.	U.S.$	Can.$	U.K.£
A-2050	15.00	30.00	25.00

Note: Models of A-2050 were originally issued on a wooden base; later models were issued on a clay base.

Mustang, turning

Model No.: A-360
Designer: Maureen Love
Height: 2 ¾", 7.0 cm
Colour: 1. Bay; gloss or matte
 2. Black pinto; gloss
 3. Buckskin; gloss or matte
Issued: Spring 1958 - fall 1959,
 1980 - fall 1984 (black pinto)

Colourways	U.S.$	Can.$	U.K.£
1. Bay	75.00	150.00	130.00
2. Black pinto	20.00	40.00	35.00
3. Buckskin	75.00	150.00	130.00

Note: Model A-360 was produced for a total of eleven seasons.

PERCHERONS

Percheron, tail down

Model No.:	A-459	
Designer:	Maureen Love	
Height:	2 ¾", 7.0 cm	
Colour:	White, grey shading; matte	
Issued:	1959, fall 1965, spring 1966	

Model No.	U.S.$	Can.$	U.K.£
A-459	80.00	160.00	140.00

Note: Model A-341 (Draft Horse, in harness), page 276, was revised to make A-459.

Percheron, tail up

Model No.:	A-3213	
Designer:	Nance Brown	
Height:	3", 7.6 cm	
Colour:	Dapple-grey	
Issued:	Fall 1996 to the present	

Model No.	U.S.$	Can.$	U.K.£
A-3213	8.00	16.00	14.00

QUARTER HORSES

Quarter Horse Foal

Model No.:	A-32	
Designer:	Maureen Love	
Height:	2", 5.1 cm	
Colour:	Buckskin; matte	
Issued:	Fall 1962 - spring 1966	

Model No.	U.S.$	Can.$	U.K.£
A-32	60.00	120.00	105.00

Note: This forms a pair with Quarter Horse Stallion (A-31).

Quarter Horse Stallion

Model No.:	A-31	
Designer:	Maureen Love	
Height:	2 ¾", 7.0 cm	
Colour:	Buckskin, matte	
Issued:	Fall 1962 - spring 1966	

Model No.	U.S.$	Can.$	U.K.£
A-31	80.00	160.00	140.00

Note: This forms a pair with Quarter Horse Foal (A-32).

Quarter Horse (On base)
Model No.:   A-2012
Designer: Maureen Love
Height: 2 1/8", 5.4 cm
Colour: Chestnut
Issued: Fall 1988 to the present
Series: Stamp Horses

Model No.	U.S.$	Can.$	U.K.£
A-2012	7.00	14.00	12.00

Note: Models of A-2012 were originally issued on a black Plexiglas base; later models were on a clay base.

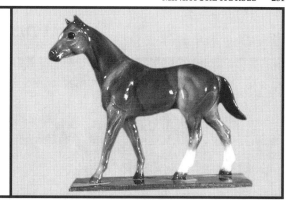

ROCKING HORSES

Rocking Horse Foal
Model No.:   A-991
Designer: Maxine Renaker
Height: 1 ¾", 4.4 cm
Colour: White; grey mane, tail and dapples;
            blue rockers
Issued: Fall 1981 - fall 1993

Model No.	U.S.$	Can.$	U.K.£
A-991	7.00	14.00	12.00

Rocking Horse Mare
Model No.:   A-990
Designer: Maxine Renaker
Height: 2", 5.0 cm
Colour: White; light grey mane, tail and
            dapples; red rockers
Issued: Fall 1981 - fall 1992

Model No.	U.S.$	Can.$	U.K.£
A-990	9.00	18.00	15.00

Note: Model A-991 is also known with red rockers.

SADDLE HORSES

Saddle Horse
Style One (Feet apart)

Model No.:	A-169
Designer:	Tom Masterson
Height:	2 ¾", 7.0 cm
Colour:	1. Bay
	2. Palomino
Issued:	Spring 1951 - fall 1951

Colourways	U.S.$	Can.$	U.K.£
1. Bay	45.00	90.00	80.00
2. Palomino	45.00	90.00	80.00

Note: Good-quality counterfeit copies of model A-169 exist.

Saddle Horse
Style Two (Feet together)

Model No.:	A-146
Designer:	Tom Masterson
Height:	2 3/8", 6.0 cm
Colour:	1. Bay
	2. Palomino
Issued:	Spring 1952 - spring 1953

Colourways	U.S.$	Can.$	U.K.£
1. Bay	40.00	80.00	70.00
2. Palomino	40.00	80.00	70.00

SHETLAND PONIES

Shetland Mare (A-3066) Shetland Foal (A-3067) Shetland Stallion (A-3065)

Shetland Mare

Model No.:	A-3066
Designer:	Maureen Love
Height:	1 15/16", 4.9 cm
Colour:	Chestnut
Issued:	Fall 1992 to the present

Model No.	U.S.$	Can.$	U.K.£
A-3066	5.00	10.00	8.00

Shetland Stallion

Model No.:	A-3065
Designer:	Maureen Love
Height:	1 7/8", 4.8 cm
Colour:	Chestnut
Issued:	Fall 1992 to the present

Model No.	U.S.$	Can.$	U.K.£
A-3065	5.00	10.00	8.00

Shetland Foal

Model No.:	A-3067
Designer:	Maureen Love
Height:	1 ½", 3.8 cm
Colour:	Chestnut
Issued:	Fall 1992 to the present

Model No.	U.S.$	Can.$	U.K.£
A-3067	4.00	8.00	6.00

Note: The colourway varies from pale golden brown to bright golden brown.

THOROUGHBREDS

Thoroughbred Racehorse 'Citation'

Model No.:	A-11
Designer:	Maureen Love
Height:	2 ¾", 7.0 cm
Colour:	Bay; matte
Issued:	Fall 1961 - fall 1968

Model No.	U.S.$	Can.$	U.K.£
A-11	70.00	140.00	120.00

Note: Race tickets were issued with earlier models of 'Citation'.

Thoroughbred Racehorse 'Native Dancer'

Model No.:	A-12
Designer:	Maureen Love
Height:	3", 7.6 cm
Colour:	Grey; matte
Issued:	Fall 1961 - spring 1966

Model No.	U.S.$	Can.$	U.K.£
A-12	70.00	140.00	120.00

Note: Race tickets were issued with earlier models of 'Native Dancer'.

Thoroughbred Racehorse 'Sea Biscuit'

Model No.:	A-10
Designer:	Maureen Love
Height:	2 ¾", 7.0 cm
Colour:	See below
Issued:	1. Buckskin — Fall 1968
	2. Chestnut — Fall 1993 to the present
	3. Dark bay — Fall 1961 - spring 1963
	4. White — 1995 in a special edition of 235

Colourways	U.S.$	Can.$	U.K.£
1. Buckskin; matte	75.00	150.00	130.00
2. Chestnut; gloss	9.00	18.00	15.00
3. Dark bay; matte	75.00	150.00	130.00
4. White	25.00	50.00	45.00

Note: Race tickets were issued with earlier models of 'Sea Biscuit'. The white colourway was issued for the Hagen-Renaker Collector's Club.

Thoroughbred Racehorse 'Silky Sullivan'

Model No.: A-030
Designer: Maureen Love
Height: 2 ¾", 7.0 cm
Colour: Chestnut; matte
Issued: Fall 1961 - fall 1970

Model No.	U.S.$	Can.$	U.K.£
A-030	65.00	130.00	115.00

Note: Race tickets were issued with earlier models of 'Silky Sullivan'.

Thoroughbred Racehorse 'Swaps'

Model No.: A-457
Designer: Maureen Love
Height: 3", 7.6 cm
Colour: Chestnut; gloss or matte
Issued: Fall 1959 - fall 1967,
fall 1991 - 1993

Description	U.S.$	Can.$	U.K.£
1. Gloss	20.00	40.00	35.00
2. Matte	65.00	130.00	115.00

Note: Race tickets were issued with earlier models of 'Swaps'.

Thoroughbred (On base)

Model No.: A-2084
Designer: Maureen Love
Height: 2 3/8", 6.0 cm
Colour: Chestnut; gloss
Issued: Fall 1990 - spring 1994

Model No.	U.S.$	Can.$	U.K.£
A-2084	15.00	30.00	25.00

Thoroughbred Foal

Model No.: A-025
Designer: Maureen Love
Height: 2", 5.0 cm
Colour: See below
Issued: Spring 1962 - spring 1975, c.1980

Colourways	U.S.$	Can.$	U.K.£
1. Bay; matte	35.00	70.00	60.00
2. Black; gloss	20.00	40.00	35.00
3. Buckskin; matte	35.00	70.00	60.00

Note: Model A-025 was produced for 27 seasons. Issued in a black colourway (c.1980), it forms with A-234.

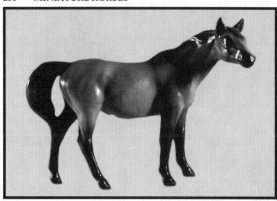

Thoroughbred Mare

Model No.:	A-024
Designer:	Maureen Love
Height:	3", 7.6 cm
Colour:	1. Bay; matte
	2. Buckskin; matte
Issued:	Spring 1962 - spring 1972

Colourways	U.S.$	Can.$	U.K.£
1. Bay	65.00	130.00	115.00
2. Buckskin	65.00	130.00	115.00

WESTERN HORSES

Western Foal

Model No.:	A-325
Designer:	Maureen Love
Height:	1 ½", 3.8 cm
Colour:	Palomino; gloss or matte
Issued:	Spring 1957 - fall 1957

Model No.	U.S.$	Can.$	U.K.£
A-325	55.00	110.00	95.00

Note: The colourway varies from soft yellow to orange-yellow.

Western Pony

Model No.:	A-323
Designer:	Maureen Love
Height:	2 ½", 6.4 cm
Colour:	1. Palomino, black saddle, blue blanket; gloss or matte
	2. Palomino, brown and silver saddle, green blanket; gloss
Issued:	1. Spring 1957
	2. spring 1979 - fall 1984

Colourways	U.S.$	Can.$	U.K.£
1. Black saddle	60.00	120.00	105.00
2. Brown saddle	20.00	40.00	35.00

Note: The palomino colourway varies from soft yellow to orange-yellow.

YEARLINGS

Yearling, head down

Model No.:   A-361
Designer: Maureen Love
Height: 1 ¾″, 4.4 cm
Colour: 1. Bay; gloss or matte
              2. Buckskin; gloss or matte
Issued: Spring 1958 - fall 1959, fall 1968

Colourways	U.S.$	Can.$	U.K.£
1. Bay	60.00	120.00	105.00
2. Buckskin	60.00	120.00	105.00

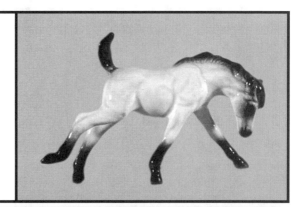

Yearling, head up

Model No.:   A-362
Designer: Maureen Love
Height: 2″, 5.1 cm
Colour: 1. Bay; gloss or matte
              2. Black pinto; gloss
              3. Buckskin; gloss or matte
Issued: Spring 1958 - fall 1959, fall 1968,
              1981 - 1984

Colourways	U.S.$	Can.$	U.K.£
1. Bay	60.00	120.00	105.00
2. Black pinto (c.1980)	18.00	36.00	30.00
3. Buckskin	60.00	120.00	105.00

Yearling, turning

Model No.:   A-363
Designer: Maureen Love
Height: 2″, 5.1 cm
Colour: 1. Bay; gloss or matte
              2. Buckskin; gloss or matte
Issued: Spring 1958 - fall 1959,
              fall 1968

Colourways	U.S.$	Can.$	U.K.£
1. Bay	60.00	120.00	105.00
2. Buckskin	60.00	120.00	105.00

MISCELLANEOUS HORSES

Colt, frisky

Model No.:	A-147
Designer:	Tom Masterson
Height:	2″, 5.1 cm
Colour:	1. Bay
	2. Palomino
Issued:	Spring 1951 - spring 1953

Colourways	U.S.$	Can.$	U.K.£
1. Bay	20.00	40.00	35.00
2. Palomino	20.00	40.00	35.00

Colt, standing

Model No.:	A-148
Designer:	Tom Masterson
Height:	1 ¾″, 4.4 cm
Colour:	1. Bay
	2. Palomino
Issued:	Spring 1952 - spring 1953

Colourways	U.S.$	Can.$	U.K.£
1. Bay	20.00	40.00	35.00
2. Palomino	20.00	40.00	35.00

Foal, lying

Model No.:	A-236
Designer:	Maureen Love
Height:	1 1/8″, 2.8 cm
Colour:	See below
Issued:	c.1953 - spring 1985

Colourways	U.S.$	Can.$	U.K.£
1. Bay; gloss	25.00	50.00	40.00
2. Buckskin; gloss	15.00	30.00	25.00
3. Palomino; gloss	25.00	50.00	40.00
4. White; matte	25.00	50.00	40.00

Note: Model A-236 was made for 18 seasons. This forms a set with models A-233 and A-235, page 290.

Horse, head down

Model No.:	A-428
Designer:	Maureen Love
Height:	2 ¼″, 5.7 cm
Colour:	See below
Issued:	Spring 1960 - spring 1968

Colourways	U.S.$	Can.$	U.K.£
1. Appaloosa (1965 - 1968)	90.00	180.00	155.00
2. Black pinto (1960)	125.00	250.00	220.00
3. Buckskin (1965)	80.00	160.00	140.00
4. Palomino (1960 - 1961)	80.00	160.00	140.00

Note: Model A-428 was made for 10 seasons.

Horse, head up

Model No.:	A-429			
Designer:	Maureen Love			
Height:	3″, 7.6 cm			
Colour:	See below			
Issued:	Spring 1960 - spring 1972			

Colourways	U.S.$	Can.$	U.K.£
1. Appaloosa (1969 - 1962)	75.00	150.00	130.00
2. Black pinto (1960)	125.00	250.00	220.00
3. Buckskin (1965)	80.00	160.00	140.00
4. Palomino (1960 - 1962)	80.00	160.00	140.00

Note: Model A-429 was made for 17 seasons.

Horse, rearing

Model No.:	A-234			
Designer:	Maureen Love			
Height:	3 ½″, 8.9 cm			
Colour:	1. Bay; gloss			
	2. Black; gloss			
	3. Brown; matte			
	4. Buckskin; matte			
	5. Palomino; gloss			
	6. White; matte			
Issued:	Fall 1954 - spring 1985			

Colourways	U.S.$	Can.$	U.K.£
1. Bay	60.00	125.00	100.00
2. Black	25.00	50.00	40.00
3. Brown (1958)	60.00	125.00	100.00
4. Buckskin (1958)	60.00	125.00	100.00
5. Palomino	60.00	125.00	100.00
6. White	60.00	125.00	100.00

Note: Model A-234 was made intermittently for 19 seasons. During the 1980s it was produced in the black colourway as a set with A-025.

Horse, reclining

Model No.:	A-209			
Designer:	Tom Masterson			
Height:	1 ½″, 3.8 cm			
Colour:	1. Bay			
	2. Palomino			
Issued:	Spring 1951 - spring 1952			

Colourways	U.S.$	Can.$	U.K.£
1. Bay	40.00	80.00	70.00
2. Palomino	40.00	80.00	70.00

Note: Good-quality counterfeit copies of model A-209 exist.

Indian Pony (On ceramic base)
Model No.:   A-3110
Designer: Maureen Love
Height: 2", 5.1 cm
Colour: Brown pinto, beige ceramic base
Issued: Fall 1993 to the present

Model No.	U.S.$	Can.$	U.K.£
A-3110	7.00	14.00	12.00

Foal, running
Model No.:   A-235
Designer: Maureen Love
Height: 2", 5.08 cm
Colour: See below
Issued: Fall 1954 to the present

Colourways	U.S.$	Can.$	U.K.£
1. Bay; gloss	30.00	60.00	50.00
2. Buckskin; gloss	6.00	12.00	10.00
3. Palomino; gloss	30.00	60.00	50.00
4. White; matte	30.00	60.00	50.00

Mare, running
Model No.:   A-233
Designer: Maureen Love
Height: 2 ¾", 7.0 cm
Colour: See below
Issued: Fall 1954 to the present

Colourways	U.S.$	Can.$	U.K.£
1. Bay; gloss	65.00	130.00	115.00
2. Buckskin; gloss	7.00	14.00	12.00
3. Palomino; gloss	65.00	130.00	115.00
4. White; matte	65.00	130.00	115.00

Note: Models A-233 and A-235 have been in production for 40 seasons.

Mini Mini Horses

Mare (A-451)   Foal (A-453)   Stallion (A-452)

Mini Mini Mare, prancing

Model No.:	A-451
Designer:	Maureen Love
Height:	1 ¼", 3.2 cm
Colour:	See below
Issued:	1. Brown; matte — Fall 1958
	2. Buckskin; gloss — 1970 - 1992
	3. Buckskin; matte — Fall 1964 - 1971
	4. Palomino; gloss — 1990 - 1992
	5. White; matte — Fall 1964 - 1971

Colourways	U.S.$	Can.$	U.K.£
1. Brown; matte	25.00	50.00	45.00
2. Buckskin; gloss	8.00	16.00	14.00
3. Buckskin; matte	25.00	50.00	45.00
4. Palomino; gloss	8.00	16.00	14.00
5. White; matte	25.00	50.00	45.00

Mini Mini Foal

Model No.:	A-453
Designer:	Maureen Love
Height:	1", 2.5 cm
Colour:	See below
Issued:	1. Brown; matte — Fall 1958
	2. Buckskin; gloss — 1970 - 1992
	3. Buckskin; matte — Fall 1964 - 1971
	4. Palomino; gloss — 1990 - 1992
	5. White; matte — Fall 1964 - 1971

Mini Mini Stallion, standing

Model No.:	A-452
Designer:	Maureen Love
Height:	1 ¼", 3.2 cm
Colour:	See below
Issued:	1. Brown; matte — Fall 1958
	2. Buckskin; gloss — 1970 - 1992
	3. Buckskin; matte — Fall 1964 - 1971
	4. Palomino; gloss — 1990 - 1992
	5. White; matte — Fall 1964 - 1971

Colourways	U.S.$	Can.$	U.K.£
1. Brown; matte	25.00	50.00	45.00
2. Buckskin; gloss	8.00	16.00	14.00
3. Buckskin; matte	25.00	50.00	45.00
4. Palomino; gloss	8.00	16.00	14.00
5. White; matte	25.00	50.00	45.00

Colourways	U.S.$	Can.$	U.K.£
1. Brown; matte	15.00	30.00	25.00
2. Buckskin; gloss	3.00	6.00	5.00
3. Buckskin; matte	15.00	30.00	25.00
4. Palomino; gloss	3.00	6.00	5.00
5. White; matte	15.00	30.00	25.00

Note: Models A-451, A-452 and A-453 were made for 54 seasons between c.1970 and fall 1992.

'Misty of Chincoteague'

Model No.:	Unknown
Designer:	Maureen Love
Height:	3 ¼", 8.3 cm
Colour:	Light brown and white
Issued:	1993

Description	U.S.$	Can.$	U.K.£
1. With stool	55.00	110.00	95.00
2. Without stool	50.00	100.00	85.00

Note: This model was retailed by Breyer. Due to breakages during shipping, in later models the stool was not glued to the horse's hoof.

Pony, head down, without harness

Model No.:	A-315
Designer:	Maureen Love
Height:	2 ¼", 5.7 cm
Colour:	Chestnut; matte
Issued:	Fall 1956 - spring 1957

Model No.	U.S.$	Can.$	U.K.£
A-315	75.00	150.00	130.00

Note: See Circus Pony, head down (A-267), page 274.

Pony, head up, without harness

Model No.:	A-314
Designer:	Maureen Love
Height:	2 3/8", 6.03 cm
Colour:	Unknown
Issued:	Fall 1956 - spring 1957

Model No.	U.S.$	Can.$	U.K.£
A-314	75.00	150.00	130.00

Note: See also Circus Pony, head up (A-266), page 274.

Stallion, rearing

Model No.:	A-480
Designer:	Maureen Love
Height:	3 ½", 8.9 cm
Colour:	1. Brown; matte
	2. Palomino; matte
Issued:	Spring 1961 - spring 1972

Model No.	U.S.$	Can.$	U.K.£
A-480	75.00	150.00	130.00

PEGASUS

Pegasus, lying

Model No.:	A-832
Designer:	Helen Perrin Farnlund
Height:	1", 2.5 cm
Colour:	White, grey wings, yellow flowers
Issued:	Spring 1984 to the present

Model No.	U.S.$	Can.$	U.K.£
A-832	7.00	14.00	12.00

Note: Model A-832 was produced for 26 seasons. The flowers were yellow until fall 1986 and then changed to blue. Pair with model A-831.

Pegasus, standing

Model No.:	A-831
Designer:	Helen Perrin Farnlund
Height:	2", 5.1 cm
Colour:	White; grey wings; blue, green or lavender flowers
Issued:	Spring 1984 to the present

Model No.	U.S.$	Can.$	U.K.£
A-831	8.00	16.00	14.00

Note: Model A-831 has been in production for 26 seasons. Pair with model A-832.

UNICORNS

Unicorn Baby
Style One

Model No.:	A-956
Designer:	Maxine Renaker
Height:	1 ½", 3.8 cm
Colour:	White; gloss
Issued:	Spring 1978 to the present

Model No.	U.S.$	Can.$	U.K.£
A-956	6.00	12.00	10.00

Note: This forms a pair with Unicorn Papa, Style One (A-941), page 294.

Unicorn Baby
Style Two

Model No.:	A-3210
Designer:	Helen Perrin Farnlund
Height:	1 ¾", 4.4 cm
Colour:	White with gold hooves and horn
Issued:	Spring 1996 to the present

Model No.	U.S.$	Can.$	U.K.£
A-3210	6.00	12.00	10.00

Unicorn, head down

Model No.:   A-801
Designer: Maureen Love
Height: 1 ½", 3.8 cm
Colour: White with gold hooves and horn,
               light blue and gold or lime and gold
               collar
Issued: Spring 1982 - fall 1986

Model No.	U.S.$	Can.$	U.K.£
A-801	10.00	20.00	17.00

Unicorn, head up

Model No.:   A-800
Designer: Maureen Love
Height: 2", 5.0 cm
Colour: White with gold hooves and horn,
               light blue collar
Issued: Spring 1982 to the present

Model No.	U.S.$	Can.$	U.K.£
A-800	7.00	14.00	12.00

Unicorn Papa
Style One

Model No.:   A-941
Designer: Maxine Renaker
Height: 2 ½", 6.4 cm
Colour: White; gold horn, hooves, neck and
               chain; gloss
Issued: Spring 1978 - spring 1996

Model No.	U.S.$	Can.$	U.K.£
A-941	6.00	12.00	10.00

Note: Pair with Unicorn Baby, Style One (A-956),
page 293.

Unicorn Papa
Style Two

Model No.:   A-3206
Designer: Helen Perrin Farnlund
Height: 2 ½", 6.4 cm
Colour: White, gold hooves and horn,
               light blue collar
Issued: Spring 1996 to the present

Model No.	U.S.$	Can.$	U.K.£
A-3206	7.00	14.00	12.00

Unicorn, turning

Model No.:	A-802
Designer:	Maureen Love
Height:	2", 5.0 cm
Colour:	White with gold hooves and horn, light blue and gold or lavender and gold collar
Issued:	Spring 1982 - spring 1990

Model No.	U.S.$	Can.$	U.K.£
A-802	10.00	20.00	17.00

BURROS, DONKEYS AND MULES

Burro in Harness

Model No.:	A-2082
Designer:	Robert McGuinness
Height:	1 5/8", 4.1 cm
Colour:	1. Brown; blue and black harness
	2. Brown; red and black harness
Issued:	Fall 1990 - fall 1991

Colourways	U.S.$	Can.$	U.K.£
1. Blue harness	9.00	18.00	15.00
2. Red harness	8.00	16.00	14.00

Donkey Baby, standing

Model No.:	A-021
Designer:	Helen Perrin Farnlund
Height:	1 ½", 3.8 cm
Colour:	Grey; gloss or matte
Issued:	Fall 1965 - spring 1986

Description	U.S.$	Can.$	U.K.£
1. Gloss	5.00	10.00	9.00
2. Matte	10.00	20.00	17.00

Note: This forms a pair with Donkey Mama (A-202), page 297.

Donkey Baby

Model No.:	A-151
Designer:	Tom Masterson
Height:	1 5/8", 4.1 cm
Colour:	1. Grey (Monrovia)
	2. Tan(San Dimas)
Issued:	Spring 1951 - c.1970

Description	U.S.$	Can.$	U.K.£
1. Monrovia	10.00	20.00	17.00
2. San Dimas	7.00	14.00	12.00

Donkey Baby, seated, ears to sides

Model No.:	A-304
Designer:	Nell Bortell
Height:	1", 2.5 cm
Colour:	Pale brown; black mouth, tail, eyes and hooves
Issued:	Fall 1956

Model No.	U.S.$	Can.$	U.K.£
A-304	30.00	60.00	50.00

Donkey or Democratic Donkey

Model No.:	A-303
Designer:	Nell Bortells
Height:	2", 5.0 cm
Colour:	Grey with darker grey shading
Issued:	Fall 1956, fall 1967

Description	U.S.$	Can.$	U.K.£
1. Without hat/flag	20.00	40.00	35.00
2. With hat/flag	30.00	60.00	50.00

Note: The Democratic Donkey wears a hat and has a hole in its mouth to hold a small flag.

Donkey Mama, seated

Model No.:	A-150
Designer:	Tom Masterson
Height:	2 ¼", 5.7 cm
Colour:	1. Grey (Monrovia)
	2. Tan (San Dimas)
Issued:	Spring 1951 - c.1970

Description	U.S.$	Can.$	U.K.£
1. Monrovia	15.00	30.00	25.00
2. San Dimas	10.00	20.00	17.00

Note: Model A-150 was made for 7 seasons between 1951 and c.1970. Earlier models have a hole in the mouth to hold a flower.

Donkey Mama, standing

Model No.: A-202
Designer: Helen Perrin Farnlund
Height: 2", 5.0 cm
Colour: Grey; gloss or matte
Issued: Fall 1965 - spring 1981

Description	U.S.$	Can.$	U.K.£
1. Gloss	10.00	20.00	17.00
2. Matte	20.00	40.00	35.00

Note: This forms a pair with Donkey Baby (A-201), page 295.

Donkey Papa, standing

Model No.: A-149
Designer: Tom Masterson
Height: 2 ¼", 5.7 cm
Colour: 1. Grey (Monrovia)
2. Tan (San Dimas)
Issued: Spring 1951 - c.1970

Description	U.S.$	Can.$	U.K.£
1. Monrovia	15.00	30.00	25.00
2. San Dimas	10.00	20.00	17.00

Note: Model A-149 was made for 7 seasons between 1951 and c.1970. Some models have a hole in the mouth to hold a flower.

Mule (On ceramic base)

Model No.: A-3074
Designer: Maureen Love
Height: 2 ¾", 7.0 cm
Colour: Grey, cream ceramic base
Issued: Fall 1992 - fall 1994

Model No.	U.S.$	Can.$	U.K.£
A-3074	20.00	40.00	35.00

Draft Foal (A-62); Draft Horse, comical (A-61)

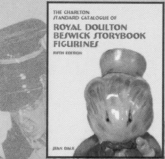

SEA CREATURES

Octopus (A-3198)

ALLIGATORS

Alligator Baby

Model No.:	A-853
Designer:	Helen Perrin Farnlund
Height:	3/8", 0.9 cm
Colour:	Green
Issued:	Spring 1985 - spring 1988

Model No.	U.S. $	Can. $	U.K. £
A-853	6.00	12.00	10.00

Alligator Mama

Model No.:	A-852
Designer:	Helen Perrin Farnlund
Height:	5/6", 2.1 cm
Colour:	Green
Issued:	Spring 1985 - spring 1988

Model No.	U.S. $	Can. $	U.K. £
A-852	8.00	16.00	14.00

FISH

Fantail Fish

Model No.:	A-426
Designer:	Helen Perrin Farnlund
Height:	7/8", 2.2 cm
Colour:	Orange
Issued:	Spring 1960 - spring 1965

Model No.	U.S. $	Can. $	U.K. £
A-426	15.00	30.00	25.00

Note: See also Specialties Section, page 476.

Flat Fish

Model No.:	A-423
Designer:	Helen Perrin Farnlund
Height:	1", 2.5 cm
Colour:	Pink with black details
Issued:	Spring 1960 - spring 1965

Model No.	U.S. $	Can. $	U.K. £
A-423	15.00	30.00	25.00

Note: See also Specialties Section, page 475.

MANATEE

Manatee

Model No.:	A-3186
Designer:	Robert McGuinness
Height:	13/16", 2.1 cm
Colour:	Grey
Issued:	Fall 1995 - fall 1997

Model No.	U.S. $	Can. $	U.K. £
A-3186	6.00	12.00	10.00

OCTOPUS

Octopus

Model No.:	A-3198
Designer:	Helen Perrin Farnlund
Height:	2/3", 1.7 cm
Colour:	Pink-grey, blue eyes
Issued:	Fall 1996 to the present

Model No.	U.S. $	Can. $	U.K. £
A-3198	3.00	6.00	5.00

OTTERS

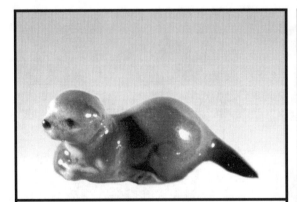

Sea Otter Baby

Model No.:	A-2061
Designer:	Shi Yi Chen
Height:	7/16", 1.1 cm
Colour:	Brown
Issued:	Fall 1989 - spring 1992

Model No.	U.S. $	Can. $	U.K. £
A-2061	4.00	8.00	7.00

Note: This forms a pair with Sea Otter Mama (A-2060).

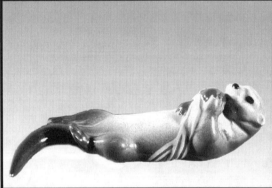

Sea Otter Mama

Model No.:	A-2060
Designer:	Shi Yi Chen
Size:	2/3" x 2 7/8", 1.7 x 7.3 cm
Colour:	Brown
Issued:	Fall 1989 - fall 1994

Model No.	U.S. $	Can. $	U.K. £
A-2060	7.00	14.00	12.00

Note: This forms a pair with Sea Otter Baby (A-2061).

PLATYPUS

Platypus Baby
Model No.:	A-3093
Designer:	Robert McGuinness
Height:	½", 1.3 cm
Colour:	Brown, white shell
Issued:	Spring 1994 - fall 1995

Model No.	U.S. $	Can. $	U.K. £
A-3093	6.00	12.00	10.00

Note: This forms a pair with Platypus Mama (A-3092).

Platypus Mama
Model No.:	A-3092
Designer:	Robert McGuinness
Size:	½" x 2 5/8", 1.3 x 6.7 cm
Colour:	Brown
Issued:	Spring 1994 - fall 1995

Model No.	U.S. $	Can. $	U.K. £
A-3092	12.00	24.00	20.00

Note: This forms a pair with Platypus Baby (A-3093).

PORPOISE

Porpoise, jumping
Model No.:	A-965
Designer:	Helen Perrin Farnlund
Height:	1 ½", 3.8 cm
Colour:	Dark blue and grey
Issued:	Spring 1977 to the present

Model No.	U.S. $	Can. $	U.K. £
A-965	3.00	6.00	5.00

Note: This forms a set with A-964 and A-966, page 304.

Porpoise, posing
Model No.:	A-966
Designer:	Helen Perrin Farnlund
Height:	1 ½", 3.8 cm
Colour:	Dark blue and grey
Issued:	Spring 1977 - fall 1978

Model No.	U.S. $	Can. $	U.K. £
A-966	8.00	16.00	14.00

Note: This forms a set with A-964 and A-965, page 304.

Porpoise, swimming
Model No.:   A-964
Designer: Helen Perrin Farnlund
Height: ¾", 1.9 cm
Colour: Dark blue and grey
Issued: Spring 1977 - spring 1988

Model No.	U.S. $	Can. $	U.K. £
A-964	6.00	12.00	10.00

Note: This forms a set with A-965 and A-966, page 303.

SEAHORSE

Seahorse (On coral)
Model No.:   A-424
Designer: Helen Perrin Farnlund
Height: 1 3/8", 3.5 cm
Colour: Black with green face
Issued: Spring 1960 - spring 1961

Model No.	U.S. $	Can. $	U.K. £
A-424	20.00	40.00	35.00

Note: For information on Coral (A-425), see page 389.

SEALS

Circus Seal Baby
Model No.:   A-259
Designer: Maureen Love
Height: 7/8", 2.2 cm
Colour: 1. Black, coloured ball; matte
                  2. Brown; gloss
Issued: See below

Description	U.S. $	Can. $	U.K. £
1. With ball (1955-1956)	12.00	24.00	20.00
2. Without ball (1956-1976)	4.00	8.00	7.00

Note: Model A-259 was revised 1956-2976.

Circus Seal
Model No.:   A-258
Designer: Maureen Love
Height: With ball — 2 ¼", 5.7 cm
                  Without ball — 1 ¾", 4.4 cm
Colour: See below
Issued: Spring 1955 - spring 1956

Description	U.S. $	Can. $	U.K. £
1. Black; coloured ball	20.00	40.00	35.00
2. Black; without ball	12.00	24.00	20.00

Harp Seal

Model No.:	A-2014
Designer:	Shi Yi Chen
Height:	½", 1.3 cm
Colour:	White
Issued:	Fall 1988 to the present

Model No.	U.S. $	Can. $	U.K. £
A-2014	2.00	4.00	3.50

Seal Baby, chubby

Model No.:	A-974
Designer:	Helen Perrin Farnlund
Height:	5/8", 1.6 cm
Colour:	Brown; gloss
Issued:	Spring 1977 to the present

Model No.	U.S. $	Can. $	U.K. £
A-974	2.00	4.00	3.50

Seal Baby on Belly

Model No.:	A-975
Designer:	Helen Perrin Farnlund
Height:	¼", 0.6 cm
Colour:	Brown
Issued:	Spring 1977 - spring 1978

Model No.	U.S. $	Can. $	U.K. £
A-975	5.00	10.00	8.50

Seal Mama

Model No.:	A-972
Designer:	Helen Perrin Farnlund
Height:	1 1/8", 2.8 cm
Colour:	Dark brown
Issued:	Spring 1977 to the present

Model No.	U.S. $	Can. $	U.K. £
A-972	3.00	6.00	5.00

Note: This is also called Seal Papa.

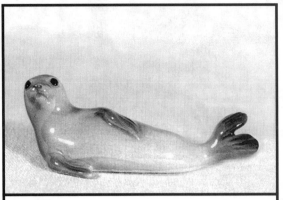

Seal Mama on Belly

Model No.:	A-973
Designer:	Helen Perrin Farnlund
Height:	¾", 1.9 cm
Colour:	Brown
Issued:	Spring 1977 - spring 1978

Model No.	U.S. $	Can. $	U.K. £
A-973	6.00	12.00	10.00

Seal Mama on Side

Model No.:	A-3139
Designer:	Robert McGuinness
Height:	7/8", 2.2 cm
Colour:	Brown-grey
Issued:	Spring 1994 to the present

Model No.	U.S. $	Can. $	U.K. £
A-3139	3.00	6.00	5.00

Note: This forms a pair with Seal Pup (A-3140).

Seal Papa

Model No.:	A-258
Designer:	Maureen Love
Height:	1 ¾", 4.4 cm
Colour:	Brown; gloss
Issued:	Fall 1965 - spring 1976

Model No.	U.S. $	Can. $	U.K. £
A-258	9.00	18.00	15.00

Note: Model A-258 was also used to make Circus Seal, page 304.

Seal Pup

Model No.:	A-3140
Designer:	Robert McGuinness
Height:	¾", 1.9 cm
Colour:	Brown-grey
Issued:	Spring 1994 to the present

Model No.	U.S. $	Can. $	U.K. £
A-3140	2.00	4.00	3.50

Note: This forms a pair with Seal Mama on Side (A-3139).

SHARKS

Great White Shark

Model No.:	A-3145
Designer:	Robert McGuinness
Size:	1 ¼" x 3 7/8", 3.2 x 9.8 cm
Colour:	White with blue shading
Issued:	Spring 1994 to the present

Model No.	U.S. $	Can. $	U.K. £
A-3145	6.00	12.00	10.00

Hammerhead Shark

Model No.:	A-3187
Designer:	Robert McGuinness
Size:	1 1/8" x 3 5/8", 2.8 x 9.2 cm
Colour:	Pale blue
Issued:	Fall 1995 - fall 1997

Model No.	U.S. $	Can. $	U.K. £
A-3187	6.00	12.00	10.00

TORTOISE

Desert Tortoise

Model No.:	A-3229
Designer:	Maureen Love
Height:	1 1/8", 2.8 cm
Colour:	Light brown
Issued:	Spring 1997 to the present

Model No.	U.S. $	Can. $	U.K. £
A-3229	6.00	12.00	10.00

Tortoise
Style One

Model No.:	A-332
Designer:	Don Winton
Height:	1 ¼", 3.2 cm
Colour:	See below
Issued:	Spring 1957
Reissued:	Fall 1970 - spring 1975

Colourways	U.S. $	Can. $	U.K. £
1. Brown	10.00	20.00	17.00
2. Dark green and gold	25.00	50.00	45.00

Tortoise
Style Two

Model No.:	A-2000		
Designer:	Nell Bortells		
Height:	1 ¼", 3.2 cm		
Colour:	Green, brown shell		
Issued:	Spring 1988 - fall 1989		

Model No.	U.S. $	Can. $	U.K. £
A-2000	10.00	20.00	17.00

Note: This forms a pair with Hare (A-2001), page 363.

Tortoise
Style Three

Model No.:	A-3239		
Designer:	Helen Perrin Farnlund		
Height:	1", 2.5 cm		
Colour:	Light brown, blue number cloth		
Issued:	Spring 1997 - fall 1998		

Model No.	U.S. $	Can. $	U.K. £
A-3239	7.00	14.00	12.00

Note: This forms a pair with Hare (A-3238), page 363.

TURTLES

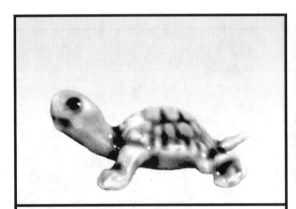

Box Turtle Baby

Model No.:	A-479		
Designer:	Helen Perrin Farnlund		
Height:	½", 1.3 cm		
Colour:	Green		
Issued:	1960 to the present		

Description	U.S. $	Can. $	U.K. £
1. Monrovia	10.00	20.00	17.00
2. Current	2.00	4.00	3.50

Note: Model A-479 has been in production for 54 seasons.

Box Turtle Mama

Model No.:	A-419		
Designer:	Helen Perrin Farnlund		
Height:	5/8", 1.6 cm		
Colour:	1. Green		
	2. Green, darker green shell, black outlined mouth and toenails		
Issued:	1960 to the present		

Colourways	U.S. $	Can. $	U.K. £
1. Green	2.00	4.00	3.50
2. Green/yellow/black	16.00	32.00	28.00

Note: Model A-419 has been produced for 54 seasons.

Coin Turtle Baby

Model No.:	A-317
Designer:	Helen Perrin Farnlund
Height:	5/8", 1.6 cm
Colour:	Green
Issued:	Spring 1957 - spring 1992

Description	U.S. $	Can. $	U.K. £
1. Monrovia	5.00	10.00	8.50
2. San Dimas	3.00	6.00	5.00

Coin Turtle Mama

Model No.:	A-316
Designer:	Helen Perrin Farnlund
Height:	7/8", 2.2 cm
Colour:	Green
Issued:	Spring 1957 - spring 1992

Description	U.S. $	Can. $	U.K. £
1. Monrovia	8.00	16.00	14.00
2. San Dimas	5.00	10.00	8.50

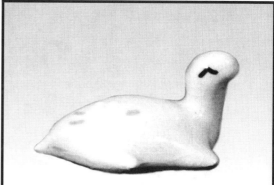

Turtle

Model No.:	A-3091
Designer:	Edith Carrion
Height:	1 ¼", 3.2 cm
Colour:	Grey
Issued:	Spring 1993 - fall 1994

Model No.	U.S. $	Can. $	U.K. £
A-3091	7.00	14.00	12.00

Turtle Baby

Model No.:	None
Designer:	Helen Perrin Farnlund
Height:	1 ¼", 3.2 cm
Colour:	1. Blue
	2. Pink
Issued:	Spring 1949 - fall 1949

Colourways	U.S. $	Can. $	U.K. £
1. Blue	8.00	16.00	14.00
2. Pink	8.00	16.00	14.00

Note: This model forms a pair with Turtle Mama, page 310.

Turtle Baby

Model No.:	A-204
Designer:	Helen Perrin Farnlund
Height:	½", 1.3 cm
Colour:	1. Green allover glaze
	2. Green glazed neck and legs, Auerspurse brown on shell
Issued:	c.1950, c.1970

Colourways	U.S. $	Can. $	U.K. £
1. Green	4.00	8.00	7.00
2. Green/Auerspurse	6.00	12.00	10.00

Turtle Baby

Model No.:	A-161
Designer:	Tom Masterson
Height:	3/8", 0.9 cm
Colour:	1. Green with gold details
	2. Tan; yellow, black and gold shell
Issued:	Spring 1952 - spring 1955

Colourway	U.S. $	Can. $	U.K. £
1. Green/gold	10.00	20.00	17.00
2. Tan/gold	10.00	20.00	17.00

Note: The pattern on the shell may vary.

Turtle Mama

Model No.:	None
Designer:	Helen Perrin Farnlund
Height:	2", 5.0 cm
Colour:	1. Blue with white, red and green details
	2. Pink with white and green details
Issued:	Spring 1949 - fall 1949

Colourways	U.S. $	Can. $	U.K. £
1. Blue	14.00	28.00	24.00
2. Pink	14.00	28.00	24.00

Note: This model forms a pair with Turtle Baby, page 309.

Turtle Mama

Model No.:	A-162
Designer:	Tom Masterson
Height:	15/16", 2.4 cm
Colour:	1. Green, gold details
	2. Tan; yellow, black and gold shell
Issued:	Spring 1952 - spring 1955

Colourways	U.S. $	Can. $	U.K. £
1. Green/gold	18.00	36.00	30.00
2. Tan/gold	18.00	36.00	30.00

Note: The pattern on the shell may vary.

Turtle Mama

Model No.:	A-203
Designer:	Helen Perrin Farnlund
Height:	1", 2.5 cm
Colour:	1. Green allover glaze
	2. Green glazed neck and legs, Auerspurse brown on shell
Issued:	c.1955 - c.1979

Colourways	U.S. $	Can. $	U.K. £
1. Green	8.00	16.00	14.00
2. Green/Auerspurse	12.00	24.00	20.00

Note: Model A-203 was produced for 54 seasons.

WALRUS

Walrus
Style One

Model No.:	A-968
Designer:	Helen Perrin Farnlund
Height:	1 5/8", 4.1 cm
Colour:	Dark brown, white tusks
Issued:	Spring 1977 - spring 1981

Model No.	U.S. $	Can. $	U.K. £
A-968	9.00	18.00	15.00

Walrus
Style Two

Model No.:	A-3209
Designer:	Robert McGuinness
Height:	1 ¼", 3.2 cm
Colour:	Golden brown, white tusks
Issued:	Fall 1996 to the present

Model No.	U.S. $	Can. $	U.K. £
A-3209	5.00	10.00	8.50

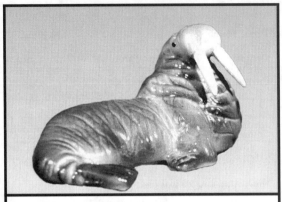

Walrus Baby

Model No.:	A-2081
Designer:	Shi Yi Chen
Height:	2/3", 1.7 cm
Colour:	Light brown
Issued:	Spring 1990 - fall 1991

Model No.	U.S. $	Can. $	U.K. £
A-2081	7.00	14.00	12.00

Walrus Mama

Model No.:	A-2071
Designer:	Shi Yi Chen
Height:	1 1/8", 2.8 cm
Colour:	Light brown, white tusks
Issued:	Fall 1989 - spring 1992

Model No.	U.S. $	Can. $	U.K. £
A-2071	10.00	20.00	17.00

WHALES

Grey Whale

Model No.:	A-3191
Designer:	Maureen Love
Size:	1" x 3", 2.5 x 7.6 cm
Colour:	Grey
Issued:	Fall 1995 - spring 1997

Model No.	U.S. $	Can. $	U.K. £
A-3191	5.00	10.00	8.50

Humpback Whale, tail down

Model No.:	A-2079
Designer:	Maureen Love
Height:	1 5/8", 4.1 cm
Colour:	Black and white
Issued:	Spring 1990 - spring 1992

Description	U.S. $	Can. $	U.K. £
1. With base	14.00	28.00	24.00
2. Without base	9.00	18.00	15.00

Note: This was originally issued on a base.

Humpback Whale, tail up

Model No.:   A-2080
Designer: Maureen Love
Height: 1 3/8", 3.5 cm
Colour: Black and white
Issued: Spring 1990 - fall 1997

Description	U.S. $	Can. $	U.K. £
1. With base	14.00	28.00	24.00
2. Without base	4.00	8.00	7.00

Note: This was originally issued on a base.

Killer Whale Flukes

Model No.:   A-887
Designer: Maureen Love
Height: ¾", 1.9 cm
Colour: Black
Issued: Spring 1987 - fall 1987

Model No.	U.S. $	Can. $	U.K. £
A-887	6.00	12.00	10.00

Killer Whale 'Lotta'

Model No.:   A-886
Designer: Maureen Love
Height: 1 5/8", 4.1 cm
Colour: Black and white
Issued: Spring 1987 to the present

Model No.	U.S. $	Can. $	U.K. £
A-886	4.00	8.00	7.00

Killer Whale 'Sam'

Model No.:   A-885
Designer: Maureen Love
Height: 1 5/8", 4.1 cm
Colour: Black and white
Issued: Spring 1987 to the present

Model No.	U.S. $	Can. $	U.K. £
A-885	4.00	8.00	7.00

Whale Baby (Cartoon)
Model No.:   A-845
Designer: Nell Bortells
Height: 1", 2.5 cm
Colour: Black and brown
Issued: Spring 1984 - spring 1992

Model No.	U.S. $	Can. $	U.K. £
A-845	4.00	8.00	7.00

Whale Mama (Cartoon)
Model No.:   A-803
Designer: Nell Bortells
Height: 1 ¾", 4.4 cm
Colour: Black and brown
Issued: Spring 1982 - fall 1997

Model No.	U.S. $	Can. $	U.K. £
A-803	5.00	10.00	8.50

MINIATURE WILD ANIMALS

INDEX TO MINIATURE WILD ANIMALS

Lynx (A-3141)

ANTEATER

Anteater

Model No.:	A-69
Designer:	Unknown
Height:	1 11/16", 4.3 cm
Colour:	Black and grey, orange eyes
Issued:	Fall 1966

Model No.	U.S. $	Can. $	U.K. £
A-69	30.00	60.00	50.00

Note: This model may have a wire tongue.
It forms a pair with Ant, Style One (A-073), page 407.

ARMADILLOS

Armadillo Baby

Model No.:	A-938
Designer:	Helen Perrin Farnlund
Height:	½", 1.3 cm
Colour:	Grey
Issued:	Spring 1981- spring 1985

Model No.	U.S. $	Can. $	U.K. £
A-938	4.00	8.00	7.00

Armadillo Mama

Model No.:	A-937
Designer:	Helen Perrin Farnlund
Height:	1 ½", 3.1 cm
Colour:	Grey
Issued:	Spring 1981 - spring 1986

Model No.	U.S. $	Can. $	U.K. £
A-937	7.00	14.00	12.00

BADGERS

Badger Baby

Model No.:	A-851
Designer:	Helen Perrin Farnlund
Height:	½", 1.3 cm
Colour:	Black and white
Issued:	Fall 1984 - spring 1986

Model No.	U.S. $	Can. $	U.K. £
A-851	5.00	10.00	8.50

Note: This forms a pair with Badger Mama (A-850).

Badger Mama

Model No.:	A-850
Designer:	Helen Perrin Farnlund
Height:	7/8", 2.3 cm
Colour:	Black and white
Issued:	Fall 1984 - spring 1986

Model No.	U.S. $	Can. $	U.K. £
A-850	8.00	16.00	14.00

Note: This forms a pair with Badger Baby (A-851).

BEARS

Bear Ma or Bear Pa

Model No.:	A-226
Designer:	Helen Perrin Farnlund
Height:	2 ½", 6.4 cm
Colour:	Brown; gloss or matte
Issued:	Spring 1954 - fall 1980

Description	U.S. $	Can. $	U.K. £
1. Gloss	8.00	16.00	14.00
2. Matte	13.00	26.00	23.00

Note: Model A-226, made for 15 seasons, can be called either Bear Ma or Bear Pa.

Bear Baby

Model No.:	A-30
Designer:	Helen Perrin Farnlund
Height:	1 ¼", 3.2 cm
Colour:	Light brown
Issued:	1949 - 1950

Model No.	U.S. $	Can. $	U.K. £
A-30	30.00	60.00	50.00

Note: This forms a set with Bear Papa (A-10) and Bear Mama (A-1), page 322. Beachstone used the baby as an ornament in the 1980s.

Bear Cub Brother

Model No.:	A-397
Designer:	Helen Perrin Farnlund
Height:	¾", 1.9 cm
Colour:	1. Dark brown; gloss
	2. Light brown; matte, Auerspurse
Issued:	Spring 1960 - spring 1988

Colourways	U.S. $	Can. $	U.K. £
1. Dark brown	5.00	10.00	8.50
2. Light brown	15.00	30.00	25.00

Note: Model A-397 was made for 41 seasons. Set with models A-401 and A-404 (Bee's Nest), page 390.

Bear Cub Sister

Model No.:	A-401
Designer:	Helen Perrin Farnlund
Height:	1", 2.5 cm
Colour:	1. Dark brown, gloss
	2. Light brown; matte, Auerspurse
Issued:	Spring 1960 - Spring 1988

Colourways	U.S. $	Can. $	U.K. £
1. Dark brown	5.00	10.00	8.50
2. Light brown	15.00	30.00	25.00

Note: Model A-401 was made for 41 seasons. Set with models A-397 and A-404 (Bee's Nest), page 390.

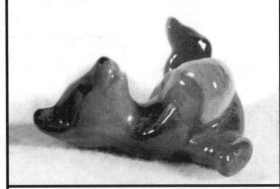

Bear Cub, standing

Model No.:	A-215
Designer:	Helen Perrin Farnlund
Height:	1 ½", 3.8 cm
Colour:	Brown, tan face and belly; gloss or matte
Issued:	Spring 1954 - fall 1980

Description	U.S. $	Can. $	U.K. £
1. Gloss	5.00	10.00	8.50
2. Matte	10.00	20.00	17.00

Note: Model A-215 was made for 17 seasons.

Bear Cub With Honey

Model No.:	A-3011
Designer:	Robert McGuinness
Height:	¾", 1.9 cm
Colour:	Dark brown; gloss
Issued:	Spring 1991 - fall 1992

Model No.	U.S. $	Can. $	U.K. £
A-3011	5.00	10.00	8.50

Bear Mama

Model No.:	A-1
Designer:	Helen Perrin Farnlund
Height:	2", 5.0 cm
Colour:	Light brown, yellow apron and umbrella
Issued:	1949 - 1950

Model No.	U.S. $	Can. $	U.K. £
A-1	35.00	70.00	60.00

Note: This forms a set with Bear Papa (A-10) and Bear Baby (A-30), page 321.

Bear Papa

Model No.:	A-10
Designer:	Helen Perrin Farnlund
Height:	2", 5.0 cm
Colour:	Light brown, yellow bow tie
Issued:	1949 - 1950

Model No.	U.S. $	Can. $	U.K. £
A-10	35.00	70.00	60.00

Note: This forms a set with Bear Mama (A-1) and Bear Baby (A-30), page 321.

Big Brother Teddy
Model No.: A-466
Designer: Helen Perrin Farnlund
Height: ¾", 1.9 cm
Colour: Light brown; gloss
Issued: Spring 1959 to the present

Description	U.S. $	Can. $	U.K. £
1. Monrovia	10.00	20.00	17.00
2. San Marcos	2.00	4.00	3.50

Note: Model A-466 has been made for over 25 years. Forms a set with A-465, page 326 and A-467, page 325.

Black Bear
Model No.: A-3136
Designer: Robert McGuinness
Height: 1 3/8", 3.5 cm
Colour: Black
Issued: Fall 1993 - fall 1995

Model No.	U.S. $	Can. $	U.K. £
A-3136	7.00	14.00	12.00

Brown Bisque Bear, Big Brother
Model No.: B-102
Designer: Helen Perrin Farnlund
Height: 2 1/8", 5.4 cm
Colour: Brown, blue cap, white and blue bow tie
Issued: Spring 1983 - fall 1983

Model No.	U.S. $	Can. $	U.K. £
B-102	20.00	40.00	35.00

Note: The head was moulded separately and attached by an elastic band. This model forms a set with models B-101 and B-103, page 324.

Brown Bisque Bear, Big Sister
Model No.: B-101
Designer: Helen Perrin Farnlund
Height: 1 7/8", 4.8 cm
Colour: Brown, pink bow
Issued: Spring 1983 - fall 1983

Model No.	U.S. $	Can. $	U.K. £
B-101	20.00	40.00	35.00

Note: The head was moulded separately and attached by an elastic band. This model forms a set with models B-102 and B-103, page 324.

Brown Bisque Bear, Little Brother

Model No.:	B-103
Designer:	Helen Perrin Farnlund
Height:	1", 2.5 cm
Colour:	Brown, blue shirt
Issued:	Spring 1983 - fall 1983

Model No.	U.S. $	Can. $	U.K. £
B-103	20.00	40.00	35.00

Note: The head was moulded separately and attached by an elastic band. This model forms a set with models B-101 and B-102, page 323.

Crabby Cub

Model No.:	A-216
Designer:	Helen Perrin Farnlund
Height:	1 ¼", 3.2 cm
Colour:	Brown, tan face and belly; gloss or matte
Issued:	Spring 1954 - c.1975

Description	U.S. $	Can. $	U.K. £
1. Gloss	5.00	10.00	8.50
2. Matte	8.00	16.00	14.00

Note: Model A-216 was made intermittently for 17 seasons, mostly in the 1970s.

Grizzly Bear, head forward

Model No.:	A-328
Designer:	Don Winton
Height:	1 ¼", 3.2 cm
Colour:	See below
Issued:	Spring 1957, fall 1969, 1973, fall 1987 - spring 1988

Colourways	U.S. $	Can. $	U.K. £
1. Brown; gloss	8.00	16.00	14.00
2. Brown; matte	18.00	36.00	30.00
3. White; gloss	14.00	28.00	24.00

Note: This forms a pair with Grizzly Bear Cub (A-329), page 325.

Grizzly Bear, looking up

Model No.:	A-3084
Designer:	Maureen Love
Height:	1 ½", 3.8 cm
Colour:	Brown
Issued:	Fall 1992 - fall 1995

Model No.	U.S. $	Can. $	U.K. £
A-3984	8.00	16.00	14.00

Note: This forms a set with models A-3085 and A-3086, page 325.

Grizzly Bear Cub, seated

Model No.: A-329
Designer: Don Winton
Height: 1", 2.5 cm
Colour: 1. Brown; matte
2. White; gloss
Issued: Spring 1957,
spring 1980 - spring 1988

Colourways	U.S. $	Can. $	U.K. £
1. Brown	10.00	20.00	17.00
2. White	5.00	10.00	8.50

Note: This forms a pair with model A-328, page 324.

Grizzly Bear Cub, seated

Model No.: A-3086
Designer: Maureen Love
Height: 1 ¼", 3.2 cm
Colour: Brown
Issued: Fall 1992 - spring 1993

Model No.	U.S. $	Can. $	U.K. £
A-3086	5.00	10.00	8.50

Note: This forms a set with models A-3085 and A-3084, page 324.

Grizzly Bear Cub, walking

Model No.: A-3085
Designer: Maureen Love
Height: 1 ¼", 3.2 cm
Colour: Brown
Issued: Fall 1992 - spring 1993

Model No.	U.S. $	Can. $	U.K. £
A-3085	5.00	10.00	8.50

Note: This forms a set with models A-3086 and A-3084, page 324.

Little Brother Teddy

Model No.: A-467
Designer: Helen Perrin Farnlund
Height: 5/8", 1.6 cm
Colour: Light brown, dark eyes
Issued: Spring 1959 to the present

Description	U.S. $	Can. $	U.K. £
1. Monrovia	8.00	16.00	14.00
2. Current	2.00	4.00	3.50

Note: Model A-467 has been made for over 25 years. It forms a set with A-466, page 323, and A-465, page 326. See also Disney (5062A), page 505.

Ski Bear 'Gussie'

Model No.:   A-876
Designer: Helen Perrin Farnlund
Height: 1 5/8", 4.1 cm
Colour: Brown, red wooden skis
Issued: Spring 1987 - spring 1988

Model No.	U.S. $	Can. $	U.K. £
A-876	13.00	26.00	23.00

Note: This forms a set with models A-877 and A-878.

Ski Bear 'Hot Dog'

Model No.:   A-877
Designer: Helen Perrin Farnlund
Height: 2", 5.0 cm
Colour: Brown, red wooden skis
Issued: Spring 1987 - spring 1988

Model No.	U.S. $	Can. $	U.K. £
A-877	13.00	26.00	23.00

Note: This forms a set with models A-876 and A-878.

Ski Bear 'Sitzmark'

Model No.:   A-878
Designer: Helen Perrin Farnlund
Height: 7/8", 2.2 cm
Colour: Brown, red wooden skis
Issued: Spring 1987 - spring 1988

Model No.	U.S. $	Can. $	U.K. £
A-878	13.00	26.00	23.00

Note: This forms a set with models A-876 and A-877.

Teddy Bear Mama

Model No.:   A-465
Designer: Helen Perrin Farnlund
Height: 1 1/8", 2.8 cm
Colour: Light brown, dark eyes, green skirt
Issued: Spring 1959 - spring 1979

Description	U.S. $	Can. $	U.K. £
1. With porridge bowl	24.00	48.00	40.00
2. Without bowl (Monrovia)	17.00	34.00	30.00
3. Without bowl (San Dimas)	7.00	14.00	12.00

Note: Model A-465 was made for 14 seasons. Forms a set with A-466, page 323 and A-467, page325. Earlier models came with a porridge bowl.

BEAVERS

Beaver, paws down

Model No.:	A-398
Designer:	Helen Perrin Farnlund
Height:	7/8", 2.2 cm
Colour:	1. Brown; Auerspurse
	2. Dark brown
	3. Red-brown
Issued:	Spring 1960 - spring 1989

Colourways	U.S. $	Can. $	U.K. £
1. Brown/Auerspurse	10.00	20.00	17.00
2. Dark brown	8.00	16.00	14.00
3. Red-brown	5.00	10.00	8.50

Beaver, paws up

Model No.:	A-399
Designer:	Helen Perrin Farnlund
Height:	1", 2.5 cm
Colour:	1. Brown; Auerspurse
	2. Dark brown
	3. Red-brown
Issued:	Spring 1960 - fall 1990

Colourways	U.S. $	Can. $	U.K. £
1. Brown/Auerspurse	10.00	20.00	17.00
2. Dark brown	8.00	16.00	14.00
3. Red-brown	5.00	10.00	8.50

Stump

Model No.:	A-400
Designer:	Helen Perrin Farnlund
Height:	¾", 1.9 cm
Colour:	1. Grey, bisque
	2. Dark brown
	3. Red-brown
Issued:	Spring 1960 - spring 1989

Colourways	U.S. $	Can. $	U.K. £
1. Bisque	10.00	20.00	17.00
2. Dark brown	5.00	10.00	8.50
3. Red-brown	8.00	16.00	14.00

Note: The beavers were made for 20 seasons and the stump, for 16 seasons. A boxed set with a painted bisque finish was issued in 1960; value $30.00 (USF).

BIGHORN SHEEP

BISON

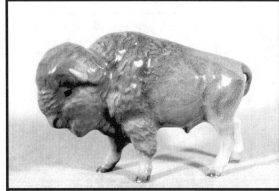

Bighorn Sheep

Model No.:	A-3051
Designer:	Robert McGuinness
Height:	1 7/8", 4.8 cm
Colour:	Brown and white
Issued:	Spring 1992 - fall 1993

Model No.	U.S. $	Can. $	U.K. £
A-3051	7.00	14.00	12.00

Bison

Model No.:	A-3134
Designer:	Maureen Love
Height:	1 7/8", 4.8 cm
Colour:	Red-brown
Issued:	Fall 1994 - fall 1998

Model No.	U.S. $	Can. $	U.K. £
A-3134	8.00	16.00	13.00

CAMELS

Camel Baby

Model No.:	A-282
Designer:	Helen Perrin Farnlund
Height:	7/8", 2.2 cm
Colour:	1. Light brown with red fez
	2. Light brown without fez
Issued:	Spring 1956, spring 1968
Reissued:	Spring 1995 - spring 1996
Series:	Circus Collection

Description	U.S. $	Can. $	U.K. £
1. With fez	20.00	40.00	35.00
2. Without fez	5.00	10.00	8.50

Camel Mama

Model No.:	A-281
Designer:	Helen Perrin Farnlund
Height:	1 5/8", 4.1 cm
Colour:	1. Light brown with red fez
	2. Light brown without fez
Issued:	Spring 1956, spring 1968
Reissued:	Spring 1995 to the present
Series:	Circus Collection

Description	U.S. $	Can. $	U.K. £
1. With fez	25.00	50.00	45.00
2. Without fez	5.00	10.00	8.50

CHIPMUNKS

Chipmunk, arms open

Model No.:	A-82
Designer:	Helen Perrin Farnlund
Height:	1 ¼", 3.2 cm
Colour:	Light and dark brown
Issued:	c.1968 for 24 seasons

Model No.	U.S. $	Can. $	U.K. £
A-82	4.00	8.00	7.00

Note: See Disney model 5035 (Dale™), page 501.

Chipmunk, holding acorn

Model No.:	A-81
Designer:	Helen Perrin Farnlund
Height:	1 ¼", 3.2 cm
Colour:	Light and dark brown chipmunk, green and yellow acorn
Issued:	c.1968 for 24 seasons

Model No.	U.S. $	Can. $	U.K. £
A-81	4.00	8.00	7.00

Note: See Disney model 5034 (Chip™ with Acorn), page 501.

Chipmunk Mama, facing right

Model No.:	A-200
Designer:	Helen Perrin Farnlund
Height:	1 ¼", 3.2 cm
Colour:	Red-brown body, tan underbelly and face, black and white stripes, well-defined eyes
Issued:	Fall 1953 - spring 1955

Model No.	U.S. $	Can. $	U.K. £
A-200	10.00	20.00	17.00

Chipmunk Baby, seated

Model No.:	A-201
Designer:	Helen Perrin Farnlund
Height:	7/8", 1.9 cm
Colour:	Red-brown body, tan underbelly and face, black and white stripes, well-defined eyes
Issued:	Fall 1953 - spring 1955

Model No.	U.S. $	Can. $	U.K. £
A-201	8.00	16.00	14.00

Chipmunk Baby, seated

Model No.:	A-334
Designer:	Helen Perrin Farnlund
Height:	¾", 2.2 cm
Colour:	Red-brown body, tan face and underbelly, black and white stripes, black pupils
Issued:	Spring 1957 - fall 1987

Model No.	U.S. $	Can. $	U.K. £
A-334	3.00	6.00	5.00

Chipmunk Mama, facing left

Model No.:	A-333
Designer:	Helen Perrin Farnlund
Height:	1 ¼", 3.2 cm
Colour:	Red-brown body, tan face and underbelly, black and white stripes, black pupils
Issued:	Spring 1957 - fall 1987

Model No.	U.S. $	Can. $	U.K. £
A-333	4.00	8.00	7.00

Chipmunk Baby, running

Model No.:	A-859
Designer:	Helen Perrin Farnlund
Height:	½", 1.3 cm
Colour:	Red-brown body, tan face and underbelly, black and white stripes, black pupils
Issued:	Fall 1985 - fall 1988

Model No.	U.S. $	Can. $	U.K. £
A-859	5.00	10.00	8.50

Note: Models A-333 and A-334 were made for 40 seasons.

COYOTE

Coyote
Model No.: A-3016
Designer: Maureen Love
Height: 2 ½", 6.4 cm
Colour: Tan with brown shading
Issued: Spring 1991 to the present

Model No.	U.S. $	Can. $	U.K. £
A-3016	6.00	12.00	10.00

DEER

Deer Papa
Model No.: A-189
Designer: Helen Perrin Farnlund
Height: 2 ¾", 7.0 cm
Colour: 1. Dark brown
2. Light brown
Issued: Spring 1953 for 80 seasons

Colourways	U.S. $	Can. $	U.K. £
1. Dark brown	15.00	30.00	25.00
2. Light brown	6.00	12.00	10.00

Fawn, lying
Model No.: A-190
Designer: Helen Perrin Farnlund
Height: 7/8", 2.2 cm
Colour: 1. Dark brown
2. Light brown
Issued: Spring 1953 - spring 1993

Colourways	U.S. $	Can. $	U.K. £
1. Dark brown	8.00	16.00	14.00
2. Light brown	4.00	8.00	7.00

Note: The illustrated model A-189 has a broken tail.
A variation of A-190 exists.

Deer Sister

Model No.:	A-188
Designer:	Helen Perrin Farnlund
Height:	1 ½", 3.8 cm
Colour:	Light brown, dark brown shading
Issued:	Fall 1953 - spring 1958

Model No.	U.S. $	Can. $	U.K. £
A-188	17.00	34.00	30.00

Deer Family

Tiny Buck

Model No.:	A-416
Designer:	Maureen Love
Height:	2", 5.0 cm
Colour:	Red-brown; gloss or matte
Issued:	Fall 1959, spring 1962

Description	U.S. $	Can. $	U.K. £
1. Gloss	25.00	50.00	45.00
2. Matte	20.00	40.00	35.00

Doe

Model No.:	A-417
Designer:	Maureen Love
Height:	1 ¼", 3.2 cm
Colour:	Brown
Issued:	Fall 1959, spring 1962

Model No.	U.S. $	Can. $	U.K. £
A-417	20.00	40.00	35.00

Fawn, lying

Model No.:	A-418
Designer:	Maureen Love
Height:	5/8", 1.6 cm
Colour:	Red-brown
Issued:	Fall 1959, spring 1962

Model No.	U.S. $	Can. $	U.K. £
A-418	10.00	20.00	17.00

Note: The illustrated model A-416 is damaged.

Doe

Model No.:	A-202
Designer:	Helen Perrin Farnlund
Height:	2 ¼", 5.7 cm
Colour:	1. Dark brown
	2. Light brown
Issued:	Spring 1953 - fall 1982

Colourways	U.S. $	Can. $	U.K. £
1. Dark brown	15.00	30.00	25.00
2. Light brown	5.00	10.00	8.50

Fawn, lying, leg out

Model No.:	A-435
Designer:	Helen Perrin Farnlund
Height:	7/8", 2.2 cm
Colour:	1. Dark brown
	2. Light brown
	3. Tan bisque; Auerspurse
Issued:	Fall 1960 - fall 1961
	spring 1993 to the present

Colourways	U.S. $	Can. $	U.K. £
1. Dark brown	15.00	30.00	25.00
2. Light brown	8.00	16.00	14.00
3. Tan bisque	3.50	7.00	6.00

Fawn, facing left

Model No.:	A-15
Designer:	Helen Perrin Farnlund
Height:	1 ½", 3.8 cm
Colour:	Light brown with darker brown shading
Issued:	Fall 1961

Model No.	U.S. $	Can. $	U.K. £
A-15	20.00	40.00	35.00

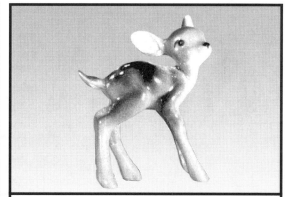

Fawn, facing right

Model No.:	A-875
Designer:	Helen Perrin Farnlund
Height:	1 5/8", 4.1 cm
Colour:	Light brown with darker brown shading
Issued:	Spring 1987 to the present

Model No.	U.S. $	Can. $	U.K. £
A-875	3.50	7.00	6.00

Note: See also Disney model 5028 (Bambi™/Faline™), page 490.

Fawn, sleeping

Model No.:	A-96
Designer:	Helen Perrin Farnlund
Height:	5/8", 1.6 cm
Colour:	1. Brown; gloss
	2. Grey; gloss
Issued:	1949 - 1952,
	1965

Colourways	U.S. $	Can. $	U.K. £
1. Brown	8.00	16.00	14.00
2. Grey	8.00	16.00	14.00

Fawn, standing

Model No.:	A-85
Designer:	Helen Perrin Farnlund
Height:	2 5/8", 6.7 cm
Colour:	1. Brown; gloss
	2. Grey; gloss
Issued:	1950 - 1952

Colourways	U.S. $	Can. $	U.K. £
1. Brown	8.00	16.00	14.00
2. Grey	8.00	16.00	14.00

Fawn, waking

Model No.:	A-32
Designer:	Helen Perrin Farnlund
Height:	1 ½", 3.8 cm
Colour:	1. Brown; gloss
	2. Grey; gloss
Issued:	1949 - 1952,
	1965

Colourways	U.S. $	Can. $	U.K. £
1. Brown	8.00	16.00	14.00
2. Grey	8.00	16.00	14.00

Note: Model A-85 has been seen with ceramic flowers.

ELEPHANTS

African Elephant Baby
Model No.:	A-191
Designer:	Helen Perrin Farnlund
Height:	2", 5.0 cm
Colour:	Grey, dark brown shading; gloss or matte
Issued:	Fall 1953 - spring 1957

Model No.	U.S. $	Can. $	U.K. £
A-191	10.00	20.00	17.00

African Elephant Mama
Model No.:	A-192
Designer:	Helen Perrin Farnlund
Height:	2 ½", 6.4 cm
Colour:	Grey, dark brown shading, pink inner ears; gloss or matte
Issued:	Fall 1953 - spring 1956

Model No.	U.S. $	Can. $	U.K. £
A-192	12.00	24.00	20.00

Elephant, head down
Model No.:	A-880
Designer:	Maureen Love
Height:	2 ½", 6.4 cm
Colour:	1. Grey elephant, blue and pink base
	2. Grey elephant, blue and white base
Issued:	Spring 1987 - fall 1989

Colourways	U.S. $	Can. $	U.K. £
1. Blue/pink	18.00	36.00	30.00
2. Blue/white	16.00	32.00	28.00

Note: Earlier models had the blue and pink base. This forms a set with models A-879 and A-881, page 336.

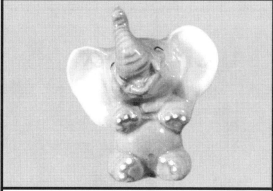

Elephant, laughing
Model No.:	A-23/88
Designer:	Helen Perrin Farnlund
Height:	2", 5.0 cm
Colour:	1. Brown; gloss
	2. Grey, pink inner ears; gloss
	3. White
Issued:	Spring 1949 - spring 1953

Colourways	U.S. $	Can. $	U.K. £
1. Brown	15.00	30.00	25.00
2. Grey	15.00	30.00	25.00
3. White	15.00	30.00	25.00

Note: The height of the model varies from 1 7/8" to 2".

Elephant, seated

Model No.:	A-879
Designer:	Maureen Love
Height:	2 ¾", 7.0 cm
Colour:	1. Grey elephant, blue and pink base
	2. Grey elephant, blue and white base
	3. Grey elephant, navy and white base
Issued:	Spring 1987 to the present

Colourways	U.S. $	Can. $	U.K. £
1. Blue/pink	15.00	30.00	25.00
2. Blue/white (current)	5.00	10.00	8.50
3. Navy/white	13.00	26.00	23.00

Note: Earlier models had the blue and pink base. Set with A-880, page 335, and A-881.

Elephant, standing

Model No.:	A-881
Designer:	Maureen Love
Height:	1 2/3", 4.2 cm
Colour:	1. Grey elephant, blue and pink base
	2. Grey elephant, blue and white base
	3. Grey elephant, navy and white base
Issued:	Spring 1987 - fall 1997

Colourways	U.S. $	Can. $	U.K. £
1. Blue/pink	15.00	30.00	25.00
2. Blue/white	5.00	10.00	8.50
3. Navy/white	13.00	26.00	23.00

Note: Earlier models had the blue and pink base. This forms a set with A-879 and A-880, page 335.

Elephant Baby

Model No.:	A-22/89
Designer:	Helen Perrin Farnlund
Height:	1 ½", 3.8 cm
Colour:	Grey, pink inner ears; gloss
Issued:	Spring 1949 - fall 1951

Model No.	U.S. $	Can. $	U.K. £
A-22/89	10.00	20.00	17.00

Elephant Baby

Model No.:	A-264
Designer:	Maureen Love
Height:	1 3/8", 3.5 cm
Colour:	1. Dark brown, decorated toenails, pink inner ears; matte
	2. Dark grey; gloss
Issued:	Fall 1955 to the present

Colourways	U.S. $	Can. $	U.K. £
1. Dark brown	10.00	20.00	17.00
2. Dark grey	3.50	7.00	6.00

Note: Made for 58 seasons. Pair with A-263, page 337.

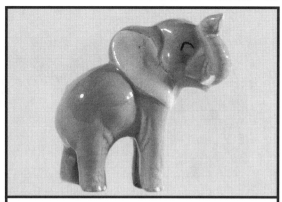

Elephant Mama, facing left

Model No.:	A-263
Designer:	Maureen Love
Height:	2 3/8", 6.0 cm
Colour:	1. Dark brown, decorated toenails, pink inner ears; matte
	2. Dark grey; gloss
Issued:	Fall 1955 to the present

Colourways	U.S. $	Can. $	U.K. £
1. Dark brown	22.00	44.00	38.00
2. Dark grey	5.00	10.00	8.50

Note: Model A-263 has been made for 58 seasons. Pair with Elephant Baby (A-264), page 336.

Elephant Mama, facing right

Model No.:	A-4/90
Designer:	Helen Perrin Farnlund
Height:	2", 5.0 cm
Colour:	Grey, pink inner ears; gloss
Issued:	Spring 1949 - fall 1951

Model No.	U.S. $	Can. $	U.K. £
A-4/90	12.00	24.00	20.00

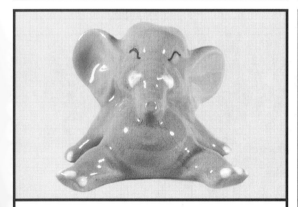

Elephant Mama, seated

Model No.:	A-159
Designer:	Tom Masterson
Height:	1 ½", 3.8 cm
Colour:	Grey; gloss
Issued:	1952

Model No.	U.S. $	Can. $	U.K. £
A-159	15.00	30.00	25.00

Indian Elephant Baby

Model No.:	A-17
Designer:	Helen Perrin Farnlund
Height:	1 ¼", 3.2 cm
Colour:	Brown, pink inner ears; gloss or matte
Issued:	1. Matte — Fall 1962 - fall 1967
	2. Gloss — 1976

Description	U.S. $	Can. $	U.K. £
1. Matte	5.00	10.00	8.50
2. Gloss	9.00	18.00	15.00

Note: Forms a pair with Indian Elephant Mama (A-16), page 338. The gloss edition, issued for the Bicentennial.

Indian Elephant Mama

Model No.:	A-16
Designer:	Helen Perrin Farnlund
Height:	2 ½", 6.4 cm
Colour:	Brown, pink inner ears; matte
Issued:	Spring 1962 - fall 1963

Model No.	U.S. $	Can. $	U.K. £
A-16	35.00	70.00	60.00

Note: The model illustrated is damaged. Model A-16 forms a pair with Indian Elephant Baby (A-17), page 337.

Republican Elephant

Model No.:	A-308
Designer:	Nell Bortells
Height:	1 2/3", 4.2 cm
Colour:	Grey, pink inner ears
Issued:	Fall 1956, fall 1967

Description	U.S. $	Can. $	U.K. £
1. With flag	23.00	46.00	40.00
2. Without flag	20.00	40.00	35.00

Note: These models had a flag glued to the elephant's trunk.

FERRET

Ferret

Model No.:	A-3097
Designer:	Helen Perrin Farnlund
Height:	1", 2.5 cm
Colour:	Brown; black eyes, paws and tail end
Issued:	Fall 1993 - spring 1995

Model No.	U.S. $	Can. $	U.K. £
A-3097	8.00	16.00	14.00

FOXES

Fox Baby, seated

Model No.:	A-2012
Designer:	Shi Yi Chen
Height:	15/16", 2.4 cm
Colour:	Red-brown and white
Issued:	Fall 1988 to the present

Model No.	U.S. $	Can. $	U.K. £
A-2012	2.00	4.00	3.50

Fox Baby, standing
Model No.:   A-157
Designer: Helen Perrin Farnlund
Height: 7/8", 2.2 cm
Colour: Red-brown and white
Issued: Spring 1952 - c.1970

Description	U.S. $	Can. $	U.K. £
1. Monrovia	10.00	20.00	17.00
2. San Dimas	5.00	10.00	8.50

Note: Model A-157 was made intermittently for 18 seasons between 1952 and c.1970.

Fox Mama, on hind legs
Model No.:   A-160
Designer: Helen Perrin Farnlund
Height: 1 5/8", 4.1 cm
Colour: Red-brown and white
Issued: 1952, 1969

Description	U.S. $	Can. $	U.K. £
1. Monrovia	15.00	30.00	25.00
2. San Dimas	10.00	20.00	17.00

Note: The height of model A-160 ranges from 1 5/8" to 2".

Fox Mama, standing
Model No.:   A-2020
Designer: Shi Yi Chen
Height: 1 ¼", 3.2 cm
Colour: Red-brown and white
Issued: Fall 1988 to the present

Model No.	U.S. $	Can. $	U.K. £
A-2020	3.50	7.00	6.00

Fox Papa
Model No.:   A-179
Designer: Helen Perrin Farnlund
Height: 2 ½", 6.4 cm
Colour: Red-brown and white
Issued: Spring 1952 - fall 1978

Description	U.S. $	Can. $	U.K. £
1. Monrovia	20.00	40.00	35.00
2. San Dimas	15.00	30.00	25.00

Note: Model A-179 was produced for 15 seasons.

GIRAFFES

Giraffe Baby, head up
Model No.:   A-182
Designer: Helen Perrin Farnlund
Height: 1", 2.5 cm
Colour: Pale yellow with brown spots
Issued: Fall 1952 - spring 1953

Model No.	U.S. $	Can. $	U.K. £
A-182	15.00	30.00	25.00

Note: This model forms a set with models A-170 and A-171.

Giraffe Baby, head down
Model No.:   A-170
Designer: Helen Perrin Farnlund
Height: 1", 2.5 cm
Colour: Pale yellow with brown spots
Issued: Fall 1952 - spring 1953

Model No.	U.S. $	Can. $	U.K. £
A-170	15.00	30.00	25.00

Giraffe Mama, facing left
Model No.:   A-171
Designer: Helen Perrin Farnlund
Height: 3", 7.6 cm
Colour: Pale yellow with brown spots
Issued: Fall 1952 - spring 1953

Model No.	U.S. $	Can. $	U.K. £
A-171	35.00	70.00	60.00

Note: These form a set with Giraffe Baby, head up (A-182).

Giraffe Baby, facing left

Model No.:	A-842
Designer:	Helen Perrin Farnlund
Height:	1 ¼", 3.2 cm
Colour:	Pale yellow with brown spots
Issued:	Spring 1982 - fall 1984

Model No.	U.S. $	Can. $	U.K. £
A-842	8.00	16.00	14.00

Giraffe Mama, facing right

Model No.:	A-841
Designer:	Helen Perrin Farnlund
Height:	2 ½", 6.4 cm
Colour:	Pale yellow with brown spots
Issued:	Spring 1982 - fall 1984

Model No.	U.S. $	Can. $	U.K. £
A-841	10.00	20.00	17.00

GUINEA PIG

Guinea Pig

Model No.:	A-3221
Designer:	Kristina Lucas
Height:	1", 2.5 cm
Colour:	Tan
Issued:	Fall 1996 - fall 1997

Model No.	U.S. $	Can. $	U.K. £
A-3221	5.00	10.00	8.50

HEDGEHOG

HIPPOPOTAMUSES

Hedgehog

Model No.:	A-2074
Designer:	Parastone
Height:	7/8", 2.2 cm
Colour:	Black and white
Issued:	Spring 1990 - fall 1990

Model No.	U.S. $	Can. $	U.K. £
A-2074	8.00	16.00	14.00

Note: Model A-2074 was released in Europe by The Parastone Company.

Half Hippo (Swimming)

Model No.:	A-992
Designer:	Helen Perrin Farnlund
Height:	½", 1.3 cm
Colour:	Grey, black shading, salmon muzzle, black dot eyes
Issued:	c.1970 - c.1972

Model No.	U.S. $	Can. $	U.K. £
A-992	8.00	16.00	14.00

Note: Model A-992 was made for three seasons in the early 1970s.

**Hippo Baby
First Version**

Model No.:	A-409
Designer:	Helen Perrin Farnlund
Height:	1 ¼", 3.2 cm
Colour:	Dark brown, rose muzzle, black eyebrows and pupils
Issued:	Fall 1958 - spring 1959

Description	U.S. $	Can. $	U.K. £
First version	10.00	20.00	17.00

**Hippo Mama
First Version**

Model No.:	A-408
Designer:	Helen Perrin Farnlund
Height:	2", 5.0 cm
Colour:	Dark brown, rose muzzle, black eyebrows and pupils
Issued:	Fall 1958 - spring 1959

Description	U.S. $	Can. $	U.K. £
First version	20.00	40.00	35.00

Note: The original 1958 issues were made to complement the Circus Collection.

Hippo Baby
Second Version

Model No.:	A-409
Designer:	Helen Perrin Farnlund
Height:	7/8", 0.9 cm
Colour:	Grey, black shading, salmon muzzle, black dot eyes
Issued:	Fall 1966 - fall 1980

Description	U.S. $	Can. $	U.K. £
Second version	7.00	14.00	12.00

Hippo Mama
Second Version

Model No.:	A-408
Designer:	Helen Perrin Farnlund
Height:	1 9/16", 4.0 cm
Colour:	Grey, black shading, salmon muzzle, black dot eyes
Issued:	Fall 1966 - fall 1980

Description	U.S. $	Can. $	U.K. £
Second version	10.00	20.00	17.00

Note: Models A-408 and A-409 were produced for 32 seasons.

Hippo Baby

Model No.:	None
Designer:	Maxine Renaker
Height:	15/16", 2.4 cm
Colour:	1. Pale blue
	2. Pale pink
Issued:	Spring 1949 - fall 1949

Description	U.S. $	Can. $	U.K. £
1. With flowers	10.00	20.00	17.00
2. Without flowers	8.00	16.00	14.00

Note: This model can be found with a flower decoration on the rump. This forms a pair with Hippo Mama, page 323.

Hippo Baby

Model No.:	A-407
Designer:	Maxine Renaker
Height:	15/16", 2.4 cm
Colour:	Grey, black shading, salmon muzzle, black dot eyes
Issued:	c.1970 - c.1975

Model No.	U.S. $	Can. $	U.K. £
A-407	7.00	14.00	12.00

Note: Model A-407 was made for seven seasons in the early 1970s.

Hippo Baby

Model No.: A-3193
Designer: Robert McGuinness
Height: 2/3", 1.7 cm
Colour: Grey
Issued: Spring 1996 - fall 1998

Model No.	U.S. $	Can. $	U.K. £
A-3193	6.00	12.00	10.00

Note: This forms a pair with Hippo Mama, mouth open (A-3192).

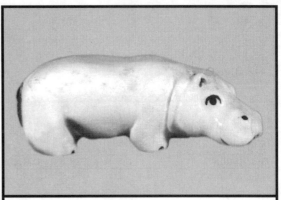

Hippo Mama, mouth closed

Model No.: None
Designer: Maxine Renaker
Height: 1", 2.5 cm
Colour: 1. Pale blue
  2. Pale pink
Issued: Spring 1949 - fall 1949

Description	U.S. $	Can. $	U.K. £
1. With flowers	15.00	30.00	25.00
2. Without flowers	10.00	20.00	17.00

Note: This model can be found with a flower decoration on the rump. This forms a pair with Hippo Baby, page 343.

Hippo Mama, mouth open

Model No.: A-3192
Designer: Robert McGuinness
Height: 1 5/6", 4.65 cm
Colour: Grey
Issued: Spring 1996 to the present

Model No.	U.S. $	Can. $	U.K. £
A-3192	5.00	10.00	8.50

Note: This forms a pair with Hippo Baby (A-3193).

Hippo River

Model No.: A-993
Designer: Helen Perrin Farnlund
Size: 5 ½" x 5", 14.0 x 12.7 cm
Colour: Pale brown with green shading
Issued: Fall 1976 - fall 1977

Description	U.S. $	Can. $	U.K. £
1. River	20.00	40.00	35.00
2. River with hippos	35.00	70.00	60.00

Note: Model A-993 was available with or without hippos A-408, A-409 and A-992; see page 342.

JAGUAR

Jaguar

Model No.:	A-2096
Designer:	Shi Yi Chen
Height:	1", 2.5 cm
Colour:	Golden brown with dark brown markings
Issued:	Spring 1991 - fall 1993

Model No.	U.S. $	Can. $	U.K. £
A-2096	7.00	14.00	12.00

KANGAROOS

Kangaroo Baby

Model No.:	A-280
Designer:	Helen Perrin Farnlund
Height:	7/8", 2.2 cm
Colour:	See below
Issued:	Spring 1956 - fall 1980

Colourways	U.S. $	Can. $	U.K. £
1. Brown	5.00	10.00	8.50
2. Dark grey, eye detail	10.00	20.00	17.00
3. Pale grey, eye dots	8.00	16.00	14.00

Kangaroo Mama
First Version (Without joey)

Model No.:	A-279
Designer:	Helen Perrin Farnlund
Height:	2 1/8", 5.4 cm
Colour:	1. Dark grey, eye dots
	2. Pale grey, eye detail
Issued:	1956, 1969

Colourways	U.S. $	Can. $	U.K. £
1. Dark grey	15.00	30.00	25.00
2. Pale grey	25.00	50.00	45.00

Kangaroo Mama, Second Version
(Joey's left ear attached to mama's body)

Model No.:	A-279
Designer:	Helen Perrin Farnlund
Height:	1 5/8", 4.1 cm
Colour:	Grey, red-brown shading, pink or blue apron
Issued:	Spring 1970 - spring 1975

Model No.	U.S. $	Can. $	U.K. £
A-279	8.00	16.00	14.00

Note: A third version of this model has the joey's head faces away from the mother's body.

Kangaroo Papa

Model No.:	A-278
Designer:	Helen Perrin Farnlund
Height:	1 7/8", 4.76 cm
Colour:	Grey, red-brown shading
Issued:	Spring 1979 - fall 1980

Model No.	U.S. $	Can. $	U.K. £
A-278	8.00	16.00	14.00

KOALA TREE SET

The Koala Tree Set was designed by Helen Perrin Farnlund. The koalas, which were available for 20 seasons between 1979 and 1988, are grey in colour. The tree is a green-brown colour.

Baby Koala

Model No.:	A-949
Height:	½", 1.2 cm
Issued:	1979 - 1988

Mama Koala

Model No.:	A-950
Height:	1 1/8", 2.8 cm
Issued:	1979 - 1988

Koala Tree

Model No.:	A-946
Height:	4 ¾", 12.1 cm
Issued:	1979

Uncle Koala, facing left

Model No.:	A-947A
Height:	1 1/8", 2.8 cm
Issued:	Spring 1978 - fall 1979

Uncle Koala, facing right

Model No.:	A-947B
Height:	1 1/8", 2.8 cm
Issued:	Spring 1978 - fall 1979

Name	U.S. $	Can. $	U.K. £
Baby Koala	8.00	16.00	14.00
Mama Koala	10.00	20.00	17.00
Koala Tree	20.00	40.00	35.00
Uncle Koala, facing left	15.00	30.00	25.00
Uncle Koala, facing right	15.00	30.00	25.00
Complete set	30.00	60.00	50.00

LIONS

Lion
Style One

Model No.:	A-410
Designer:	Helen Perrin Farnlund
Height:	1 ½", 3.8 cm
Colour:	Tan
Issued:	Fall 1958, fall 1975 - fall 1979
Series:	Circus Collection

Description	U.S. $	Can. $	U.K. £
1. Monrovia	15.00	30.00	25.00
2. San Dimas	8.00	16.00	14.00

Note: Earlier models had more detailed eyes.

Lion
Style Two

Model No.:	A-3172
Designer:	Robert McGuinness
Height:	1 ½", 3.8 cm
Colour:	Tan
Issued:	Spring 1995 to the present

Model No.	U.S. $	Can. $	U.K. £
A-3172	6.50	13.00	11.00

Lion Cub
Style One

Model No.:	A-411
Designer:	Helen Perrin Farnlund
Height:	5/8", 1.6 cm
Colour:	Tan
Issued:	Fall 1958, fall 1975 - fall 1979
Series:	Circus Collection

Description	U.S. $	Can. $	U.K. £
1. Monrovia	10.00	20.00	17.00
2. San Dimas	4.00	8.00	7.00

Note: Earlier models had more detailed eyes.

Lion Cub
Style Two

Model No.:	A-3174
Designer:	Robert McGuinness
Height:	½", 1.3 cm
Colour:	Tan
Issued:	Spring 1995 - fall 1998

Model No.	U.S. $	Can. $	U.K. £
A-3174	3.00	6.00	5.00

Lioness
Style One
Model No.:   A-412
Designer: Maxine Renaker
Height: 1 ½", 3.8 cm
Colour: Tan
Issued: Fall 1975 - fall 1978

Model No.	U.S. $	Can. $	U.K. £
A-412	8.00	16.00	14.00

Lioness
Style Two
Model No.:   A-3173
Designer: Robert McGuinness
Height: 1 ¼", 3.2 cm
Colour: Tan
Issued: Spring 1995 - fall 1996

Model No.	U.S. $	Can. $	U.K. £
A-3174	6.00	12.00	10.00

Mountain Lion, lying
Model No.:   A-3235
Designer: Maureen Love
Height: 1 5/8", 4.1 cm
Colour: Brown, white chest
Issued: Spring 1997 - fall 1998

Model No.	U.S. $	Can. $	U.K. £
A-3235	8.00	16.00	14.00

Mountain Lion, standing
Model No.:   A-3054
Designer: Shi Yi Chen
Height: 1 5/8", 4.1 cm
Colour: Brown, white chest
Issued: Spring 1992 - fall 1993

Model No.	U.S. $	Can. $	U.K. £
A-3054	5.00	10.00	8.50

LLAMAS

Llama

Model No.:	A-872
Designer:	Helen Perrin Farnlund
Height:	1 5/8", 4.1 cm
Colour:	1. Cream
	2. White with black markings
Issued:	Spring 1986 - fall 1987

Colourways	U.S. $	Can. $	U.K. £
1. Cream	9.00	18.00	15.00
2. White/black	8.00	16.00	14.00

Note: Pair with Llama Baby (A-873).

Llama Baby

Model No.:	A-873
Designer:	Helen Perrin Farnlund
Height:	1 1/8", 2.8 cm
Colour:	1. Cream
	2. White with black markings
Issued:	Spring 1986 - fall 1987

Colourways	U.S. $	Can. $	U.K. £
1. Cream	6.00	12.00	10.00
2. White/black	5.00	10.00	8.50

Note: Pair with Llama (A-872).

LYNX

MEERKAT

Lynx

Model No.:	A-3141
Designer:	Robert McGuinness
Height:	1 1/8", 2.8 cm (without base)
Colour:	White
Issued:	Spring 1994 - spring 1996

Description	U.S. $	Can. $	U.K. £
1. With base	10.00	20.00	17.00
2. Without base	8.00	16.00	14.00

Note: This piece was sold with and without the base.

Meerkat

Model No.:	3278
Designer:	Robert McGuinness
Height:	1 5/8", 4.1 cm
Colour:	Brown
Issued:	Fall 1998 to the present

Model No.	U.S. $	Can. $	U.K. £
3278	3.00	6.00	5.00

MICE

Big Brother Mouse

Model No.:	A-295
Designer:	Helen Perrin Farnlund
Height:	1 ¼", 3.2 cm
Colour:	Brown-grey, pink inner ears
Issued:	Fall 1956 - spring 1991

Description	U.S. $	Can. $	U.K. £
1. Monrovia	10.00	20.00	17.00
2. San Dimas	5.00	10.00	8.50

Note: Model A-295, which was also used to make City Mouse, First Version, was made for 32 seasons..

City Mouse
First Version

Model No.:	A-295
Designer:	Helen Perrin Farnlund
Height:	1 ½", 3.2 cm
Colour:	Brown-grey, pink inner ears, purple hat, black cane
Issued:	Fall 1956 - c.1959

Description	U.S. $	Can. $	U.K. £
First version	20.00	40.00	35.00

Note: Model A-295 was also used to make Big Brother Mouse.

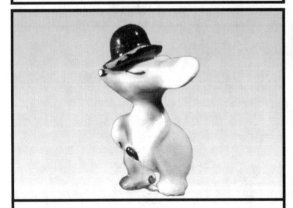

City Mouse
Second Version

Model No.:	A-133/356
Designer:	Helen Perrin Farnlund
Height:	1 ¼", 3.2 cm
Colour:	White-grey, black hat and cane
Issued:	Fall 1985 - spring 1994

Description	U.S. $	Can. $	U.K. £
Second version	8.00	16.00	14.00

Confederate Mouse

Model No.:	A-3072
Designer:	Helen Perrin Farnlund
Height:	1 ½", 3.8 cm
Colour:	Light grey mouse, pink inner ears, dark grey uniform, black hat and belt
Issued:	Fall 1992 - fall 1994

Model No.	U.S. $	Can. $	U.K. £
A-3072	4.00	8.00	7.00

Note: This forms a pair with Yankee Mouse (A-3073), page 354.

Country Mouse

Model No.:	A-294
Designer:	Helen Perrin Farnlund
Height:	1 ¼", 3.2 cm
Colour:	Brown-grey, pink inner ears, yellow shawl, blue bag
Issued:	1956 - fall 1990

Description	U.S. $	Can. $	U.K. £
1. Monrovia	20.00	40.00	35.00
2. San Dimas	10.00	20.00	17.00

Note: Model A-294 was in production for 16 seasons. A colourway with a blue shawl exists.

Little Brother Mouse

Model No.:	A-296
Designer:	Nell Bortells
Height:	¾", 1.9 cm
Colour:	1. Grey, white chest, pink inner ears, black tail
	2. Grey, white chest, pink inner ears, without tail
Issued:	c.1950 - spring 1988

Description	U.S. $	Can. $	U.K. £
1. With tail	15.00	30.00	25.00
2. Without tail	5.00	10.00	8.50

Note: Model A-296 made intermittently for 39 seasons.

Mouse, crouched, front paws up

Model No.:	A-007
Designer:	Helen Perrin Farnlund
Height:	¾", 1.9 cm
Colour:	Brown-grey, pink inner ears
Issued:	Fall 1961 - c.1985

Model No.	U.S. $	Can. $	U.K. £
A-007	8.00	16.00	14.00

Note: Model A-007, also called Mrs. New Mouse, was made for 10 seasons.

Mouse, crouched, straight tail

Model No.:	A-180
Designer:	Helen Perrin Farnlund
Height:	5/16", 0.8 cm
Colour:	Dark grey, light brown-grey, pink inner ears
Issued:	Fall 1953 to the present

Description	U.S. $	Can. $	U.K. £
1. Monrovia	10.00	20.00	17.00
2. San Dimas (current)	2.00	4.00	3.50

Note: Model A-180, also called Baby Mouse, was made for 73 seasons. A white colourway model exists.

Mouse, holding tail near chin

Model No.:	A-008
Designer:	Helen Perrin Farnlund
Height:	1", 2.5 cm
Colour:	1. Brown-grey, pink inner ears
	2. Grey, yellow hat
Issued:	Fall 1961 - spring 1968

Description	U.S. $	Can. $	U.K. £
1 Brown/without hat	5.00	10.00	8.50
2. Grey/with hat	15.00	30.00	25.00
3. Grey/without hat	10.00	20.00	17.00

Note: Model A-008, also called Mrs. New Mouse, was produced for 30 seasons.

Mouse, large bottom, pointy tail

Model No.:	A-70
Designer:	Helen Perrin Farnlund
Height:	5/8", 1.6 cm
Colour:	Steel grey, pink inner ears
Issued:	c.1950 - c.1970

Description	U.S. $	Can. $	U.K. £
1. Monrovia	10.00	20.00	17.00
2. San Dimas	5.00	10.00	8.50

Note: Model A-70 may vary slightly in size and have a wire tail.

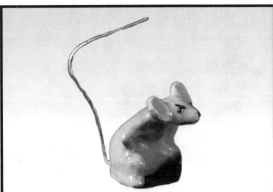

Mouse, large bottom, small shoulders

Model No.:	A-240
Designer:	Helen Perrin Farnlund
Height:	9/16", 1.4 cm
Colour:	Light brown-grey, pink inner ears
Issued:	c.1950 - c.1970

Description	U.S. $	Can. $	U.K. £
1. Monrovia	10.00	20.00	17.00
2. San Dimas	5.00	10.00	8.50

Note: Model A-240 has been seen with a wire tail.

Mouse, nose forward
First Version

Model No.:	A-241
Designer:	Helen Perrin Farnlund
Height:	9/16", 1.4 cm
Colour:	Grey, pink inner ears, wire tail
Issued:	c.1955

Model No.	U.S. $	Can. $	U.K. £
A-241	10.00	20.00	17.00

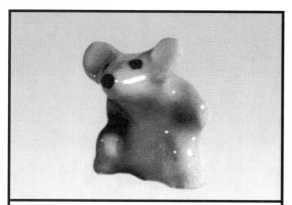

Mouse, nose forward
Second Version

Model No.:	A-241
Designer:	Helen Perrin Farnlund
Height:	9/16", 1.4 cm
Colour:	Light brown-grey, pink inner ears
Issued:	c.1975

Model No.	U.S. $	Can. $	U.K. £
A-241	5.00	10.00	8.50

Mouse, reclining

Model No.:	A-358
Designer:	Helen Perrin Farnlund
Height:	5/6", 2.1 cm
Colour:	Black and grey, pink inner ears
Issued:	Fall 1957 to the present

Description	U.S. $	Can. $	U.K. £
1. Monrovia	8.00	16.00	14.00
2. Current	2.50	5.00	4.00

Note: Model A-35, which is also called Mama Mouse or Papa Mouse, has been made for 80 seasons.

Mouse Baby

Model No.:	A-009
Designer:	Helen Perrin Farnlund
Height:	¼", 0.6 cm
Colour:	Pale brown, pink markings and inner ears
Issued:	Fall 1952 to the present

Description	U.S. $	Can. $	U.K. £
1. Monrovia	5.00	10.00	8.00
2. San Dimas	2.00	4.00	3.50

Note: Model A-009 has been made intermittently for 42 seasons.

Mouse Mama, holding tail by belly

Model No.:	A-356
Designer:	Helen Perrin Farnlund
Height:	1", 2.5 cm
Colour:	1. Brown-grey, pink inner ears, black tail
	2. Brown-grey, pink inner ears, grey tail
Issued:	Fall 1950 to the present

Colourways	U.S. $	Can. $	U.K. £
1. Black tail	10.00	20.00	17.00
2. Grey tail	2.00	4.00	3.00

Note: This model has been made for 38 seasons. Earlier versions of this model have a black tail, eyes, mouth and nails.

Three Blind Mice

Model No.:	A-70
Designer:	Helen Perrin Farnlund
Height:	5/8", 1.6 cm
Colour:	Light grey, pink inner ears, black glasses
Issued:	Spring 1966 - fall 1966

Model No.	U.S. $	Can. $	U.K. £
A-70	10.00	20.00	17.00

Note: The price given is for one mouse.

Yankee Mouse

Model No.:	A-3073
Designer:	Helen Perrin Farnlund
Height:	1 ½", 3.8 cm
Colour:	Light grey, pink inner ears, blue uniform and hat, black belt
Issued:	Fall 1992 - fall 1994

Model No.	U.S. $	Can. $	U.K. £
A-3073	4.00	8.00	7.00

Note: This forms a pair with Confederate Mouse (A-3072), page 350.

MOOSE

Moose

Model No.:	A-3137
Designer:	Maureen Love
Height:	2 7/8", 7.3 cm
Colour:	Brown, beige ceramic base
Issued:	Fall 1993 to the present

Model No.	U.S. $	Can. $	U.K. £
A-3137	9.00	18.00	15.00

Note: The antlers are cast separately from the body.

Moose Baby

Model No.:	A-40
Designer:	Helen Perrin Farnlund
Height:	1", 2.5 cm
Colour:	Red-brown and cream; gloss or matte
Issued:	Fall 1959 - fall 1985

Description	U.S. $	Can. $	U.K. £
1. Gloss	10.00	20.00	17.00
2. Matte	15.00	30.00	25.00

Note: Model A-40 was made for 6 seasons. Those made in 1959 may have a matte finish. This model forms a pair with Moose Papa (A-39), page 355.

Moose Papa

Model No.:   A-39
Designer: Helen Perrin Farnlund
Height: 2 ¼", 5.7 cm
Colour: Black, brown and cream; gloss or matte
Issued: Fall 1959 - spring 1988

Description	U.S. $	Can. $	U.K. £
1. Gloss	20.00	40.00	35.00
2. Matte	30.00	60.00	50.00

Note: Model A-39 was produced for 12 seasons and forms a pair with Moose Baby (A-40), page 354. Pieces made in 1959 may have a matte finish.

OPOSSUMS

Opossum Baby

Model No.:   A-838
Designer: Helen Perrin Farnlund
Height: 3/8", 0.9 cm
Colour: Black and pink
Issued: Fall 1983 - fall 1984

Model No.	U.S. $	Can. $	U.K. £
A-838	4.00	8.00	7.00

Note: Opossums can be joined at the tail. This model forms a pair with Opossum Mama (A-837).

Opossum Mama

Model No.:   A-837
Designer: Helen Perrin Farnlund
Height: 7/8", 2.2 cm
Colour: Black and pink
Issued: Fall 1983 - spring 1985

Model No.	U.S. $	Can. $	U.K. £
A-837	8.00	16.00	14.00

Note: Opossums can be joined at the tail. This model forms a pair with Opossum Baby (A-838).

OTTERS

Otter, standing

Model No.:	A-843
Designer:	Helen Perrin Farnlund
Height:	1 7/8", 4.8 cm
Colour:	Brown and tan
Issued:	Spring 1984 - fall 1994

Model No.	U.S. $	Can. $	U.K. £
A-843	6.00	12.00	10.00

Note: This forms a pair with model A-844.

Otter, walking

Model No.:	A-844
Designer:	Helen Perrin Farnlund
Height:	7/8", 2.2 cm
Colour:	Brown
Issued:	Spring 1984 - fall 1989

Model No.	U.S. $	Can. $	U.K. £
A-844	7.00	14.00	12.00

Note: This forms a pair with model A-843.

PANDAS

Panda, on three legs, black chest

Model No.:	A-951
Designer:	Maxine Renaker
Height:	1", 2.5 cm
Colour:	Black and white
Issued:	Spring 1978 - fall 1979

Model No.	U.S. $	Can. $	U.K. £
A-951	7.00	14.00	12.00

Note: This forms a sair with Panda (A-952), page 357.

Panda, on three legs, white chest

Model No.:	A-493
Designer:	Helen Perrin Farnlund
Height:	1 1/8", 2.8 cm
Colour:	Black and white
Issued:	Spring 1961 - spring 1992

Model No.	U.S. $	Can. $	U.K. £
A-493	6.00	12.00	10.00

Note: Model A-493 was made for 24 seasons. This forms a pair with Panda (A-494), page 357.

Panda, standing, black chest
Model No.:	A-952		
Designer:	Maxine Renaker		
Height:	1 3/8", 3.5 cm		
Colour:	Black and white		
Issued:	Spring 1978 - fall 1979		

Model No.	U.S. $	Can. $	U.K. £
A-952	7.00	14.00	12.00

Note: This forms a pair with Panda (A-951), page 356.

Panda, standing, white chest
Model No.:	A-494		
Designer:	Helen Perrin Farnlund		
Height:	1 ½", 3.8 cm		
Colour:	Black and white		
Issued:	Spring 1961 - spring 1992		

Model No.	U.S. $	Can. $	U.K. £
A-494	6.00	12.00	10.00

Note: Model A-494 was made for 24 seasons. This forms a pair with Panda (A-493), page 356.

Panda Papa
Model No.:	A-2017		
Designer:	Shi Yi Chen		
Height:	1 7/8", 4.8 cm		
Colour:	Black and white		
Issued:	Fall 1988 to the present		

Model No.	U.S. $	Can. $	U.K. £
A-2017	6.00	12.00	10.00

POLAR BEARS

Piano Bear
Model No.:	A-807		
Designer:	Helen Perrin Farnlund		
Height:	2 ½", 6.4 cm		
Colour:	White; gloss		
Issued:	Spring 1982 - fall 1986		

Model No.	U.S. $	Can. $	U.K. £
A-807	12.00	24.00	20.00

Note: This model can be paired with Piano (A-808), page 392.

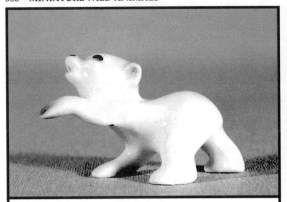

Piano Bear Cub

Model No.:	A-809		
Designer:	Helen Perrin Farnlund		
Height:	1", 2.5 cm		
Colour:	White; gloss		
Issued:	Spring 1982 - fall 1984		

Model No.	U.S. $	Can. $	U.K. £
A-809	6.00	12.00	10.00

Note: This model can be paired with Piano (A-808), page 392.

Polar Bear

Model No.:	A-942
Designer:	Helen Perrin Farnlund
Height:	1 ¼", 32. cm
Colour:	White, light brown highlights, black eyes and nose
Issued:	Spring 1980 - spring 1988

Model No.	U.S. $	Can. $	U.K. £
A-942	7.00	14.00	12.00

PORCUPINE

PRAIRIE DOG

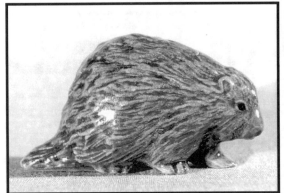

Porcupine

Model No.:	A-3133
Designer:	Robert McGuinness
Height:	1 1/8", 2.8 cm
Colour:	Brown
Issued:	Fall 1994 - fall 1995

Model No.	U.S. $	Can. $	U.K. £
A-3133	5.00	10.00	8.50

Prairie Dog

Model No.:	A-3100
Designer:	Robert McGuinness
Height:	1 7/8", 4.8 cm
Colour:	Light brown, cream belly
Issued:	Spring 1993 - fall 1994

Model No.	U.S. $	Can. $	U.K. £
A-3100	8.00	16.00	14.00

PRIMATES

Ape Baby

Model No.:   A-196
Designer: Tom Masterson
Height: 7/8", 2.2 cm
Colour: 1. Black body, white face
             2. Brown
Issued: Spring 1953 - 1979

Colourways	U.S. $	Can. $	U.K. £
1. Black (Monrovia)	10.00	20.00	17.00
2. Brown (San Dimas)	9.00	18.00	15.00

Hanging Ape

Model No.:   A-195
Designer: Tom Masterson
Length: 2 7/8", 7.3 cm
Colour: 1. Black body, white face
             2. Brown
Issued: Spring 1953 - 1979

Colourways	U.S. $	Can. $	U.K. £
1. Black (Monrovia)	20.00	40.00	35.00
2. Brown (San Dimas)	15.00	30.00	25.00

Note: Model A-196 and A-195 were available for six
seasons between 1953 and 1979.

Chimpanzee Baby

Model No.:   A-313
Designer: Helen Perrin Farnlund
Height: 1 ¼", 3.2 cm
Colour: Black, tan hands and face, yellow shirt
Issued: c.1980 - c.1992

Model No.	U.S. $	Can. $	U.K. £
A-313	10.00	20.00	17.00

Note: Model A-313 was produced for 22 seasons. The
colour of the shirt may vary.

Chimpanzee Mama

Model No.:   A-312
Designer: Helen Perrin Farnlund
Height: 2 ½", 6.4 cm
Colour: Black, tan hands and face, yellow skirt
Issued: Spring 1969 - fall 1980

Model No.	U.S. $	Can. $	U.K. £
A-312	18.00	36.00	30.00

Note: Model A-312 was produced for 7 seasons.

Flower Monkey Baby

Model No.:	A-29
Designer:	Otto Annala
Length:	1 3/8", 3.5 cm
Colour:	Red-brown, white face, pipe-cleaner tail
Issued:	Spring 1949 - fall 1950

Model No.	U.S. $	Can. $	U.K. £
A-29	8.00	16.00	14.00

Note: The model illustrated has its tail missing. This model forms a pair with Flower Monkey Mama (A-28).

Flower Monkey Mama

Model No.:	A-28
Designer:	Otto Annala
Length:	2 ½", 6.4 cm
Colour:	Red-brown, white face, pipe-cleaner tail
Issued:	Spring 1949 - fall 1950

Model No.	U.S. $	Can. $	U.K. £
A-28	15.00	30.00	25.00

Note: This forms a pair with Flower Monkey Baby (A-29).

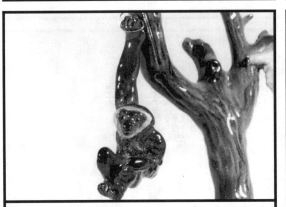

Gibbon

Model No.:	A-195
Designer:	Maureen Love
Height:	1 5/8", 4.1 cm
Colour:	Black; gloss
Issued:	1969

Model No.	U.S. $	Can. $	U.K. £
A-195	15.00	30.00	25.00

Note: The model illustrated is hanging from Koala Tree (A-946), page 395.

Monkey, climbing, arms forming circle

Model No.:	A-460
Designer:	Unknown
Height:	1 ¼", 3.2 cm
Colour:	Red-brown
Issued:	Spring 1959, fall 1966

Model No.	U.S. $	Can. $	U.K. £
A-460	15.00	30.00	25.00

Note: Monkey is attached to Koala Tree (A-946), page 395.

Monkey, climbing, right arm extended
Model No.: A-194
Designer: Tom Masterson
Length: 4", 5.0 cm
Colour: Brown with darker brown highlights
Issued: Fall 1953, fall 1969, 1979

Model No.	U.S. $	Can. $	U.K. £
A-194	15.00	30.00	25.00

Monkey, seated
Model No.: A-414
Designer: Unknown
Height: 1 ¼", 3.2 cm
Colour: Red-brown, tan face and chest
Issued: Fall 1958

Model No.	U.S. $	Can. $	U.K. £
A-414	20.00	40.00	35.00

Monkey, standing
Model No.: A-415
Designer: Unknown
Height: 1 ¼", 3.2 cm
Colour: Tan with red-brown shading
Issued: Fall 1958,
fall 1966

Description	U.S. $	Can. $	U.K. £
1. Black dot eyes	10.00	20.00	17.00
2. Detailed eyes	15.00	30.00	25.00

Note: Earlier models had painted black eyebrows and a painted black mouth line.

Orangutan With Baby
Model No.: A-3147
Designer: Robert McGuinness
Height: 1 5/8", 4.1cm
Colour: Orange with red highlights
Issued: Spring 1994 - spring 1996

Model No.	U.S. $	Can. $	U.K. £
A-3147	5.00	10.00	8.50

RABBITS AND HARES

Bunny Mama With Egg

Model No.: A-2015
Designer: Nell Bortells
Height: 2 ½", 6.4 cm
Colour: Pink bunny; white eyes, nose, inner ears and paws; yellow and blue egg
Issued: Fall 1988 - fall 1990

Model No.	U.S. $	Can. $	U.K. £
A-2015	7.00	14.00	12.00

Bunny Papa With Egg

Model No.: A-2016
Designer: Nell Bortells
Height: 2 ½", 6.4 cm
Colour: Blue bunny; white eyes, nose, inner ears and paws; yellow and blue egg
Issued: Fall 1988 - fall 1990

Model No.	U.S. $	Can. $	U.K. £
A-2016	7.00	14.00	12.00

Bunny Mama With Heart

Model No.: A-2015-1
Designer: Nell Bortells
Height: 2 ½", 6.4 cm
Colour: 1. Brown; pink nose and inner ears; white eyes, chest and paws; gold heart
2. Brown; pink nose and inner ears; white eyes, chest and paws; red heart
Issued: Fall 1988 - fall 1989

Colourways	U.S. $	Can. $	U.K. £
1. Gold heart	7.00	14.00	12.00
2. Red heart	7.00	14.00	12.00

Bunny Papa With Heart

Model No.: A-2016-1
Designer: Nell Bortells
Height: 2 ½", 6.4 cm
Colour: 1. Brown; pink nose and inner ears; white eyes, chest and paws; gold heart
2. Brown; pink nose and inner ears; white eyes, chest and paws; red heart
Issued: Fall 1988 - fall 1989

Colourways	U.S. $	Can. $	U.K. £
1. Gold heart	7.00	14.00	12.00
2. Red heart	7.00	14.00	12.00

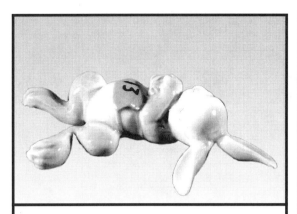

Hare, arms crossed over chest

Model No.:   A-3238
Designer: Helen Perrin Farnlund
Size: 5/8" x 3 1/8", 1.6 x 7.9 cm
Colour: White, blue number cloth
Issued: Spring 1997 - spring 1998

Model No.	U.S. $	Can. $	U.K. £
A-3238	7.00	14.00	12.00

Note: This forms a pair with Tortoise, Style Three
(A-3239), page 308.

Hare, right arm extended

Model No.:   A-2001
Designer: Nell Bortells
Height: 1 7/8", 4.8 cm
Colour: Brown; white chest, eyes and toes;
   pink nose
Issued: Spring 1988 - spring 1989

Model No.	U.S. $	Can. $	U.K. £
A-2001	10.00	20.00	17.00

Note: This forms a pair with Tortoise, Style Three
(A-2000), page 308.

Classic Whispering Rabbit Baby

Model No.:   A-199
Designer: Helen Perrin Farnlund
Height: 1 1/8", 2.8 cm
Colour: See below
Issued: Spring 1953 to the present

Colourways	U.S. $	Can. $	U.K. £
1. Blue (Monrovia)	6.00	12.00	10.00
2. Brown (Monrovia)	6.00	12.00	10.00
3. Brown (San Dimas)	4.00	8.00	7.00
4. Pink (Monrovia)	6.00	12.00	10.00
5. White (Monrovia)	6.00	12.00	10.00
6. White (San Dimas) current	2.00	4.00	3.00

Classic Whispering Rabbit Mama

Model No.:   A-198
Designer: Helen Perrin Farnlund
Height: 1 ¾", 4.4 cm
Colour: See below
Issued: Spring 1953 to the present

Colourways	U.S. $	Can. $	U.K. £
1. Blue (Monrovia)	10.00	20.00	17.00
2. Brown (Monrovia)	10.00	20.00	17.00
3. Brown (San Dimas)	6.00	12.00	10.00
4. Pink (Monrovia)	10.00	20.00	17.00
5. White (Monrovia)	10.00	20.00	17.00
6. White (San Dimas) current	3.00	6.00	5.00

Classic Whispering Rabbit Papa

Model No.:	A-197
Designer:	Helen Perrin Farnlund
Height:	1 5/8", 4.1 cm
Colour:	See below
Issued:	Spring 1953 to the present

Colourways	U.S. $	Can. $	U.K. £
1. Blue (Monrovia)	10.00	20.00	17.00
2. Brown (Monrovia)	10.00	20.00	17.00
3. Brown (San Dimas)	6.00	12.00	10.00
4. Pink (Monrovia)	10.00	20.00	17.00
5. White (Monrovia)	10.00	20.00	17.00
6. White (San Dimas-current)	3.00	6.00	5.00

Cottontail Baby

Model No.:	A-336
Designer:	Martha Armstrong
Height:	1", 2.5 cm
Colour:	1. Brown; darker brown shading; white chest, nose and eyes; pink inner ears
	2. Pale yellow
Issued:	Spring 1957 - fall 1987

Colourways	U.S. $	Can. $	U.K. £
1. Brown	10.00	20.00	17.00
2. Pale yellow	3.00	6.00	5.00

Note: Model A-336 was produced for 41 seasons and forms a pair with Cottontail Mama (A-330).

Cottontail Mama

Model No.:	A-330
Designer:	Martha Armstrong
Height:	1 ½", 3.8 cm
Colour:	1. Brown with darker brown shading; white chest, nose and eyes; pink inner ears
	2. Pale yellow
Issued:	Spring 1957 - fall 1987

Colourways	U.S. $	Can. $	U.K. £
1. Brown	15.00	30.00	25.00
2. Pale yellow	6.00	12.00	10.00

Note: Pair with Cottontail Baby (A-336).

Rabbit in Hat

Model No.:	A-3144
Designer:	Edith Carrion
Height:	1 7/8", 4.8 cm
Colour:	White rabbit, black top hat
Issued:	Spring 1994 to the present

Model No.	U.S. $	Can. $	U.K. £
A-3144	5.00	10.00	8.50

Rabbit, lop-eared, crouching
Model No.:   A-860
Designer: Helen Perrin Farnlund
Height: 1 1/8", 2.8 cm
Colour: Brown, white chest, pink inner ears
Issued: Fall 1985 to the present

Model No.	U.S. $	Can. $	U.K. £
A-860	3.00	6.00	5.00

Note: This forms a pair with model A-861.

Rabbit, lop-eared, on hind legs
Model No.:   A-861
Designer: Helen Perrin Farnlund
Height: 1 7/8", 4.8 cm
Colour: Brown, white chest, pink inner ears
Issued: Fall 1985 to the present

Model No.	U.S. $	Can. $	U.K. £
A-861	3.00	6.00	5.00

Note: This forms a pair with model A-860.

Rabbit, seated
Model No.:   A-3098
Designer: Helen Perrin Farnlund
Height: 1 ¾", 4.4 cm
Colour: Grey
Issued: Spring 1995 - spring 1996

Model No.	U.S. $	Can. $	U.K. £
A-3098	6.00	12.00	10.00

Rabbit, walking
Model No.:   A-3099
Designer: Helen Perrin Farnlund
Height: 1 7/8", 4.8 cm
Colour: Grey
Issued: Spring 1995 - spring 1996

Model No.	U.S. $	Can. $	U.K. £
A-3099	6.00	12.00	10.00

Rabbit Family
Ears together

These rabbits, designed by Helen Perrin Farnlund, were available in the folowing colourways: blue, pink and white.

Rabbit Papa, ears together

Model No.:	A-14
Designer:	Helen Perrin Farnlund
Height:	2", 5.0 cm
Colour:	See above
Issued:	1949

Colourways	U.S. $	Can. $	U.K. £
1. Blue	8.00	16.00	14.00
2. Pink	8.00	16.00	14.00
3. White	8.00	16.00	14.00

Rabbit Mama, ears together

Model No.:	A-15
Designer:	Helen Perrin Farnlund
Height:	1 5/8", 4.1 cm
Colour:	See above
Issued:	1949

Colourways	U.S. $	Can. $	U.K. £
1. Blue	8.00	16.00	14.00
2. Pink	8.00	16.00	14.00
3. White	8.00	16.00	14.00

Rabbit Baby, ears down

Model No.:	A-11
Designer:	Helen Perrin Farnlund
Height:	¾", 1.9 cm
Colour:	See above
Issued:	1949

Colourways	U.S. $	Can. $	U.K. £
1. Blue	5.00	10.00	8.50
2. Pink	5.00	10.00	8.50
3. White	5.00	10.00	8.50

Rabbit, running

Model No.:	A-36
Designer:	Helen Perrin Farnlund
Height:	1 1/8", 2.8 cm
Colour:	See above
Issued:	1949

Colourways	U.S. $	Can. $	U.K. £
1. Blue	8.00	16.00	14.00
2. Pink	8.00	16.00	14.00
3. White	8.00	16.00	14.00

Note: Rabbit Mama, ears together (A-15), is not illustrated.

Rabbit Family
Ears apart

Rabbit Mama, ears apart

Model No.:	A-127
Designer:	Helen Perrin Farnlund
Height:	1 5/8", 4.1 cm
Colour:	1. Brown
	2. White
Issued:	Fall 1950 - fall 1952

Colourways	U.S. $	Can. $	U.K. £
1. Brown	5.00	10.00	8.50
2. White	5.00	10.00	8.50

Rabbit Baby, ears apart

Model No.:	A-128
Designer:	Helen Perrin Farnlund
Height:	1", 2.5 cm
Colour:	1. Brown
	2. White
Issued:	Fall 1950 - fall 1952

Colourways	U.S. $	Can. $	U.K. £
1. Brown	5.00	10.00	8.50
2. White	5.00	10.00	8.50

Rabbit, running, ears apart

Model No.:	A-129
Designer:	Helen Perrin Farnlund
Height:	1 1/8", 2.8 cm
Colour:	1. Brown
	2. White
Issued:	Fall 1950 - fall 1952

Colourways	U.S. $	Can. $	U.K. £
1. Brown	5.00	10.00	8.50
2. White	5.00	10.00	8.50

Rabbit Baby, ears down

Model No.:	A-449
Designer:	Helen Perrin Farnlund
Height:	1", 2.5 cm
Colour:	1. White; Auerspurse
	2. White
Issued:	Fall 1960 - spring 1963

Colourways	U.S. $	Can. $	U.K. £
1. White/Auerspurse	10.00	20.00	17.00
2. White	5.00	10.00	8.50

Note: This forms a pair with Rabbit Mama (A-442).

Rabbit Baby, ears up

Model No.:	A-979
Designer:	Maxine Renaker
Height:	1", 2.5 cm
Colour:	White, pink inner ears, black
	dot eyes; gloss
Issued:	Spring 1976 - fall 1977

Model No.	U.S. $	Can. $	U.K. £
A-979	4.00	8.00	7.00

Note: This forms a pair with Rabbit Mama (A-980).

Rabbit Brother

Model No.:	A-858
Designer:	Helen Perrin Farnlund
Height:	1 ½", 3.8 cm
Colour:	Light brown, pink inner ears
Issued:	Fall 1984 to the present

Model No.	U.S. $	Can. $	U.K. £
A-858	3.00	6.00	5.00

Note: See Also Disney model 5020 (Thumper™),
page 491.

Rabbit Mama, ears down

Model No.:	A-442
Designer:	Helen Perrin Farnlund
Height:	1 ½", 3.8 cm
Colour:	1. White; Auerspurse
	2. White
Issued:	Fall 1960 - spring 1963,
	spring 1976 - fall 1977

Colourways	U.S. $	Can. $	U.K. £
1. White/Auerspurse	15.00	30.00	25.00
2. White	8.00	16.00	14.00

Rabbit Mama, ears flat

Model No.:	A-980
Designer:	Maxine Renaker
Height:	7/8", 2.2 cm
Colour:	White, pink inner ears, black dot eyes; gloss
Issued:	Spring 1976 - fall 1977

Model No.	U.S. $	Can. $	U.K. £
A-980	10.00	20.00	17.00

RACCOONS

Raccoon Baby

Model No.:	A-819
Designer:	Helen Perrin Farnlund
Height:	7/8", 2.2 cm
Colour:	Grey
Issued:	Spring 1983 - spring 1989

Model No.	U.S. $	Can. $	U.K. £
A-819	4.00	8.00	7.00

Note: This forms a pair with Raccoon Mama (A-818).

Raccoon Mama

Model No.:	A-818
Designer:	Helen Perrin Farnlund
Height:	1 ½", 3.8 cm
Colour:	Grey
Issued:	Spring 1983 - fall 1989

Model No.	U.S. $	Can. $	U.K. £
A-818	6.00	12.00	10.00

Note: This forms a pair with Raccoon Baby (A-819).

Raccoon Baby
First Version (Hole in hand)

Model No.:	A-164
Designer:	Tom Masterson
Height:	1 ½", 3.8 cm
Colour:	1. Black and grey
	2. Red-brown and grey
Issued:	1952

Colourways	U.S. $	Can. $	U.K. £
1. Black/grey	7.00	14.00	12.00
2. Red-brown	7.00	14.00	12.00

Raccoon Mama
First Version

Model No.:	A-163
Designer:	Tom Masterson
Height:	1 5/8", 4.1 cm
Colour:	1. Black and grey
	2. Red-brown and grey
Issued:	1952

Colourways	U.S. $	Can. $	U.K. £
1. Black/grey	9.00	18.00	15.00
2. Red-brown	9.00	18.00	15.00

Note: The first version of model A-164 has a hole in its hand to hold flowers.

Raccoon Baby
Second Version

Model No.:	A-164
Designer:	Tom Masterson
Height:	7/8", 2.2 cm
Colour:	Red-brown
Issued:	Fall 1972 - fall 1981

Description	U.S. $	Can. $	U.K. £
Second version	4.00	8.00	7.00

Raccoon Mama
Second Version

Model No.:	A-163
Designer:	Tom Masterson
Height:	1 ¼", 3.2 cm
Colour:	Red-brown
Issued:	Fall 1972 - fall 1981

Description	U.S. $	Can. $	U.K. £
Second version	6.00	12.00	10.00

Raccoon Family

Raccoon Mama

Model No.:	A-3095
Designer:	Robert McGuinness
Height:	1 ½", 3.8 cm
Colour:	Grey
Issued:	Spring 1993 to the present

Model No.	U.S. $	Can. $	U.K. £
A-3095	3.00	6.00	5.00

Raccoon Baby

Model No.:	A-3096
Designer:	Robert McGuinness
Height:	1 ¼", 3.2 cm
Colour:	Grey
Issued:	Spring 1993 to the present

Model No.	U.S. $	Can. $	U.K. £
A-3096	3.00	6.00	5.00

Raccoon Papa on Fence

Model No.:	A-3094
Designer:	Robert McGuinness
Height:	2 ¼", 5.7 cm
Colour:	Grey, brown fence
Issued:	Spring 1993 - spring 1996

Model No.	U.S. $	Can. $	U.K. £
A-3094	6.00	12.00	10.00

RHINOCEROS

Rhino
Model No.:   A-3194
Designer: Robert McGuinness
Height: 1 1/8", 2.8 cm
Colour: Grey
Issued: Spring 1996 - fall 1997

Model No.	U.S. $	Can. $	U.K. £
A-3194	6.00	12.00	10.00

Rhino Baby
Model No.:   A-830
Designer: Helen Perrin Farnlund
Height: ½", 1.3 cm
Colour: Grey
Issued: Fall 1983 - fall 1985

Model No.	U.S. $	Can. $	U.K. £
A-830	8.00	16.00	14.00

Note: This forms a pair with Rhino Mama (A-829).

Rhino Mama
Model No.:   A-829
Designer: Helen Perrin Farnlund
Height: ¾", 1.9 cm
Colour: Grey
Issued: Fall 1983 - fall 1985

Model No.	U.S. $	Can. $	U.K. £
A-829	10.00	20.00	17.00

Note: This forms a pair with Rhino Baby (A-830).

SKUNKS

Skunk Baby

Model No.: A-30
Designer: Maxine Renaker
Height: 1", 2.5 cm
Colour: Black and white
Issued: 1949

Model No.	U.S. $	Can. $	U.K. £
A-30	8.00	16.00	14.00

Skunk Baby

Model No.: A-84
Designer: Maxine Renaker
Height: 11/16", 1.7 cm
Colour: Black and white
Issued: 1950 - fall 1987

Model No.	U.S. $	Can. $	U.K. £
A-84	3.00	6.00	5.00

Note: Model A-84 was produced for seventy seasons.

Skunk Baby

Model No.: A-152
Designer: Tom Masterson
Height: 1 ¼", 3.2 cm
Colour: Black and white
Issued: 1951, spring 1959 - fall 1960

Model No.	U.S. $	Can. $	U.K. £
A-152	8.00	16.00	14.00

Note: Model A-152 was first released with A-144, page 374, and A-153, page 375, and later with Atomizer (A-392), page 385.

Skunk Baby

Model No.: A-3081
Designer: Helen Perrin Farnlund
Height: 7/8", 2.2 cm
Colour: Black and white
Issued: Fall 1992 to the present

Model No.	U.S. $	Can. $	U.K. £
A-3081	2.00	4.00	3.50

Skunk Mama

Model No.:	A-6
Designer:	Maxine Renaker
Height:	1 7/8", 4.8 cm
Colour:	Black and white
Issued:	1948

Model No.	U.S. $	Can. $	U.K. £
A-6	15.00	30.00	25.00

Skunk Mama

Model No.:	A-95
Designer:	Maxine Renaker
Height:	1", 2.5 cm
Colour:	Black and white
Issued:	1950 - spring 1996

Model No.	U.S. $	Can. $	U.K. £
A-95	5.00	10.00	8.50

Note: Model A-95 was produced for over 70 seasons.

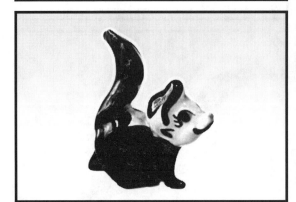

Skunk Mama

Model No.:	A-144
Designer:	Tom Masterson
Height:	1 ¾", 4.4 cm
Colour:	Black and white
Issued:	Fall 1951

Model No.	U.S. $	Can. $	U.K. £
A-144	20.00	40.00	35.00

Skunk Mama

Model No.:	A-3080
Designer:	Helen Perrin Farnlund
Height:	1 3/8", 3.5 cm
Colour:	Black and white
Issued:	Fall 1992 to the present

Model No.	U.S. $	Can. $	U.K. £
A-3080	3.00	6.00	5.00

Skunk Papa

Model No.:	A-3
Designer:	Maxine Renaker
Height:	2", 5.0 cm
Colour:	Black and white
Issued:	1949

Model No.	U.S. $	Can. $	U.K. £
A-3	15.00	30.00	25.00

Skunk Papa

Model No.:	A-153
Designer:	Tom Masterson
Height:	1 ¾", 4.4 cm
Colour:	Black and white
Issued:	Fall 1951

Model No.	U.S. $	Can. $	U.K. £
A-153	25.00	50.00	45.00

Textured Skunk Baby

Model No.:	A-84A
Designer:	Maxine Renaker
Height:	¾", 1.9 cm
Colour:	Black and white
Issued:	Spring 1977 - spring 1978

Model No.	U.S. $	Can. $	U.K. £
A-84A	5.00	10.00	8.50

Textured Skunk Mama

Model No.:	A-95A
Designer:	Maxine Renaker
Height:	1 ¼", 3.2 cm
Colour:	Black and white
Issued:	Spring 1977 - spring 1978

Model No.	U.S. $	Can. $	U.K. £
A-95A	7.00	14.00	12.00

Note: The illustrated model A-95A has been attached to a base for display purposes.

SQUIRRELS

Squirrel Baby

Model No.:	A-34
Designer:	Helen Perrin Farnlund
Height:	1 1/8", 2.8 cm
Colour:	See below
Issued:	Spring 1949 - fall 1950

Colourways	U.S. $	Can. $	U.K. £
1. Brown	7.00	14.00	12.00
2. Buff	7.00	14.00	12.00
3. Grey	7.00	14.00	12.00

Note: Forms a pair with Squirrel Mama (A-5), page 377.

Squirrel Baby

Model No.:	A-137
Designer:	Helen Perrin Farnlund
Height:	1", 2.5 cm
Colour:	1. Brown
	2. Grey
Issued:	Spring 1951 - fall 1951

Colourways	U.S. $	Can. $	U.K. £
1. Brown	8.00	16.00	14.00
2. Grey	8.00	16.00	14.00

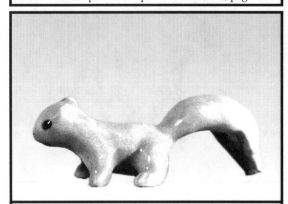

Squirrel Baby

Model No.:	A-272
Designer:	Robin Sikking
Height:	¾", 1.9 cm
Colour:	See below
Issued:	Fall 1955 - spring 1969

Colourways	U.S. $	Can. $	U.K. £
1. Brown	5.00	10.00	8.50
2. Brown/Auerspurse	10.00	20.00	17.00
3. Grey	5.00	10.00	8.50

Note: Model A-272 was produced for 28 seasons.

Squirrel Baby

Model No.:	A-340
Designer:	Helen Perrin Farnlund
Height:	15/16", 2.4 cm
Colour:	See below
Issued:	Spring 1957 - spring 1983

Colourways	U.S. $	Can. $	U.K. £
1. Brown (Monrovia)	7.00	14.00	12.00
2. Grey (San Dimas)	3.00	6.00	5.00

Note: This model was made intermittently for 10 seasons between 1957 and 1983. This forms a pair with Squirrel Mama (A-339), page 378.

Squirrel Baby

Model No.:   A-840
Designer: Helen Perrin Farnlund
Height: 7/8", 2.2 cm
Colour: 1. Brown
     2. Grey
Issued: Spring 1984 - spring 1988

Colourways	U.S. $	Can. $	U.K. £
1. Brown	6.00	12.00	10.00
2.. Grey	6.00	12.00	10.00

Note: This forms a pair with Squirrel Mama (A-839),
     page 378.

Squirrel Baby, carved tail

Model No.:   A-14
Designer: Helen Perrin Farnlund
Height: 1", 2.5 cm
Colour: Brown
Issued: c.1960 for 16 seasons

Model No.	U.S. $	Can. $	U.K. £
A-14	9.00	18.00	15.00

Note: This forms a pair with Squirrel Mama (A-13/066),
     page 378.

Squirrel Mama

Model No.:   A-5
Designer: Helen Perrin Farnlund
Height: 1 ¾", 4.4 cm
Colour: 1. Brown
     2. Buff
     3. Grey
Issued: Spring 1949 - fall 1950

Colourways	U.S. $	Can. $	U.K. £
1. Brown	7.00	14.00	12.00
2. Buff	7.00	14.00	12.00
3. Grey	7.00	14.00	12.00

Note: Pair with Squirrel Baby (A-34), page 376.

Squirrel Mama

Model No.:   A-140
Designer: Helen Perrin Farnlund
Height: 13/16", 2.1 cm
Colour: 1. Brown
     2. Grey
Issued: Spring 1951 - fall 1951

Colourways	U.S. $	Can. $	U.K. £
1. Brown	8.00	16.00	14.00
2. Grey	8.00	16.00	14.00

Note: A wire was attached to the right front paw for
     placement.

Squirrel Mama
Model No.:   A-271
Designer: Robin Sikking
Height: 2", 5.0 cm
Colour: See below
Issued: Fall 1955 - fall 1980

Colourways	U.S. $	Can. $	U.K. £
1. Brown	8.00	16.00	14.00
2. Brown/Auerspurse	15.00	30.00	25.00
3. Grey	5.00	10.00	8.50

Note: Model A-271 was produced for 28 seasons.

Squirrel Mama
Model No.:   A-839
Designer: Helen Perrin Farnlund
Height: 1 5/8", 4.1 cm
Colour: 1. Brown
              2. Grey
Issued: Spring 1984 - spring 1988

Colourways	U.S. $	Can. $	U.K. £
1. Brown	7.00	14.00	12.00
2. Grey	7.00	14.00	12.00

Note: This forms a pair with Squirrel Baby (A-840), page 377.

Squirrel Mama, carved tail
Model No.:   A-13/066
Designer: Helen Perrin Farnlund
Height: 1 ½", 3.8 cm
Colour: Brown
Issued: c.1960 for 16 seasons

Model No.	U.S. $	Can. $	U.K. £
A-13/066	10.00	20.00	17.00

Note: This forms a pair with Squirrel Baby (A-14), page 377.

Squirrel Mama, paw up
Model No.:   A-339
Designer: Helen Perrin Farnlund
Height: 1 ½", 3.8 cm
Colour: 1. Brown
              2. Grey
Issued: Spring 1957 - fall 1983

Colourways	U.S. $	Can. $	U.K. £
1. Brown (Monrovia)	10.00	20.00	17.00
2. Grey (San Dimas)	8.00	16.00	14.00

Note: Made intermittently for 10 seasons between 1957 and 1983, this model forms a pair with Squirrel Baby (A-340), page 376.

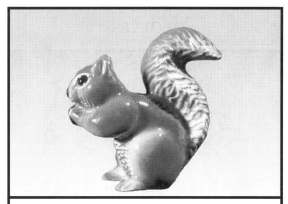

TIGERS

Squirrel
Model No.:	A-3017
Designer:	Laurilyn Burson
Height:	1 ¾", 4.4 cm
Colour:	1. Brown
	2. Grey
Issued:	Spring 1991 - fall 1992

Colourways	U.S. $	Can. $	U.K. £
1. Brown	7.00	14.00	12.00
2. Grey	7.00	14.00	12.00

Tiger
Model No.:	A-2029
Designer:	Shi Yi Chen
Height:	1", 2.5 cm
Colour:	Tan and brown
Issued:	Fall 1990 - fall 1995

Model No.	U.S. $	Can. $	U.K. £
A-2029	7.00	14.00	12.00

Note: For Stoneware version of model A-2029, see page 481.

WART HOG

Tiger Cub
Model No.:	A-411
Designer:	Helen Perrin Farnlund
Height:	5/8", 1.6 cm
Colour:	Tan with black markings
Issued:	Unknown

Model No.	U.S. $	Can. $	U.K. £
A-411		Rare	

Note: Model A-411 was also used to make Lion Cub, Style One, page 347. This may have been a special order for Sambos restaurants.

Wart Hog
Model No.:	A-3167
Designer:	Robert McGuinness
Height:	1 ¼", 3.2 cm
Colour:	Red-brown
Issued:	Spring 1995 - spring 1996

Model No.	U.S. $	Can. $	U.K. £
A-3167	8.00	16.00	13.00

WILD BOAR

WOLVES

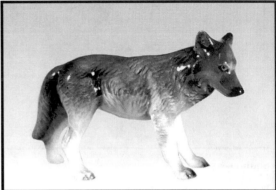

Wild Boar
Model No.: A-3168
Designer: Robert McGuinness
Height: 1 ¼", 3.2 cm
Colour: Red-brown
Issued: Spring 1995 - spring 1996

Model No.	U.S. $	Can. $	U.K. £
A-3168	8.00	16.00	14.00

Wolf
Model No.: A-3249
Designer: Maureen Love
Height: 1 7/8", 4.8 cm
Colour: Dark brown
Issued: Fall 1997 to the present

Model No.	U.S. $	Can. $	U.K. £
A-3249	4.50	9.00	8.00

Wolf Cub
Model No.: A-3250
Designer: Maureen Love
Height: 1 1/8", 2.8 cm
Colour: Dark brown
Issued: Fall 1997 to the present

Model No.	U.S. $	Can. $	U.K. £
A-3250	3.00	6.00	5.00

ZEBRAS

Zebra Baby, standing, rear legs parallel
Model No.:   A-174
Designer: Helen Perrin Farnlund
Height: 1", 2.5 cm
Colour: Black and white
Issued: Fall 1983 - fall 1986

Model No.	U.S. $	Can. $	U.K. £
A-174	15.00	30.00	25.00

Zebra Baby,
standing, right rear leg extended
Model No.:   A-413
Designer: Helen Perrin Farnlund
Height: 1 ¼", 3.2 cm
Colour: Black and white
Issued: Spring 1958 - fall 1958

Model No.	U.S. $	Can. $	U.K. £
A-413		Rare	

Zebra Mama, head forward
Model No.:   A-412
Designer: Helen Perrin Farnlund
Height: 2", 5.0 cm
Colour: Black and white
Issued: Spring 1958 - fall 1958

Model No.	U.S. $	Can. $	U.K. £
A-412		Rare	

Zebra Mama, head turned
Model No.:   A-173
Designer: Helen Perrin Farnlund
Height: 1 ½", 3.8 cm
Colour: Black and white
Issued: Fall 1983 - fall 1986

Model No.	U.S. $	Can. $	U.K. £
A-173	20.00	40.00	35.00

Cocker Spaniel With Newspaper

MISCELLANEOUS ITEMS

INDEX TO
MINIATURE MISCELLANEOUS ITEMS

ACCESSORIES

ANVIL

Anvil
Model No.:	A-394
Designer:	Will Climes
Height:	1 3/8", 3.5 cm
Colour:	Silver and brown
Issued:	Fall 1959

Model No.	U.S. $	Can. $	U.K. £
A-394	50.00	100.00	85.00

Note: Miniature horseshoes are moulded into the anvil's base.

ATOMIZER

Atomizer
Model No.:	A-392
Designer:	Will Climes
Height:	5/8", 1.6 cm
Colour:	White and gold
Issued:	Spring 1959 - fall 1960

Model No.	U.S. $	Can. $	U.K. £
A-392	20.00	40.00	35.00

Note: A pink colourway is also known.

BANANAS

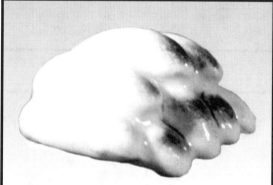

Bananas
Model No.:	A-312A
Designer:	Helen Perrin Farnlund
Height:	3/8", 0.9 cm
Colour:	Yellow, brown highlights
Issued:	Spring 1979 - spring 1980

Model No.	U.S. $	Can. $	U.K. £
A-312A	10.00	20.00	17.00

BEAR FLOOR

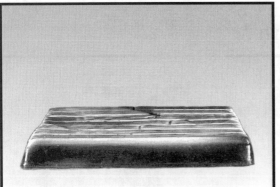

BED

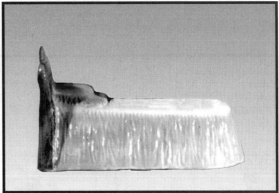

Bear Floor

Model No.:	A-996
Designer:	Maxine Renaker
Size:	4" x 2 ¾", 10.1 x 7.0 cm
Colour:	Light brown, dark brown shading
Issued:	Fall 1976 - spring 1977

Description	U.S. $	Can. $	U.K. £
1. Bear floor	20.00	40.00	35.00
2. Complete set	30.00	60.00	50.00

Note: Set with A-465 page 326, A-466 page 323, and A-467 page 325.

Bed

Model No.:	A-976
Designer:	Helen Perrin Farnlund
Size:	2" x 3 ¾", 5.1 x 9.5 cm
Colour:	Yellow
Issued:	Fall 1976 - spring 1977

Model No.	U.S.$	Can. $	U.K.£
A-976	20.00	40.00	35.00

BELL

BIRDBATH

Photograph not
available
at press time

Liberty Bell

Model No.:	A-999
Designer:	Helen Perrin Farnlund
Height:	1 ½", 3.8 cm
Colour:	Gold bell
Issued:	Fall 1983 - fall 1984

Model No.	U.S. $	Can. $	U.K. £
A-999	15.00	30.00	25.00

Birdbath

Model No.:	A-986
Designer:	Helen Perrin Farnlund
Height:	2", 5.1 cm
Colour:	White
Issued:	Fall 1976 - spring 1981

Model No.	U.S. $	Can. $	U.K. £
A-958	10.00	20.00	17.00

Note: Pair with Oriole, Style Two (A-982), page 168.

BOOK

BOTTLE

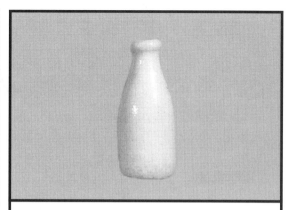

Book

Model No.:	A-421A
Designer:	Helen Perrin Farnlund
Height:	¼", 0.6 cm
Colour:	White and black, red cover
Issued:	Spring 1960 - spring 1961

Model No.	U.S. $	Can. $	U.K. £
A-421A	20.00	40.00	35.00

Note: Pair with Professor Owl (A-421), page 171.

Milk Bottle

Model No.:	A-53
Designer:	Helen Perrin Farnlund
Height:	1 ¼", 3.2 cm
Colour:	White
Issued:	Fall 1959 - fall 1960

Model No.	U.S. $	Can. $	U.K. £
A-55	15.00	30.00	125.00

Note: Forms a set with Siamese Kittens A-54 page 201, A-55 page 208, A-56 page 200, A-57 page 210.

CAVES

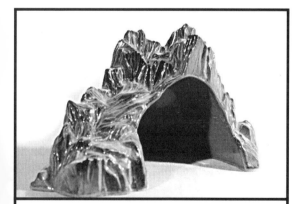

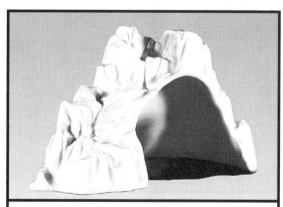

Cave

Model No.:	D-392
Designer:	Nell Bortells
Height:	3 ¼", 8.3 cm
Colour:	Brown; gloss
Issued:	1966

Model No.	U.S. $	Can. $	U.K. £
D-392	30.00	60.00	50.00

Note: This cave has a smooth mouth opening and forms a set with Cavemen, page 399.

Ice Cave

Model No.:	A-392A
Designer:	Helen Perrin Farnlund
Height:	3 ¼", 8.3 cm
Colour:	White
Issued:	Spring 1980 - 1984

Model No.	U.S. $	Can. $	U.K. £
A-392A	.00	.00	.00

Note: This forms a set with Eskimos, see page 400.

CHEESE

Cheese, half wedge

Model No.:	Unknown
Designer:	Nell Bortell
Size:	¼″ x ½″, 0.6 x 1.3 cm
Colour:	1. Bleu cheese
	2. Yellow cheese
Issued:	Unknown

Colourways	U.S. $	Can. $	U.K. £
1. Bleu cheese	8.00	15.00	12.00
2. Yellow cheese	8.00	15.00	12.00

Cheese Wedge

Model No.:	A-52/240
Designer:	Nell Bortell
Height:	½″, 1.3 cm
Colour:	1. Yellow
	2. White
Issued:	Spring 1966 - spring 1991

Model No.	U.S. $	Can. $	U.K. £
A-52/240	5.00	10.00	8.50

Note: These models are also known with red rind.

Cheese Wheel

Model No.:	A-384
Designer:	Nell Bortell
Size:	½″, 1.3 cm
Colour:	1. Yellow
	2. Yellow with red rind
Issued:	Fall 1959 - spring 1960

Colourways	U.S. $	Can. $	U.K. £
1. Yellow	18.00	35.00	30.00
2. Yellow/red rind	18.00	35.00	30.00

CORAL

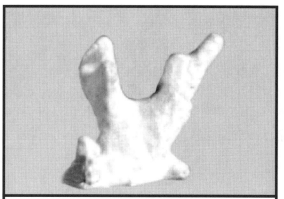

Coral
Model No.: A-425
Designer: Helen Perrin Farnlund
Height: ¾", 1.9 cm
Colour: Light brown; bisque
Issued: Spring 1960 - spring 1961

Model No.	U.S. $	Can. $	U.K. £
A-425	10.00	20.00	17.00

Note: See also Seahorse, page 304.

DISH

Dog Dish
Model No.: A-2008
Designer: Robert McGuinness
Height: 3/8", 0.9 cm
Colour: Blue, gold lettering
Issued: Spring 1988 - fall 1992

Model No.	U.S.$	Can. $	U.K.£
A-2008	5.00	10.00	8.50

Note: Variations exist in the lettering for "Dog".

DRIFTWOOD

Driftwood
Model No.: A-977
Designer: Helen Perrin Farnlund
Size: 1 1/8" x 4 1/8", 2.8 x 10.5 cm
Colour: Brown log, yellow base; bisque
Issued: Fall 1976 - spring 1977

Model No.	U.S. $	Can. $	U.K. £
A-435A	15.00	30.00	25.00

Note: Also known with a gloss base.

EGG

Photograph not
available
at press time

Egg
Model No.: A-466A
Designer: Helen Perrin Farnlund
Height: Unknown
Colour: White
Issued: Fall 1960 - fall 1961

Model No.	U.S.$	Can. $	U.K.£
A-466A	5.00	10.00	8.50

Note: This forms a set with A-445 and A-446.

HITCHING POST

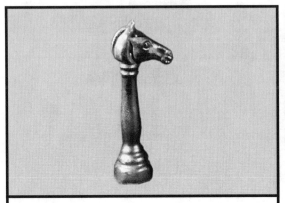

Hitching Post
Model No.:   A-51
Designer: Unknown
Height: 1 ¾", 4.4 cm
Colour: Silver
Issued: Fall 1959

Model No.	U.S.$	Can.$	U.K.£
A-51	50.00	100.00	85.00

HYDRANT

Hydrant
Model No.:   A-444/464
Designer: Helen Perrin Farnlund
Height: 1 ¼", 3.2 cm
Colour: Red
Issued: Spring 1959 - spring 1978

Model No.	U.S.$	Can. $	U.K.£
A-444/464	6.00	12.00	10.00

Note: Model A-444/464 was produced for 39 seasons.

LOG

Photograph not
available
at press time

Log
Model No.:   A-435A
Designer: Nell Bortell
Size: 5/8" x 2", 1.6 x 5.0 cm
Colour: Brown; bisque
Issued: Fall 1960 - fall 1961

Model No.	U.S. $	Can. $	U.K. £
A-435A	10.00	20.00	17.00

Note: This model forms a set with Fawn (A-435),
page 333.

MILK BOWL

Photograph not
available
at press time

Milk Bowl
Model No.:   A-383
Designer: Unknown
Height: Unknown
Colour: Unknown
Issued: Fall 1959 - spring 1960

Model No.	U.S. $	Can. $	U.K. £
A-383		Rare	

Note: Forms a set with Kittens A-385 page 202, A-386
page 203, and A-396 page 203.

NESTS

Bee's Nest
Model No.:   A-404
Designer: Helen Perrin Farnlund
Height: ½", 1.3 cm
Colour: See below
Issued: 1960, fall 1977 - fall 1978

Colourways	U.S. $	Can. $	U.K. £
1. Brown; gloss	9.00	18.00	15.00
2. Brown; matte	9.00	18.00	15.00
3. Brown/green stem; matte	9.00	18.00	15.00

Crow's Nest
Model No.:   A-393
Designer: Helen Perrin Farnlund
Height: 5/8", 1.6 cm
Colour: Brown
Issued: Fall 1959 - spring 1979

Model No.	U.S. $	Can. $	U.K. £
A-393	10.00	20.00	17.00

Note: Model A-393 was produced for 19 seasons and forms a set with A-58 and A-59, page 147.

Nest With Coloured Eggs
Model No.:   A-446
Designer: Helen Perrin Farnlund
Height: 5/8", 1.6 cm
Colour: Brown nest, yellow and blue eggs
Issued: Fall 1976 - fall 1979

Model No.	U.S. $	Can. $	U.K. £
A-446	8.00	16.00	14.00

PEDESTAL

Circus Pedestal
Model No.:   A-268A
Designer: Maureen Love
Height: 5/8", 1.6 cm
Colour: Various colours with gold decoration
Issued: Fall 1955 - spring 1956

Model No.	U.S. $	Can. $	U.K. £
A-268A	15.00	30.00	25.00

PIANOS

Piano
Style One

Model No.:	A-808
Designer:	Helen Perrin Farnlund
Height:	1 3/8", 3.5 cm
Colour:	See below
Issued:	Spring 1982 to the present

Colourways	U.S. $	Can. $	U.K. £
1. Black (current)	6.00	12.00	10.00
2. White	8.00	16.00	14.00

Note: Model A-808 can be paired with A-807 and A-809.

Piano
Style Two

Model No.:	A-3124
Designer:	Helen Perrin Farnlund
Height:	2 5/16", 5.8 cm
Colour:	Brown with a "Meowsic" decal on the music stand
Issued:	Fall 1993 to the present

Model No.	U.S.$	Can. $	U.K.£
A-3124	8.00	16.00	14.00

PIANO BENCH

POND

Photograph not
available
at press time

Piano Bench

Model No.:	A-3125-1
Designer:	Helen Perrin Farnlund
Height:	1", 2.5 cm
Colour:	Brown, purple bench
Issued:	Fall 1993 - spring 1995

Model No.	U.S.$	Can. $	U.K.£
A-3125-1	5.00	7.00	8.50

Note: This forms a set with Kitten (A-3125-1), page 199, and Piano, Style Two (A-3124).

Pond

Model No.:	A-228
Designer:	Tom Masterson
Size:	3 7/8" x 2 ½", 9.8 x 6.4 cm
Colour:	Light blue or dark blue
Issued:	Spring 1954 - fall 1992

Model No.	U.S.$	Can. $	U.K.£
A-228	4.00	8.00	7.00

Note: Model A-228 was made for 30 seasons.

SPILLED MILK

Spilled Milk

Model No.:	A-239
Designer:	Maureen Love
Height:	2/3", 1.7 cm
Colour:	Silver pail, white milk
Issued:	Fall 1954 to the present

Model No.	U.S. $	Can. $	U.K. £
A-239	3.00	6.00	5.00

Note: Model A-239 has been made intermittently for 61 seasons. Some models were painted to resemble wood.

STUMPS

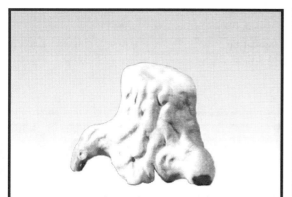

Stump, flat
Style One

Model No.:	A-387
Designer:	Helen Perrin Farnlund
Height:	7/8", 2.2 cm
Colour:	1. Brown; bisque
	2. Red-brown
Issued:	Spring 1960, fall 1989 - 1990

Colourways	U.S. $	Can. $	U.K. £
1. Bisque	10.00	20.00	17.00
2. Red-brown	5.00	10.00	8.50

Note: This stump was used as a rabbit seat.

Stump
Style Two

Model No.:	A-400
Designer:	Helen Perrin Farnlund
Height:	7/8", 2.2 cm
Colour:	1. Dark brown
	2. Grey, bisque
	3. Red-brown
Issued:	Fall 1989 - 1990

Colourways	U.S. $	Can. $	U.K. £
1. Dark brown	5.00	10.00	8.50
2. Grey, bisque	10.00	20.00	17.00
3. Red-brown	8.00	16.00	14.00

TOADSTOOLS

Toadstool

Model No.:   A-2501
Designer: Millesan Drews
Height: 3", 7.6 cm
Colour: Cream
Issued: Spring 1969 - 1973

Model No.	U.S. $	Can. $	U.K. £
A-2501	20.00	40.00	35.00

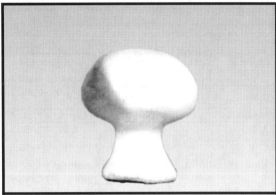

Toadstool, rounded

Model No.:   A-407
Designer: Helen Perrin Farnlund
Height: 9/16", 1.4 cm
Colour: White
Issued: Spring 1960 - spring 1966

Model No.	U.S. $	Can. $	U.K. £
A-407	8.00	16.00	14.00

Toadstool, straight

Model No.:   A-406
Designer: Helen Perrin Farnlund
Height: 7/8", 2.2 cm
Colour: Beige
Issued: Spring 1960 - fall 1965

Model No.	U.S. $	Can. $	U.K. £
A-406	8.00	16.00	14.00

Toadstool, tilted

Model No.:   A-2503
Designer: Millesan Drews
Height: 5/8", 1.6 cm
Colour: Beige
Issued: Spring 1969 - fall 1973

Model No.	U.S. $	Can. $	U.K. £
A-2503	8.00	16.00	14.00

TREES

For an illustration of
model A-946,
see Koala Tree Set, page 346

Tree

Model No.:	A-946			
Designer:	Helen Perrin Farnlund			
Height:	4 ¾", 12.1 cm			
Colour:	Green with brown shading			
Issued:	Spring 1979 - fall 1979			

Model No.	U.S. $	Can. $	U.K. £
A-946	15.00	30.00	25.00

Note: This forms part of the Koala Tree Set, page 346.

Tree

Model No.:	A-834
Designer:	Helen Perrin Farnlund
Height:	2 1/5", 5.6 cm
Colour:	Dark green
Issued:	Fall 1984 - fall 1986

Model No.	U.S. $	Can. $	U.K. £
A-834	15.00	30.00	25.00

Note: This forms a pair with Wise Old Owl (A-883), page 172.

WATER TROUGH

Water Trough

Model No.:	A-50
Designer:	Maureen Love
Height:	¾", 1.9 cm
Colour:	Brown with blue water
Issued:	Fall 1959 - spring 1960

Model No.	U.S.$	Can.$	U.K.£
A-50	20.00	40.00	35.00

HUMAN FORM

Babies

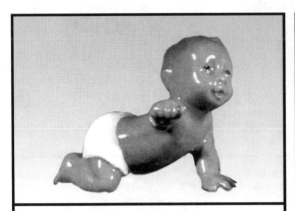

Baby, crawling

Model No.:	A-3162	
Designer:	Robert McGuinness	
Height:	1 ¼", 3.2 cm	
Colour:	1. Brown flesh tone	
	2. Pink flesh tone	
Issued:	Fall 1994 - spring 1997	

Model No.	U.S. $	Can. $	U.K. £
A-3162	10.00	20.00	17.00

Baby, seated

Model No.:	A-3164	
Designer:	Robert McGuinness	
Height:	1 ½", 3.8 cm	
Colour:	1. Brown flesh tone	
	2. Pink flesh tone	
Issued:	Fall 1994	

Model No.	U.S. $	Can. $	U.K. £
A-3164	10.00	20.00	17.00

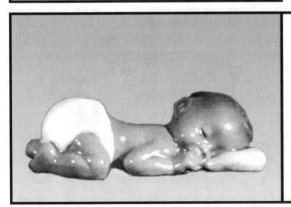

Baby, sleeping

Model No.:	A-3163	
Designer:	Robert McGuinness	
Height:	½", 1.3 cm	
Colour:	1. Brown flesh tone, blue pillow	
	2. Pink flesh tone, blue pillow	
Issued:	Fall 1994 - spring 1997	

Model No.	U.S. $	Can. $	U.K. £
A-3163	10.00	20.00	17.00

BALLERINAS

Ballerina, arms up

Model No.:	A-402
Designer:	Helen Perrin Farnlund
Height:	2 ¾", 7.9 cm
Colour:	Black leotard, blond hair, gold base
Issued:	Fall 1958 - spring 1959

Model No.	U.S. $	Can. $	U.K. £
A-402	50.00	100.00	85.00

Note: The ponytail and body were moulded separately.
This forms a set with models A-395 and A-403.

Ballerina, left arm up

Model No.:	A-395
Designer:	Helen Perrin Farnlund
Height:	2 ¾", 7.0 cm
Colour:	Black leotard, blond hair, gold base
Issued:	Fall 1958 - spring 1959

Model No.	U.S. $	Can. $	U.K. £
A-395	50.00	100.00	85.00

Note: The ponytail and body were moulded separately.
This forms a set with models A-402 and A-403.

Ballerina, left leg up

Model No.:	A-403
Designer:	Helen Perrin Farnlund
Height:	2 ½", 6.3 cm
Colour:	Black leotard, blond hair, gold base
Issued:	Fall 1958 - spring 1959

Model No.	U.S. $	Can. $	U.K. £
A-403	50.00	100.00	85.00

Note: The ponytail and body were moulded separately.
This forms a set with models A-395 and A-402.

BEACH BOYS

Beach Boy Junior, standing

Model No.: A-071
Designer: Nell Bortells
Height: 1 ¼″, 3.2 cm
Colour: Blond hair, pink flesh tone, dark eyes
Issued: 1982 - 1983

Model No.	U.S. $	Can. $	U.K. £
A-071	15.00	30.00	25.00

Surfboard

Model No.: A-805
Designer: Nell Bortells
Length: 2 3/8″, 6.0 cm
Colour: 1. Green and white
2. Yellow
Issued: 1982 - 1983

Model No.	U.S. $	Can. $	U.K. £
A-805	10.00	20.00	17.00

Beach Boy, small, seated

Model No.: A-072
Designer: Nell Bortells
Height: 1 1/8″, 2.8 cm
Colour: Blond hair, pink flesh tone, dark eyes
Issued: 1982 - 1983

Model No.	U.S. $	Can. $	U.K. £
A-072	10.00	20.00	17.00

Beach Boy Senior

Model No.: A-070
Designer: Nell Bortells
Height: 2″, 5.0 cm
Colour: Blond hair, pink flesh tone, dark eyes
Issued: 1982 - 1983

Model No.	U.S. $	Can. $	U.K. £
A-070	20.00	40.00	35.00

Skateboard

Model No.: A-806
Designer: Nell Bortells
Size: ½ ″ x 2 ½″, 1.3 x 6.4 cm
Colour: Tan, light orange wheels
Issued: Spring 1966 - spring 1972

Model No.	U.S. $	Can. $	U.K. £
A-806	10.00	20.00	17.00

Wave

Model No.: A-804
Designer: Nell Bortells
Height: 1 5/8″, 4.1 cm
Colour: Light blue with white highlights
Issued: 1982 - 1983

Model No.	U.S. $	Can. $	U.K. £
A-804	15.00	30.00	25.00

Note: Model A-072, Beach Boy, seated, is not illustrated. For an illustration of the Skateboard, see the following page. See also Cavemen, page 399, and Little Horribles, page 130.

CAVEMEN

Caveman Junior, seated
Model No.:	A-072
Designer:	Nell Bortells
Height:	1 1/8″, 2.8 cm
Colour:	Brown flesh tone, dark brown hair and beard
Issued:	Spring 1966 - spring 1972

Model No.	U.S. $	Can. $	U.K. £
A-072	15.00	30.00	25.00

Caveman Junior, standing
Model No.:	A-071
Designer:	Nell Bortells
Height:	1 ¼″, 3.2 cm
Colour:	Brown flesh tone, dark brown hair and beard
Issued:	Spring 1966 - spring 1972

Model No.	U.S. $	Can. $	U.K. £
A-071	15.00	30.00	25.00

Caveman
Model No.:	A-070
Designer:	Nell Bortells
Height:	2″, 5.0 cm
Colour:	Dark brown hair and beard, tan skin
Issued:	Spring 1966 - spring 1977

Model No.	U.S. $	Can. $	U.K. £
A-070	20.00	40.00	35.00

Note: Caveman Junior, standing, is not illustrated. These models form a set with Cave (D-392), page 387. See also Beach Boys, page 398, and Little Horribles, page 126.

ESKIMOS

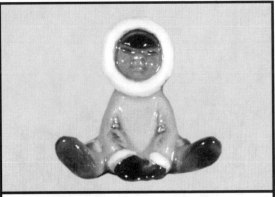

Eskimo Tot, crouched

Model No.:	A-945
Designer:	Helen Perrin Farnlund
Height:	1 3/8", 3.5 cm
Colour:	Brown face, light brown parka with white trim; gloss
Issued:	Spring 1980 - spring 1988

Description	U.S. $	Can. $	U.K. £
Gloss	8.00	16.00	14.00

Note: This forms a set with models A-943, A-944 and A-392A (Ice Cave), page 387.

Eskimo Tot, seated

Model No.:	A-943
Designer:	Helen Perrin Farnlund
Height:	1 ½", 3.8 cm
Colour:	Brown face, light brown parka with white trim; gloss
Issued:	Spring 1980 - spring 1988

Description	U.S. $	Can. $	U.K. £
Gloss	8.00	16.00	14.00

Note: This forms a set with models A-944, A-945 and. A-392A (Ice Cave), page 387.

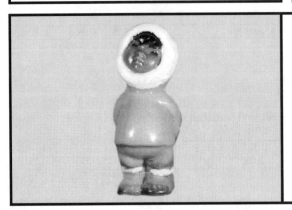

Eskimo Tot, standing

Model No.:	A-944
Designer:	Helen Perrin Farnlund
Height:	1 1/8", 2.8 cm
Colour:	Brown face, light brown parka with white trim; gloss or matte
Issued:	Spring 1980 - spring 1988 – gloss
Re-issued:	Fall 1990 - spring 1992 – matte

Description	U.S. $	Can. $	U.K. £
1. Gloss	8.00	16.00	14.00
2. Matte	10.00	20.00	17.00

Note: This forms a set with models A-943 and A-945 and A-392A (Ice Cave), page 387.

GUARDIAN ANGELS

Photograph not
available
at press time

Guardian Angel, lying (pin)

Model No.:	A-075
Designer:	Jane Manske
Height:	½", 1.3 cm
Colour:	1. Chocolate
	2. Peach
Issued:	Spring 1967 - fall 1967

Colourways	U.S. $	Can. $	U.K. £
1. Chocolate		Rare	
2. Peach		Rare	

Guardian Angel, standing (pin)

Model No.:	A-074
Designer:	Jane Manske
Height:	1", 2.5 cm
Colour:	1. Chocolate
	2. Peach
Issued:	Spring 1967

Colourways	U.S. $	Can. $	U.K. £
1. Chocolate		Rare	
2. Peach		Rare	

PIXIES

Pixie, holding stick

Model No.:   A-111
Designer: Helen Perrin Farnlund
Height: 2 ¾", 7.0 cm
Colour: Yellow and blue clothing; gold shoes
Issued: c.1950

Model No.	U.S. $	Can. $	U.K. £
A-111	30.00	60.00	50.00

Note: The model illustrated is missing the stick.
          See also Walker-Renaker, page 567.

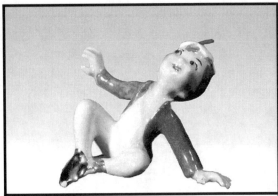

Pixie, seated

Model No.:   A-124
Designer: Helen Perrin Farnlund
Height: 2 ¼", 7.0 cm
Colour: Yellow and green clothing, gold shoes
Issued: c.1950

Model No.	U.S. $	Can. $	U.K. £
A-124	30.00	60.00	50.00

Pixie, seated on snail

Model No.:   A-110
Designer: Helen Perrin Farnlund
Height: 2 3/8", 6.03 cm
Colour: Blue and pink clothing, gold shoes,
                  green and brown snail
Issued: c.1950

Model No.	U.S. $	Can. $	U.K. £
A-110	30.00	60.00	50.00

Pixie, throwing

Model No.:   A-112
Designer: Helen Perrin Farnlund
Height: 2 7/16", 6.19 cm
Colour: Yellow and green clothing, gold shoes,
                  brown ball
Issued: c.1950

Model No.	U.S. $	Can. $	U.K. £
A-112	30.00	60.00	50.00

AMPHIBIANS

Frogs

Bullfrog Baby

Model No.:	A-345		
Designer:	Martha Armstrong		
Height:	½", 1.3 cm		
Colour:	Green		
Issued:	c.1950 - c.1970		

Model No.	U.S. $	Can. $	U.K. £
A-345	6.00	12.00	10.00

Note: Model A-345 was produced for 4 seasons in the 1950s and six seasons in the 1970s. It forms a pair with Bullfrog Papa (A-344).

Bullfrog Papa
Version One (Without crown)

Model No.:	A-344		
Designer:	Martha Armstrong		
Height:	1", 2.5 cm		
Colour:	Green		
Issued:	Fall 1957 - spring 1962, fall 1973		

Model No.	U.S. $	Can. $	U.K. £
A-344	8.00	16.00	14.00

Note: This is also called Bullfrog Mama.

Bullfrog Papa
Version Two (With crown)

Model No.:	A-344		
Designer:	Martha Armstrong		
Height:	1 ¼", 3.2 cm		
Colour:	Green		
Issued:	Fall 1975 to the present		

Model No.	U.S. $	Can. $	U.K. £
A-344	3.00	6.00	5.00

Note: This forms a pair with Bullfrog Baby (A-345) and is also called Bullfrog Mama/Frog Prince.

Photograph not
available
at press time

Frog

Model No.:	A-405
Designer:	Helen Perrin Farnlund
Height:	Unknown
Colour:	Green
Issued:	c.1960 - c.1970

Model No.	U.S. $	Can. $	U.K. £
A-405	9.00	18.00	15.00

Frog Baby, facing left

Model No.:	A-38
Designer:	Helen Perrin Farnlund
Height:	½", 1.3 cm
Colour:	Green, yellow throat
Issued:	1949 - 1952

Model No.	U.S. $	Can. $	U.K. £
A-38	3.00	6.00	5.00

Frog Baby, facing right

Model No.:	A-477
Designer:	Helen Perrin Farnlund
Height:	½", 1.3 cm
Colour:	1. Green
	2. Green with stripes
Issued:	Fall 1960 to the present

Colourways	U.S. $	Can. $	U.K. £
1. Green	2.00	4.00	3.50
2. Green with stripes	8.00	16.00	14.00

Note: Model A-477 has been made intermittently since 1960.

Frog Mama

Model No.:	A-27
Designer:	Helen Perrin Farnlund
Height:	¾", 1.9 cm
Colour:	Green, yellow throat
Issued:	1949 - 1952

Model No.	U.S. $	Can. $	U.K. £
A-27	5.00	10.00	8.50

Frog Mama

Model No.:	A-448
Designer:	Helen Perrin Farnlund
Height:	5/8", 1.6 cm
Colour:	1. Green
	2. Green with decorative stripe
Issued:	Fall 1960 to the present

Colourways	U.S. $	Can. $	U.K. £
1. Green	3.00	6.00	5.00
2. Green/stripe	10.00	20.00	17.00

Note: This is also called Frog Papa.

Mr. Froggie

Model No.:	A-867
Designer:	Nell Bortells
Height:	5/8", 1.58 cm
Colour:	Dark green, yellow throat
Issued:	Spring 1986 to the present

Model No.	U.S. $	Can. $	U.K. £
A-867	3.00	6.00	5.00

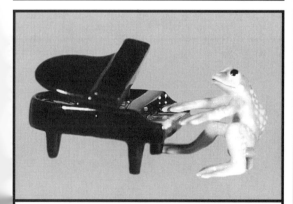

Piano-playing Frog, arms forward

Model No.:	A-3285
Designer:	Helen Perrin Farnlund
Height:	1 3/16", 3.0 cm
Colour:	Green, brown stool
Issued:	Fall 1998 to the present

Model No.	U.S. $	Can. $	U.K. £
A-3285	6.00	12.00	10.00

Note: For information on Piano (A-808), see page 392.

Piano-playing Frog, arms raised

Model No.:	A-814
Designer:	Helen Perrin Farnlund
Height:	1", 2.5 cm
Colour:	1. Dark green, brown shading
	2. Light green
Issued:	Spring 1982 - spring 1992

Colourways	U.S. $	Can. $	U.K. £
1. Dark green	7.00	14.00	12.00
2. Light green	7.00	14.00	12.00

Tadpole

Model No.: A-478
Designer: Helen Perrin Farnlund
Height: 3/8", 0.9 cm
Colour: 1. Black; bisque
2. Black; gloss
Issued: Fall 1960

Description	U.S. $	Can. $	U.K. £
1. Bisque	25.00	50.00	45.00
2. Gloss	25.00	50.00	45.00

Note: This is also known as Pollywog.

Tree Frog Baby

Model No.: A-217
Designer: Tom Masterson
Height: ½", 1.3 cm
Colour: 1. Green
2. Green with stripes
Issued: Spring 1954 - fall 1981

Colourways	U.S. $	Can. $	U.K. £
1. Green	3.00	6.00	5.00
2. Green with stripes	8.00	16.00	14.00

Note: Model A-217 was made for 28 seasons.

Salamander

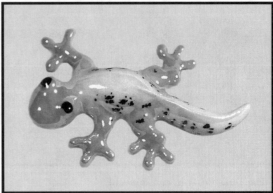

Tree Frog Mama

Model No.: A-221
Designer: Tom Masterson
Height: ¾", 1.9 cm
Colour: 1. Green
2. Green with stripes
Issued: Spring 1954 - fall 1981

Colourways	U.S. $	Can. $	U.K. £
1. Green	6.00	12.00	10.00
2. Green/stripes	14.00	28.00	24.00

Note: Model A-221 was made for 28 seasons, mostly in the 1970s.

Salamander

Model No.: 3279
Designer: Robert McGuinness
Size: ¾" x 1 7/8", 1.9 x 4.8 cm
Colour: Orange and yellow with black speckles
Issued: Fall 1998 to the present

Model No.	U.S. $	Can. $	U.K. £
3279	3.00	6.00	5.00

Bugs

Photograph not
available
at press time

Ant
Style One

Model No.:	A-073			
Designer:	Unknown			
Size:	Unknown			
Colour:	Black			
Issued:	Fall 1966			

Description	U.S. $	Can. $	U.K. £
Style one		Extremely rare	

Note: This forms a pair with Anteater (A-69), page 319.

Ant
Style Two

Model No.:	A-3157			
Designer:	Nell Bortells			
Length:	1", 2.5 cm			
Colour:	Black			
Issued:	Fall 1994 to the present			

Description	U.S. $	Can. $	U.K. £
Style two	3.00	6.00	5.00

Lady Bug

Model No.:	A-430
Designer:	Nell Bortells
Height:	1", 2.5 cm
Colour:	1. Green; Auerspurse
	2. Light green, brown bonnet and shoes
Issued:	Spring 1960 - spring 1962

Colourways	U.S. $	Can. $	U.K. £
1. Green; Auerspurse	15.00	30.00	25.00
2. Light green	15.00	30.00	25.00

Lord Bug

Model No.:	A-431
Designer:	Nell Bortells
Height:	1", 2.5 cm
Colour:	1. Green; Auerspurse
	2. White body; black hat, shoes and
	monocle; green shell
Issued:	Spring 1960 - spring 1962

Colourways	U.S. $	Can. $	U.K. £
1. Green; Auerspurse	20.00	40.00	35.00
2. White/black/green	15.00	30.00	25.00

The Bug Band

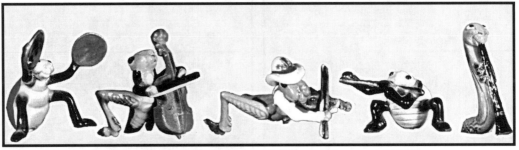

Beetle with Cymbals, Grasshopper with Cello, Grasshopper with Fiddle
Beetle with Flute, Caterpillar with Clarinet

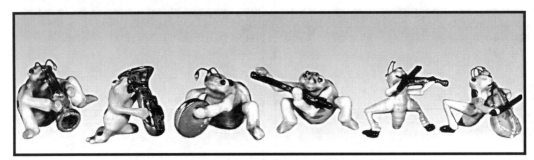

Ladybug with Saxophone, Frog with Tuba, Ladybug with Cymbals,
Ladybug with Clarinet, Grasshopper with Fiddle, Grasshopper with Cello

Designer: Helen Perrin Farnlund
Colourways:
1. Beetle With Cymbals — Red back, green underside, black legs, gold cymbals
2. Beetle With Flute — Light green, black legs
3. Caterpillar With Clarinet — Brown, black clarinet
4. Frog With Tuba — Pink and blue, gold tuba
5. Grasshopper With Cello — Pale blue, wire antenna with gold tips
6. Grasshopper With Cello — Green, black jacket, brown cello
7. Grasshopper With Fiddle — Pale blue, wire antenna with gold tips, black shoes, gold fiddle
8. Grasshopper With Fiddle — Pale blue, white arms, yellow hat, brown shoes and fiddle
9. Ladybug With Clarinet — Pink and blue, wire antenna with gold tips
10. Ladybug With Cymbals — Pink and blue, wire antenna with gold tips
11. Ladybug With Saxophone — Pink and blue, wire antenna with gold tips

Name	Model No.	Height	Issued	U.S. $	Can. $	U.K. £
1. Beetle/cymbals	A-939	1 ¾", 4.4 cm	1981 - 1983	12.00	24.00	20.00
2. Beetle/flute	A-248	1", 2.54 cm	1981 - 1984	12.00	24.00	20.00
3. Caterpillar/clarinet	A-940	2", 5.0 cm	1981 - 1982	12.00	24.00	20.00
4. Frog/tuba	A-245	1 1/8", 2.85 cm	1955	25.00	50.00	45.00
5. Grasshopper/cello	A-250	1 ½", 3.81 cm	1955	19.00	38.00	33.00
6. Grasshopper/cello	A-250	1 ½", 3.81 cm	1981	12.00	24.00	20.00
7. Grasshopper/fiddle	A-244	1 ¾", 4.40 cm	1955	19.00	38.00	33.00
8. Grasshopper/fiddle	A-244	¾", 1.90 cm	1982 - 1985	12.00	24.00	20.00
9. Ladybug/clarinet	A-248	1", 2.54 cm	1955	20.00	40.00	35.00
10. Ladybug/cymbals	A-248	7/8", 2.22 cm	1955	20.00	40.00	35.00
11. Ladybug/saxophone	A-248	1", 2.54 cm	1955	20.00	40.00	35.00

Note: In spring 1981, the name "Ladybug" was changed to "Beetle". In 1955, Ladybug With Saxophone was replaced by Ladybug With Cymbals and the arms were altered to fit the instrument.

Dinosaurs

Anatosaurus

Model No.: A-961
Designer: Helen Perrin Farnlund
Height: 1 3/8", 3.5 cm
Colour: Green
Issued: Fall 1977 - fall 1978

Model No.	U.S. $	Can. $	U.K. £
A-961	8.00	16.00	14.00

Anatosaurus, Baby

Model No.: A-960
Designer: Helen Perrin Farnlund
Height: ½", 1.3 cm
Colour: Green
Issued: Fall 1977 - fall 1978

Model No.	U.S. $	Can. $	U.K. £
A-960	8.00	16.00	14.00

Diplodocus

Model No.: A-971
Designer: Helen Perrin Farnlund
Height: 1 ½", 3.8 cm
Colour: Light green with brown shading
Issued: Spring 1977 - fall 1979,
spring 1987 - spring 1988

Model No.	U.S. $	Can. $	U.K. £
A-971	8.00	16.00	14.00

Diplodocus, Baby

Model No.: A-970
Designer: Helen Perrin Farnlund
Height: ¾", 1.9 cm
Colour: Green
Issued: Spring 1977 - fall 1979,
fall 1987 - spring 1988

Model No.	U.S. $	Can. $	U.K. £
A-970	8.00	16.00	14.00

Pterodactyl

Model No.:	A-2048
Designer:	Helen Perrin Farnlund
Height:	1 ½", 3.8 cm
Colour:	Green
Issued:	Spring 1989 - fall 1990

Model No.	U.S. $	Can. $	U.K. £
A-2048	8.00	16.00	14.00

Triceratops Mama

Model No.:	A-962
Designer:	Helen Perrin Farnlund
Height:	¾", 1.9 cm
Colour:	Green, brown shading
Issued:	Fall 1977 - 1978, fall 1987 - spring 1988

Model No.	U.S. $	Can. $	U.K. £
A-962	8.00	16.00	14.00

Triceratops Baby

Model No.:	A-963
Designer:	Helen Perrin Farnlund
Height:	½", 1.3 cm
Colour:	Green, brown shading
Issued:	Fall 1977 - fall 1978

Model No.	U.S. $	Can. $	U.K. £
A-963	8.00	16.00	14.00

Tyrannosaurus

Model No.: A-967
Designer: Helen Perrin Farnlund
Height: 1 5/8", 4.1 cm
Colour: 1. Brown
2. Green, black spots
Issued: Spring 1977 - fall 1978,
fall 1987 - spring 1988

Colourways	U.S. $	Can. $	U.K. £
1. Brown	8.00	16.00	14.00
2. Green	8.00	16.00	14.00

Tyrannosaurus, Baby

Model No.: A-969
Designer: Helen Perrin Farnlund
Height: ¾", 1.9 cm
Colour: 1. Brown
2. Green, black spots
Issued: Spring 1977 - fall 1978

Colourways	U.S. $	Can. $	U.K. £
1. Brown	8.00	16.00	14.00
2. Green	8.00	16.00	14.00

Dragons

Dragon

Model No.: A-892
Designer: Helen Perrin Farnlund
Height: 1 ½", 3.8 cm
Colour: 1. Green
2. Turquoise
Issued: Spring 1986 to the present

Colourways	U.S. $	Can. $	U.K. £
1. Green	7.00	14.00	12.00
2. Turquoise	7.00	14.00	12.00

Dragon Baby, arms up

Model No.: A-893
Designer: Helen Perrin Farnlund
Height: ¾", 1.9 cm
Colour: 1. Green
2. Turquoise
Issued: Spring 1986 - fall 1988

Colourways	U.S. $	Can. $	U.K. £
1. Green	8.00	16.00	14.00
2. Turquoise	8.00	16.00	14.00

Dragon Family
First Version (With wings)

Designer: Don Winton
Colour: Grey-green, pale green underbelly, pale yellow wings
Issued: Fall 1956 - spring 1957

Name	Model No.	Height	U.S. $	Can. $	U.K. £
Dragon Baby	A-311	7/8", 2.2 cm	20.00	40.00	35.00
Dragon Mama	A-309	1", 2.5 cm	25.00	50.00	45.00
Dragon Papa	A-310	1 ½", 3.8 cm	25.00	50.00	45.00

Second Version (Without wings)

Designer: Don Winton
Height: Dragon Baby (A-311) — 7/8", 2.2 cm
 Dragon Mama (A-309) — 1", 2.5 cm
 Dragon Papa (A-310) — 1½", 3.8 cm
Colour: Kelly green
Issued: Fall 1965 - fall 1988

Name / Model No.	U.S. $	Can. $	U.K. £
Dragon Baby / A-311	5.00	10.00	7.00
Dragon Mama / A-309	8.00	16.00	14.00
Dragon Papa / A-310	8.00	16.00	14.00

Note: The dragons were made for a total of 49 seasons.

Snakes

Cobra in Basket
Model No.: A-3082
Designer: Edith Carrion
Height: 3 1/16", 7.8 cm
Colour: Light brown snake in yellow basket
Issued: Fall 1992 - fall 1993

Model No.	U.S. $	Can. $	U.K. £
A-3082	8.00	16.00	14.00

Snails

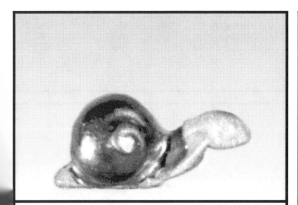

Escargot Bébé
Model No.: A-80
Designer: Helen Perrin Farnlund
Height: 3/8", 0.9 cm
Colour: Grey body, gold shell and antenna tips
Issued: 1950 - fall 1977

Model No.	U.S. $	Can. $	U.K. £
A-80	8.00	16.00	14.00

Note: Model A-80, shown here without antennae, was produced for 22 seasons. It forms a pair with Escargot Maman (A-79).

Escargot Maman
Model No.: A-79
Designer: Helen Perrin Farnlund
Height: 7/8", 2.2 cm
Colour: Grey body, gold shell and antenna tips
Issued: 1950 - fall 1977

Model No.	U.S. $	Can. $	U.K. £
A-79	10.00	20.00	17.00

Note: Model A-79 was produced for 22 seasons. It forms a pair with Escargot Bébé (A-80).

Sea Snail

Model No.:	A-427	
Designer:	Helen Perrin Farnlund	
Height:	½", 1.3 cm	
Colour:	Yellow body, brown shell	
Issued:	Spring 1960, spring 1973	

Model No.	U.S. $	Can. $	U.K. £
A-427	20.00	40.00	35.00

Snail

Model No.:	A-2045	
Designer:	Nell Bortells	
Height:	1", 2.5 cm	
Colour:	1. Brown-grey	
	2. Grey, lustre shell	
Issued:	Spring 1989 - fall 1990	

Colourways	U.S. $	Can. $	U.K. £
1. Brown-grey	7.00	14.00	12.00
2. Grey/lustre	7.00	14.00	12.00

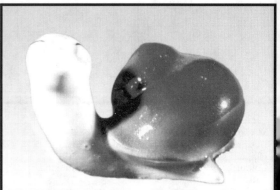

Snail Baby

Model No.:	A-488	
Designer:	Helen Perrin Farnlund	
Height:	½", 1.3 cm	
Colour:	1. Grey body, green shell	
	2. Yellow body, brown shell	
Issued:	Spring 1961 - c.1975	

Colourways	U.S. $	Can. $	U.K. £
1. Grey/green	5.00	10.00	8.50
2. Yellow/brown	5.00	10.00	8.50

Note: Model A-488 was produced for nine seasons between 1961 and c.1975. It forms a pair with Snail Mama (A-487).

Snail Mama

Model No.:	A-487	
Designer:	Helen Perrin Farnlund	
Height:	1", 2.5 cm	
Colour:	1. Grey body, green shell	
	2. Yellow body, brown shell	
Issued:	Spring 1961 - c.1975	

Colourways	U.S. $	Can. $	U.K. £
1. Grey/green	6.00	12.00	10.00
2. Yellow/brown	6.00	12.00	10.00

Note: This forms a pair with Snail Baby (A-488).

WORMS

Inchworm Baby

Model No.:	A-486
Designer:	Helen Perrin Farnlund
Height:	½", 1.3 cm
Colour:	See below
Issued:	Spring 1961 - fall 1977, fall 1991

Colourways	U.S. $	Can. $	U.K. £
1. Auerspurse	8.00	16.00	14.00
2. Green/yellow/red	8.00	16.00	14.00

Note: Pair with Inchworm Mama (A-485).

Inchworm Mama

Model No.:	A-485
Designer:	Helen Perrin Farnlund
Height:	1", 2.5 cm
Colour:	1. Auerspurse
	2. Green, yellow belly, red hat
Issued:	Spring 1961 - fall 1977

Colourways	U.S. $	Can. $	U.K. £
1. Auerspurse	8.00	16.00	14.00
2. Green/yellow/red	10.00	20.00	17.00

Note: Model A-485 is also called Inchworm Papa.
Pair with Inchworm Baby (A-486).

Worm With Hat 'Homer'

Model No.:	A-3083
Designer:	Edith Carrion
Height:	1½", 3.8 cm
Colour:	Green worm, blue hat
Issued:	Fall 1992 to the present

Model No.	U.S. $	Can. $	U.K. £
A-3083	5.00	10.00	8.50

Worm With Hat 'Homer' (A-3083)

PEDIGREE DOG LINE

Tom Masterson was the primary designer for the Pedigree Dog Line, which was created in 1954 and ran until the fall of 1968, at which time it was phased into the Designer's Workshop line.

On the fall 1954 list, six large-sized dogs were designated as "Champions," but the following season these dogs were listed as part of the regular Pedigree line. Pedigree dogs were listed by name and breed only until spring 1959, when mould numbers were added, and, in spring 1962, the names were dropped.

In spring 1964, miniature dogs were added to the Pedigree line and removed from the Miniatures list, but in fall 1969 they were returned to the Miniatures list. Fall 1972 was the last season for the production of dogs at the San Dimas factory. A few dogs were produced at the San Marcos factory.

With the Pedigree Dog Line, as with the Designer's Workshop Line, Hagen-Renaker experimented with the showy gloss finish versus the more realistic matte finish on several models. At San Marcos, the dogs, along with other Designer's Workshop pieces, were finally offered in gloss or matte at the same time so that collector's could enjoy both.

INDEX TO
PEDIGREE DOG LINE

Afghan Hound 'Monicle'
Model No.: H-1002
Designer: Tom Masterson
Size: 4" x 5 ½", 10.1 x 14.0 cm
Colour: Fawn; matte
Issued: 1958 - spring 1959, 1972

Description	U.S. $	Can. $	U.K. £
1. Monrovia	55.00	110.00	95.00
2. San Dimas	40.00	80.00	70.00

Airedale 'Gypsy'
Model No.: H-1004
Designer: Tom Masterson
Size: 3" x 3 ¼", 7.6 x 8.3 cm
Colour: Black and tan; gloss or matte
Issued: 1958 - spring 1959, spring 1968, 1972

Description	U.S. $	Can. $	U.K. £
1. Monrovia	55.00	110.00	95.00
2. San Dimas	40.00	80.00	70.00

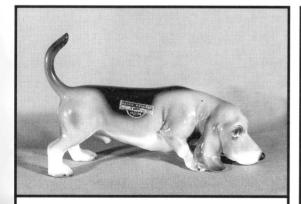

Basset Hound 'Benny'
Model No.: H-1502
Designer: Tom Masterson
Size: 4 ½" x 6 ¼", 11.9 x 15.9 cm
Colour: Brown, black and white; gloss or matte
Issued: Fall 1954, spring 1955, 1956, 1957, spring 1959, fall 1961 - 1962, spring 1966 - spring 1968
Series: Champion Line

Description	U.S. $	Can. $	U.K. £
1. Gloss (Monrovia)	50.00	100.00	85.00
2. Matte (San Dimas)	65.00	130.00	115.00

Basset Hound 'Sherlock'
Model No.: H-1585
Designer: Tom Masterson
Size: 3 ½" x 4", 8.9 x 10.1 cm
Colour: Brown, black and white; matte
Issued: Fall 1960 - spring 1961, fall 1964 - 1965, spring 1968 - spring 1969

Description	U.S. $	Can. $	U.K. £
1. Monrovia	55.00	110.00	95.00
2. San Dimas	40.00	80.00	70.00

Beagle 'Beau', adult male seated

Model No.: H-1561
Designer: Tom Masterson
Height: 2 ½", 6.4 cm
Colour: Brown, black and white; gloss or matte
Issued: 1954 - spring 1955, 1964, 1965, 1974

Description	U.S. $	Can. $	U.K. £
1. Monrovia	30.00	60.00	50.00
2. San Dimas	25.00	50.00	45.00

Beagle Puppy 'Beau', walking

Model No.: H-1523
Designer: Tom Masterson
Size: 1 5/8" x 2 ¾", 4.1 x 7.0 cm
Colour: Brown, black and white; matte
Issued: Spring 1959

Model No.	U.S. $	Can. $	U.K. £
H-1523		Rare	

Beagle 'Belle', seated

Model No.: H-1522
Designer: Tom Masterson
Size: 3 ¾" x 3 ½", 9.5 x 8.9 cm
Colour: Brown, black and white; gloss or matte
Issued: Spring 1959

Model No.	U.S. $	Can. $	U.K. £
H-1522		Rare	

Beagle 'Belle', standing

Model No.: H-1011
Designer: Tom Masterson
Height: 2 ¼", 5.7 cm
Colour: Brown, black and white; gloss or matte
Issued: 1954 - spring 1955, 1964, 1965

Description	U.S. $	Can. $	U.K. £
1. Monrovia	30.00	60.00	50.00
2. San Dimas	25.00	50.00	45.00

Sam (H-1558), Sally (H-1522), Ralph (H-1599)

Beagle 'Sally', adult standing

Model No.:	H-1522
Designer:	Tom Masterson
Height:	5", 12.7 cm
Colour:	Brown, black and white; gloss or matte
Issued:	Spring 1955 - fall 1957, fall 1961 - fall 1962, fall 1966 - spring 1968

Description	U.S. $	Can. $	U.K. £
Monrovia	60.00	120.00	105.00

Beagle Puppy 'Sam', crouching

Model No.:	H-1558
Designer:	Tom Masterson
Height:	2 ¼", 5.7 cm
Colour:	Brown, black and white; gloss or matte
Issued:	Spring 1955 - fall 1957, fall 1961 - fall 1962, fall 1966

Description	U.S. $	Can. $	U.K. £
Monrovia	35.00	70.00	60.00

Beagle Puppy 'Ralph', walking

Model No.:	H-1559
Designer:	Tom Masterson
Height:	1 7/8", 4.8 cm
Colour:	Brown, black and white; gloss or matte
Issued:	Fall 1955 - spring 1968

Description	U.S. $	Can. $	U.K. £
Monrovia	40.00	80.00	70.00

Note: Model H-1558 was also used to make Dalmatian Puppy 'Flint,' page 437, and model H-1559 was also used to make Dalmatian Puppy 'Tinder,' page 437.

Bloodhound

Model No.: H-1005
Designer: Tom Masterson
Height: 2 5/8", 6.6 cm
Colour: 1. Dark red-brown; matte
2. Light brown, darker brown shading; gloss
Issued: Spring 1958, spring 1968, 1972

Description	U.S. $	Can. $	U.K. £
1. Red-brown (Monrovia)	55.00	110.00	95.00
2. Light brown (San Dimas)	40.00	80.00	70.00

Borzoi

Model No.: H-1003
Designer: Tom Masterson
Height: 3 5/8", 9.2 cm
Colour: White with caramel spots; matte
Issued: 1972

Model No.	U.S. $	Can. $	U.K. £
H-1003	60.00	120.00	105.00

Note: Model H-1003 was also used to make Russian Wolfhound, page 446.

Boston Terrier 'Chips'

Model No.: H-1008
Designer: Tom Masterson
Height: 2 ¾", 7.0 cm
Colour: Black and white; gloss
Issued: Spring 1958 - spring 1959

Model No.	U.S. $	Can. $	U.K. £
H-1008	60.00	120.00	105.00

Boston Terrier 'Roland'

Model No.: H-1508
Designer: Tom Masterson
Height: 4 1/8", 10.5 cm
Colour: Black and white; gloss
Issued: 1955

Model No.	U.S. $	Can. $	U.K. £
H-1508		Rare	

Note: This forms a pair with Boston Terrier Puppy 'Chester' (H-1512), page 423.

Boston Terrier Puppy 'Chester'
Model No.:   H-1512
Designer: Tom Masterson
Height: 2 ¼", 5.7 cm
Colour: Black and white; gloss
Issued: 1955

Model No.	U.S. $	Can. $	U.K. £
H-1512	75.00	150.00	130.00

Note: This forms a pair with Boston Terrier 'Roland' (H-1508), page 422. Model H-1512 was also used to make Boxer Puppy, page 427.

Boxer 'Bing'
Model No.:   H-1562
Designer: Tom Masterson
Height: 4 ¼", 10.8 cm
Colour: Fawn; matte
Issued: Fall 1959 - spring 1961, 1965, spring 1970

Model No.	U.S. $	Can. $	U.K. £
H-1562	50.00	100.00	85.00

Note: This forms a set with 'Bruce' (H-1563) and Boxer puppies 'Max' (H-1564) and 'King' (H-1565); see page 426.

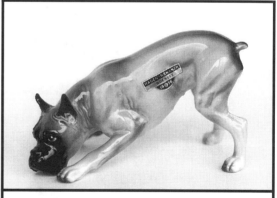

Boxer 'Bruce'
Model No.:   H-1563
Designer: Tom Masterson
Height: 2 ¾", 7.0 cm
Colour: Fawn; gloss or matte
Issued: Fall 1959 - spring 1961, 1965, spring 1970

Description	U.S. $	Can. $	U.K. £
1. Monrovia	65.00	130.00	115.00
2. San Dimas	50.00	100.00	85.00

Note: This forms a set with 'Bing' (H-1562) and Boxer puppies 'Max' (H-1564) and 'King' (H-1565); see page 426.

Boxer 'Duchess'
Model No.:   H-1525
Designer: Tom Masterson
Height: 3 ¼", 8.3 cm
Colour: Fawn; gloss or matte
Issued: Spring 1956 - fall 1959

Model No.	U.S. $	Can. $	U.K. £
H-1525	55.00	110.00	95.00

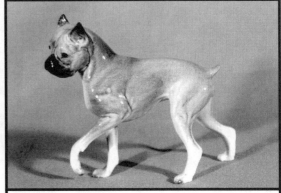

Boxer 'Jiggs'

Model No.:	H-1010
Designer:	Tom Masterson
Height:	2", 5.0 cm
Colour:	Fawn; gloss or matte
Issued:	Spring 1954 - fall 1956, spring 1959 - spring 1961

Model No.	U.S. $	Can. $	U.K. £
H-1010	40.00	80.00	70.00

Note: This is the mate to Boxer 'Maggie' (H-1009).

Boxer 'Maggie'
Style One (walking)

Model No.:	H-1009
Designer:	Tom Masterson
Height:	2 ¾", 7.0 cm
Colour:	Fawn; gloss or matte
Issued:	Spring 1954 - fall 1956, spring 1959 - spring 1961, spring 1964 - fall 1965

Model No.	U.S. $	Can. $	U.K. £
H-1009	40.00	80.00	70.00

Note: This is the mate to Boxer 'Jiggs' (H-1010).

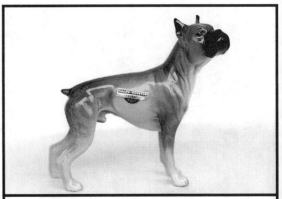

Boxer 'Maggie'
Style Two (seated)

Model No.:	H-1541
Designer:	Tom Masterson
Height:	11 ½", 29.2 cm
Colour:	Fawn; matte
Issued:	1957 - spring 1958, 1967 - spring 1968
Varieties:	Also called 'Maggie II'

Model No.	U.S. $	Can. $	U.K. £
H-1541	150.00	300.00	260.00

Boxer 'Prince'

Model No.:	H-1507
Designer:	Tom Masterson
Height:	5 ½", 14.0 cm
Colour:	Fawn; gloss
Issued:	1955, 1956

Model No.	U.S. $	Can. $	U.K. £
H-1507	55.00	110.00	95.00

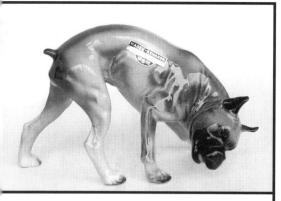

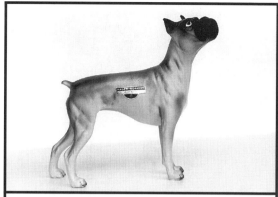

Boxer 'Princess'

Model No.:	H-1526
Designer:	Tom Masterson
Height:	3 ½", 8.9 cm
Colour:	Fawn; gloss or matte
Issued:	Spring 1956 - fall 1959

Model No.	U.S. $	Can. $	U.K. £
H-1526	55.00	110.00	95.00

Note: This forms a pair with Bone (H-1526A), page 449.

Boxer 'Queenie'

Model No.:	H-1516
Designer:	Tom Masterson
Height:	5 ½", 14.0 cm
Colour:	Fawn; matte
Issued:	Spring 1957 - fall 1959, fall 1961, 1962, spring 1966 - spring 1968

Model No.	U.S. $	Can. $	U.K. £
H-1516	50.00	100.00	85.00

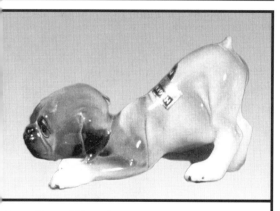

Boxer Puppy 'Champ'
Style One (crouched)

Model No.:	H-1527
Designer:	Tom Masterson
Height:	1 ½", 3.8 cm
Colour:	Fawn; gloss or matte
Issued:	1956
	Fall 1961 - fall 1962

Model No.	U.S. $	Can. $	U.K. £
H-1527	40.00	80.00	70.007

Boxer Puppy 'Champ'
Style Two (seated)

Model No.:	H-1544
Designer:	Tom Masterson
Height:	5 ¼", 13.3 cm
Colour:	Fawn; matte
Issued:	1957 - spring 1958, spring 1959, 1967
Varieties:	Also called 'Champ II'

Model No.	U.S. $	Can. $	U.K. £
H-1544	50.00	100.00	85.00

Note: This is the puppy to 'Maggie' (H-1541), page 424.

Boxer Puppy 'Duke'
Style One (seated)
Model No.:	H-1517
Designer:	Tom Masterson
Height:	2 ½", 6.4 cm
Colour:	Fawn; gloss
Issued:	1955 - 1956

Model No.	U.S. $	Can. $	U.K. £
H-1517	30.00	60.00	50.00

Boxer Puppy 'Duke'
Style Two (walking)
Model No.:	H-1547
Designer:	Tom Masterson
Height:	2", 5.0 cm
Colour:	Fawn; matte
Issued:	Spring 1957 - spring 1959

Model No.	U.S. $	Can. $	U.K. £
H-1547	40.00	80.00	70.00

Note: This is the puppy to 'Queenie' (H-1516), page 425.

Boxer Puppy 'King'
Model No.:	H-1565
Designer:	Tom Masterson
Height:	1 ½", 3.8 cm
Colour:	Fawn; matte
Issued:	Fall 1959 - spring 1961, 1965

Model No.	U.S. $	Can. $	U.K. £
H-1565	40.00	80.00	70.00

Boxer Puppy 'Max'
Model No.:	H-1564
Designer:	Tom Masterson
Height:	1 ¾", 4.4 cm
Colour:	Fawn; matte
Issued:	Fall 1959 - spring 1961, 1965

Model No.	U.S. $	Can. $	U.K. £
H-1564	45.00	90.00	80.00

Note: This forms a set with 'Bing' (H-1562) and 'Bruce' (H-1563), page 423, and 'Max' (H-1564).

Note: This forms a set with 'Bing' (H-1562) and 'Bruce' (H-1563), page 423, and 'King' (H-1565).

Boxer Puppy

Model No.:	H-1512	
Designer:	Tom Masterson	
Height:	2 ¼", 5.7 cm	
Colour:	Fawn; gloss or matte	
Issued:	Fall 1966 - fall 1967	

Model No.	U.S. $	Can. $	U.K. £
H-1512	45.00	90.00	80.00

Note: Model H-1512 was also used to make Boston Terrier Puppy 'Chester', see page 423.

Chihuahua 'Carmencita'

Model No.:	H-1529	
Designer:	Tom Masterson	
Height:	4 ¼", 10.8 cm	
Colour:	Tan; gloss or matte	
Issued:	Spring 1956 - spring 1962, fall 1966 - 1967	

Model No.	U.S. $	Can. $	U.K. £
H-1529	50.00	100.00	85.00

Note: 'Pancho Villa' is the puppy of 'Carmencita.' Their stickers were often switched.

Chihuahua Puppy 'Pancho Villa'

Model No.:	H-1528	
Designer:	Tom Masterson	
Height:	2", 5.0 cm	
Colour:	Tan; gloss or matte	
Issued:	Spring 1956 - spring 1962, fall 1966 - spring 1968	

Model No.	U.S. $	Can. $	U.K. £
H-1528	25.00	50.00	45.00

Note: 'Pancho Villa' is the puppy of 'Carmencita'. Their stickers were often switched.

Cocker Spaniel

Model No.:	A-1542	
Designer:	Don Winton	
Height:	5 ¼", 13.3 cm	
Colour:	Buff, white chest, red-brown collar with yellow tag	
Issued:	1968	

Model No.	U.S. $	Can. $	U.K. £
A-1542		Rare	

Note: Model A-1542 was first used to make Cocker Spaniel 'Butch', page 428.

Cocker Spaniel 'Butch', large

Model No.: H-1542
Designer: Don Winton
Height: 5 ¼", 13.3 cm
Colour: Black and white; gloss
Issued: Spring 1957 - fall 1959

Model No.	U.S. $	Can. $	U.K. £
H-1542	50.00	100.00	85.00

Cocker Spaniel 'Butch', miniature

Model No.: A-1542
Designer: Don Winton
Height: 1 ¾", 4.4 cm
Colour: Black and white; gloss
Issued: 1957

Model No.	U.S. $	Can. $	U.K. £
A-1542	50.00	100.00	85.00

Note: This is also seen in a black, white and grey decoration colourway. Model H-1542 is engraved 'A. Staehle' on the base. Butch was owned by the American illustrator Albert Staehle and appeared on the covers of *The Saturday Evening Post* in the 1940s and *The American Weekly* in the 1950s.
In 1968, model A-1542 was used to make a buff-coloured cocker spaniel, page 425.

Above, 1954 Version - Below, 1959 Version

Cocker Spaniel Puppy 'Dash', chasing tail

Model No.: B/H-556
Designer: Helen Perrin Farnlund
Height: 2 ½", 6.4 cm
Colour: White, black spots and shading; gloss
Issued: 1954, spring 1959

Description	U.S. $	Can. $	U.K. £
1. 1954	65.00	130.00	115.00
2. 1959	55.00	110.00	95.00

Cocker Spaniel Puppy 'Dot', scratching ear

Model No.: B/H-557
Designer: Helen Perrin Farnlund
Height: 3", 7.6 cm
Colour: White, black spots and shading; gloss
Issued: 1954, spring 1959

Description	U.S. $	Can. $	U.K. £
1. 1954	65.00	130.00	115.00
2. 1959	55.00	110.00	95.00

Cocker Spaniel 'Queenie', adult walking

Model No.: B/H-563
Designer: Helen Perrin Farnlund
Height: 4 ¾", 12.1 cm
Colour: White, black spots and shading; gloss
Issued: 1954

Description	U.S. $	Can. $	U.K. £
1954	110.00	220.00	190.00

Note: The 1959 versions of 'Dot' and 'Dash' were decorated to match 'Butch', (H-1542).

Cocker Spaniel 'His Nibs'

Model No.:	H-1014/86
Designer:	Tom Masterson
Height:	2 ½", 6.4 cm
Colour:	1. Tan; glossy or matte
	2. White with black patches; gloss/matte
Issued:	1954 - spring 1955,
	1964, 1972,
	fall 1984 - spring 1985

Colourways	U.S. $	Can. $	U.K. £
1. Black/white	20.00	40.00	35.00
2. Tan	30.00	60.00	50.00

Cocker Spaniel 'Pip Emma'

Model No.:	H-1013
Designer:	Tom Masterson
Height:	2 ½", 6.4 cm
Colour:	Tan; gloss
Issued:	1954, fall 1955

Model No.	U.S. $	Can. $	U.K. £
H-1013	35.00	70.00	60.00

Cocker Spaniel 'Honey Girl'

Model No.:	H-1518
Designer:	Maureen Love
Height:	5 ½", 14.0 cm
Colour:	Tan; gloss or matte
Issued:	Fall 1955 - spring 1958,
	fall 1961 - fall 1962,
	fall 1966, spring 1968

Description	U.S. $	Can. $	U.K. £
1. Monrovia	45.00	90.00	80.00
2. San Dimas	30.00	60.00	50.00

Cocker Spaniel Puppy 'Patsy'

Model No.:	H-1519
Designer:	Maureen Love
Height:	2 ¾", 7.0 cm
Colour:	Tan; gloss or matte
Issued:	Fall 1955 - spring 1958,
	fall 1961 - fall 1962,
	fall 1966, spring 1968

Description	U.S. $	Can. $	U.K. £
1. Monrovia	40.00	80.00	70.00
2. San Dimas	25.00	50.00	45.00

Note: Model H-1519 has also been seen in white with red-brown speckles and black dot eyes. This colourway is considered rare.

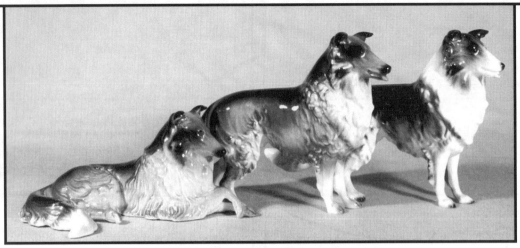

'Bonnie' (H-1006), 'Gaylord' (H-1007) decoration variances

Collie 'Bonnie'

Model No.:	H-1006
Designer:	Tom Masterson
Height:	2", 5.0 cm
Colour:	1. Brown and white; gloss or matte
	2. Brown, black and white; gloss or matte
Issued:	Spring 1954 - fall 1956, spring 1959 - spring 1961, spring 1970

Description	U.S. $	Can. $	U.K. £
1. Monrovia	45.00	90.00	80.00
2. San Dimas	45.00	90.00	80.00

Collie 'Gaylord'
Style One (small)

Model No.:	H-1007
Designer:	Tom Masterson
Height:	3 3/8", 8.6 cm
Colour:	1. Black and white; gloss or matte
	2. Brown, black and white; gloss or matte
Issued:	Spring 1954 - fall 1956, spring 1959 - spring 1961, 1964, spring 1970

Description	U.S. $	Can. $	U.K. £
1. Monrovia	75.00	150.00	130.00
2. San Dimas	45.00	90.00	80.00

Collie 'Gaylord', Style Two (large)

Model No.:	H-1543
Designer:	Tom Masterson
Height:	10", 25.4 cm
Colour:	1. Brown and white; matte
	2. Golden brown and white; matte
Issued:	1957, 1958, 1962, 1967, spring 1968

Colourways	U.S. $	Can. $	U.K. £
1. Brown/white	175.00	350.00	300.00
2. Golden brown/white	150.00	300.00	260.00

Collie 'Golden Lady'

Model No.:	H-1515
Designer:	Tom Masterson
Size:	6" x 8", 15.0 x 20.3 cm
Colour:	Brown and white; gloss
Issued:	1955, 1956

Model No.	U.S. $	Can. $	U.K. £
H-1515	90.00	180.00	155.00

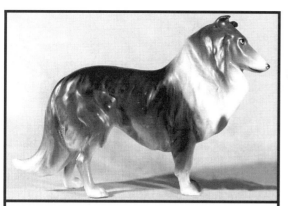

Collie 'Marmion'

Model No.:	H-1553
Designer:	Tom Masterson
Height:	5", 12.7 cm
Colour:	Brown and white; matte
Issued:	Spring 1957 - fall 1959, fall 1961 - fall 1962, 1966 - spring 1968

Model No.	U.S. $	Can. $	U.K. £
H-1553	75.00	150.00	130.00

Collie Puppy 'Laddie'

Model No.:	H-1532
Designer:	Tom Masterson
Height:	2 ½", 6.4 cm
Colour:	1. Brown and white; gloss
	2. Brown, black and white; gloss or matte
Issued:	1956, fall 1961

Colourways	U.S. $	Can. $	U.K. £
1. Brown and white	45.00	90.00	80.00
2. Brown, black and white	45.00	90.00	80.00

Curbstone Setter 'Albert'

Model No.:	H-1581
Designer:	Nell Bortells
Height:	2 ¾", 7.0 cm
Colour:	White, brown and black shading; matte
Issued:	Fall 1960 - spring 1961

Model No.	U.S. $	Can. $	U.K. £
H-1581	40.00	80.00	70.00

Curbstone Setter 'Mutt', lying

Model No.:	89
Designer:	Nell Bortells
Height:	1", 2.5 cm
Colour:	1. Black, brown and white; gloss or matte
	2. Dark brown; gloss or matte
	3. Tan; gloss or matte
Issued:	Fall 1984 - spring 1985

Colourways	U.S. $	Can. $	U.K. £
1. Brown/black/white	25.00	50.00	45.00
2. Dark brown	25.00	50.00	45.00
3. Tan	25.00	50.00	45.00

Note: Original mould was Percival (H-1582), page 432.

Curbstone Setter 'Mutt', reclining

Model No.: 90
Designer: Nell Bortells
Height: 1", 2.5 cm
Colour: 1. Brown; gloss or matte
2. Brown, black and white; gloss or matte
3. Tan; gloss or matte
Issued: Fall 1984 - spring 1985

Colourways	U.S. $	Can. $	U.K. £
1. Brown	20.00	40.00	35.00
2. Brown/black/white	20.00	40.00	35.00
3. Tan	20.00	40.00	35.00

Curbstone Setter 'Mutt', seated

Model No.: 88
Designer: Nell Bortells
Height: 3", 7.6 cm
Colour: 1. Brown, black and white; gloss or matte
2. Dark brown; gloss or matte
3. Tan; gloss or matte
Issued: Fall 1984 - spring 1985

Colourways	U.S. $	Can. $	U.K. £
1. Brown/black/white	20.00	40.00	35.00
2. Dark brown	20.00	40.00	35.00
3. Tan	20.00	40.00	35.00

Note: Original mould was K-9 from Zany Zoo, page 521.

Curbstone Setter 'Percival'

Model No.: H-1582
Designer: Nell Bortells
Height: 1", 2.5 cm
Colour: Brown and white
Issued: Fall 1960 - spring 1961

Model No.	U.S. $	Can. $	U.K. £
H-1582	50.00	100.00	85.00

Note: See also Curbstone Setter 'Mutt', lying, page 431.
The model illustrated has a broken tail.

Dachshund 'Beanbag'

Model No.: H-1567
Designer: Tom Masterson
Height: 2", 5.0 cm
Colour: 1. Dark brown; gloss
2. Red-brown; gloss
Issued: Fall 1959 - spring 1961, 1965, 1968 - spring 1970

Description	U.S. $	Can. $	U.K. £
1. Monrovia	45.00	90.00	80.00
2. San Dimas	45.00	90.00	80.00

Dachshund 'Bernie'

Model No.: H-1545
Designer: Tom Masterson
Size: 6 ½" x 14", 16.5 x 35.5 cm
Colour: Dark brown; gloss or matte
Issued: Fall 1957, 1962,
1967 - spring 1968

Description	U.S. $	Can. $	U.K. £
1. Monrovia (gloss)	150.00	300.00	260.00
2. San Dimas (matte)	150.00	300.00	260.00

Note: The original issue price was $12.00.

Dachshund 'Brunhilda'

Model No.: H-1520
Designer: Tom Masterson
Height: 4", 10.1 cm
Colour: Brown; gloss or matte
Issued: Fall 1955 - spring 1962

Model No.	U.S. $	Can. $	U.K. £
H-1520	60.00	120.00	105.00

Dachshund 'Greta'

Model No.: H-1016
Designer: Tom Masterson
Height: 2", 5.0 cm
Colour: Brown; gloss or matte
Issued: Fall 1954 - fall 1955

Model No.	U.S. $	Can. $	U.K. £
H-1016	60.00	120.00	105.00

Note: This forms a pair with 'Schnapsie' (H-1017/87).

Dachshund 'Schnapsie'

Model No.: H-1017/87
Designer: Tom Masterson
Height: 2", 5.0 cm
Colour: Brown; gloss or matte
Issued: Fall 1954 - 1955,
fall 1984 - spring 1985

Description	U.S. $	Can. $	U.K. £
1. Monrovia	45.00	90.00	80.00
2. San Dimas	20.00	40.00	35.00

Note: This forms a pair with Dachshund 'Greta'
(H-1016).

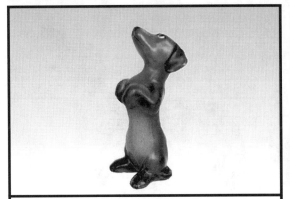

Dachshund Puppy 'Greta', begging

Model No.: H-1522
Designer: Tom Masterson
Height: 2 ¾", 7.0 cm
Colour: Brown; gloss or matte
Issued: Fall 1955 - fall 1961

Model No.	U.S. $	Can. $	U.K. £
H-1522	35.00	70.00	60.00

Dachshund Puppy 'Hymie'

Model No.: H-1521
Designer: Tom Masterson
Height: 2", 5.0 cm
Colour: Brown; gloss or matte
Issued: Spring 1957 - spring 1961, 1964

Model No.	U.S. $	Can. $	U.K. £
H-1521	35.00	70.00	60.00

1959 — DACHSHUND FAMILY

'Dutch' (H-1574)

'Elsa' (H-1571)

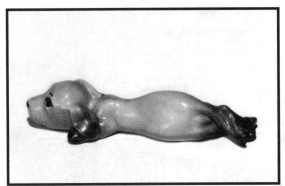

'Lenk' (H-1560)

'Tiger' (H-1572)

'Henessy' (H-1568)

'Kutchen' (H-1573)

These models were designed by Tom Masterson and issued in three colourways:

1. Dark brown; gloss or matte   2. Red-brown; gloss or matte   3. Yellow-tan; gloss

Dachshund Puppy 'Henessy', seated,
right paw up, mouth open

Model No.:	H-1568
Height:	1 ½", 3.8 cm
Issued:	Fall 1959 - spring 1961, spring 1968

Model No.	U.S. $	Can. $	U.K. £
H-1568	40.00	80.00	70.00

Dachshund Puppy 'Cornball', seated

Model No.:	H-1570
Height:	1 ¼", 3.2 cm
Issued:	Fall 1959 - spring 1961

Model No.	U.S. $	Can. $	U.K. £
H-1570	40.00	80.00	70.00

Dachshund Puppy 'Dutch', standing,
head turned left

Model No.:	H-1574
Height:	1 ¼", 3.2 cm
Issued:	Fall 1959 - spring 1961

Model No.	U.S. $	Can. $	U.K. £
H-1574	40.00	80.00	70.00

Dachshund Puppy 'Elsa', seated, scratching

Model No.:	H-1571
Height:	1 ½", 3.8 cm
Issued:	Fall 1959 - spring 1961, spring 1968

Model No.	U.S. $	Can. $	U.K. £
H-1571	40.00	80.00	70.00

Dachshund Puppy 'Kutchen', standing,
right paw up, facing right

Model No.:	H-1573
Height:	1 ¼", 3.2 cm
Issued:	Fall 1959 - spring 1961, spring 1968

Model No.	U.S. $	Can. $	U.K. £
H-1573	40.00	80.00	70.00

Dachshund 'Knobby', standing

Model No.:	H-1566
Height:	2 ¼", 5.7 cm
Issued:	Fall 1959 - spring 1961, 1965, 1968 - 1969, 1972

Description	U.S. $	Can. $	U.K. £
1. Monrovia	50.00	100.00	85.00
2. San Dimas	30.00	60.00	50.00

Dachshund Puppy 'Lenk', lying

Model No.:	H-1560
Size:	½" x 2 ½", 1.3 x 6.4 cm
Issued:	Fall 1959 - spring 1961

Model No.	U.S. $	Can. $	U.K. £
H-1560	40.00	80.00	70.00

Dachshund Puppy 'Tiger', standing,
left front paw up

Model No.:	H-1572
Height:	1 ¼", 3.2 cm
Issued:	Fall 1959 - spring 1961, spring 1968

Model No.	U.S. $	Can. $	U.K. £
H-1572	40.00	80.00	70.00

Note: Illustrations of 'Knobby' and 'Conrball' not available at press time.

Dalmatian 'Lady'
Model No.:   H-1536
Designer: Tom Masterson
Height: 10", 25.4 cm
Colour: White, black spots; matte
Issued: Fall 1956 - spring 1958, 1962

Model No.	U.S. $	Can. $	U.K. £
H-1536	200.00	400.00	350.00

Dalmatian 'Spooky', lying
Model No.:   H-1557
Designer: Tom Masterson
Height: 2 ½", 6.4 cm
Colour: White, black spots; matte
Issued: Fall 1958 - spring 1961

Model No.	U.S. $	Can. $	U.K. £
H-1557	60.00	120.00	105.00

Dalmatian 'Spooky', seated
Model No.:   H-1506
Designer: Tom Masterson
Height: 5 ½", 14.0 cm
Colour: White, black spots; gloss or matte
Issued: Fall 1954 - fall 1957,
               fall 1961, 1966 - spring 1968
Series: Champion Line

Description	U.S. $	Can. $	U.K. £
1. Monrovia	75.00	150.00	130.00
2. San Dimas	50.00	100.00	85.00
2. San Marcos	50.00	100.00	85.00

Note: 'Spooky' first made at San Marcos, however the factory closed before he was added to order forms.

Dalmatian Puppy 'Sparky', running

Model No.: H-1511
Designer: Maureen Love
Height: 2 ½", 6.4 cm
Colour: White, black spots; gloss or matte
Issued: Spring 1955 - fall 1957,
fall 1961,
fall 1966 - 1967

Model No.	U.S. $	Can. $	U.K. £
H-1511	40.00	80.00	70.00

'Flint' (H-1558), 'Tinder' (H-1559), 'Sparky' (H-1556)

Dalmatian Puppy 'Flint', playing

Model No.: H-1558
Designer: Tom Masterson
Height: 2 ¼", 5.7 cm
Colour: White, black spots; matte
Issued: Fall 1958 - spring 1961

Model No.	U.S. $	Can. $	U.K. £
H-1559	50.00	100.00	85.00

Dalmatian Puppy 'Sparky', begging

Model No.: H-1556
Designer: Tom Masterson
Height: 2 ¼", 5.7 cm
Colour: White, black spots; matte
Issued: Fall 1958 - fall 1959

Model No.	U.S. $	Can. $	U.K. £
H-1556	50.00	100.00	85.00

Dalmatian Puppy 'Tinder', walking

Model No.: H-1559
Designer: Tom Masterson
Height: 2", 5.0 cm
Colour: White, black spots; matte
Issued: Fall 1958 - fall 1959

Model No.	U.S. $	Can. $	U.K. £
H-1558	75.00	150.00	130.00

Note: Model H-1559 was also used to make Beagle Puppy 'Ralph', page 421, and model H-1558 was used to make Beagle Puppy 'Sam', page 421. Illustrated models H-1558 and H-1559 have broken tails.

Doberman Pinscher 'Diana'

Model No.:   H-1539
Designer: Tom Masterson
Height: 5 ¾", 14.6 cm
Colour: Brown; gloss or matte
Issued: 1. Gloss — 1957
              2. Matte — Fall 1967

Description	U.S. $	Can. $	U.K. £
1. Monrovia	90.00	180.00	155.00
2. San Dimas	95.00	190.00	165.00

Doberman Pinscher 'Helga'

Model No.:   H-1540
Designer: Tom Masterson
Height: 5 7/8", 14.9 cm
Colour: Brown; gloss or matte
Issued: 1. Gloss — 1957
              2. Matte — Fall 1967 - spring 1968

Description	U.S. $	Can. $	U.K. £
1. Monrovia	90.00	180.00	155.00
2. San Dimas	95.00	190.00	165.00

English Bulldog 'Bing'

Model No.:   H-1002
Designer: Tom Masterson
Height: 1 ¾", 4.4 cm
Colour: 1. Fawn; gloss or matte
              2. Spotted; gloss or matte
Issued: 1954 - spring 1955,
              1964, 1972

Colourways	U.S. $	Can. $	U.K. £
1. Fawn	40.00	80.00	70.00
2. Spotted	40.00	80.00	70.00

English Bulldog 'Pam'

Model No.:   H-1001
Designer: Tom Masterson
Height: 1 ¾", 4.4 cm
Colour: 1. Fawn; gloss or matte
              2. Spotted; gloss or matte
Issued: 1954 - spring 1955

Colourways	U.S. $	Can. $	U.K. £
1. Fawn	40.00	80.00	70.00
2. Spotted	40.00	80.00	70.00

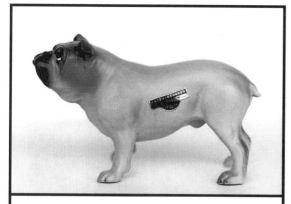

English Bulldog 'Winston'
Model No.:   H-1501
Designer: Tom Masterson
Height: 3 ½", 8.9 cm
Colour: Fawn; gloss or matte
Issued: Fall 1954 - fall 1957, fall 1961, 1964,
               spring 1966 - spring 1968
Series: Champion Line

Description	U.S. $	Can. $	U.K. £
1. Monrovia	65.00	130.00	115.00
2. San Dimas	65.00	130.00	115.00

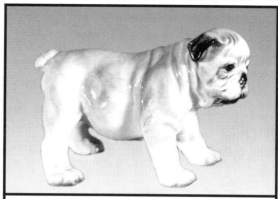

English Bulldog Puppy 'Bobby'
Model No.:   H-1510
Designer: Maureen Love
Height: 2", 5.0 cm
Colour: Fawn; gloss or matte
Issued: 1955 - spring 1956

Description	U.S. $	Can. $	U.K. £
1. Gloss	40.00	80.00	70.00
2. Matte	40.00	80.00	70.00

English Bulldog Puppy 'Nobby'
Model No.:   H-1509
Designer: Maureen Love
Size: 1 ¾" x 3 1/3", 4.4 x 8.5 cm
Colour: 1. Fawn; gloss or matte
               2. Spotted; gloss or matte
Issued: Spring 1955 - fall 1957, fall 1961,
               fall 1966 - 1967

Colourways	U.S. $	Can. $	U.K. £
1. Fawn	40.00	80.00	70.00
2. Spotted	40.00	80.00	70.00

Note: This forms a pair with Shoe (H-1509A), page 449.

English Setter 'Squire'
Model No.:   H-1504
Designer: Tom Masterson
Height: 5 ¼", 13.3 cm
Colour: Grey, brown shading and spots
Issued: Fall 1954 -spring 1956
Serie: Champion Line

Model No.	U.S. $	Can. $	U.K. £
H-1504	75.00	150.00	130.00

Note: Model H-1504 was also used to make Irish Setter,
Style One, page 442.

German Shepherd 'Baron'

Model No.:	H-1005
Designer:	Tom Masterson
Height:	3 ¼", 8.3 cm
Colour:	Tan with brown and black shading; gloss or matte
Issued:	Spring 1954 - fall 1955, 1964 - 1965, fall 1984 - spring 1985

Description	U.S. $	Can. $	U.K. £
1. Monrovia	50.00	100.00	85.00
2. San Dimas	30.00	60.00	50.00
3. San Marcos	20.00	40.00	35.00

Note: Model H-1005 became model 85 at San Marcos.

German Shepherd 'Duchess'

Model No.:	H-1020
Designer:	Tom Masterson
Height:	2 ¼", 5.7 cm
Colour:	Tan with brown and black shading, white chest; gloss or matte
Issued:	Fall 1954, 1955, 1972

Description	U.S. $	Can. $	U.K. £
1. Monrovia	60.00	120.00	105.00
2. San Dimas	50.00	100.00	85.00

German Shepherd 'Herman'

Model No.:	H-1580
Designer:	Tom Masterson
Height:	4", 10.1 cm
Colour:	Black and tan; matte
Issued:	Fall 1960 - spring 1961, 1968 - spring 1969

Model No.	U.S. $	Can. $	U.K. £
H-1580	55.00	110.00	95.00

German Shepherd 'Von'

Model No.:	H-1505
Designer:	Tom Masterson
Height:	6", 15.0 cm
Colour:	Light and dark brown; gloss or matte
Issued:	Fall 1954 - spring 1958, fall 1961 - fall 1962
Series:	Champion Line

Description	U.S. $	Can. $	U.K. £
1. Gloss	50.00	100.00	85.00
2. Matte	75.00	150.00	130.00

**German Shepherd Puppy 'Fritzi',
standing on hind legs**

Model No.:	H-1530
Designer:	Tom Masterson
Size:	3" x 4", 7.6 x 10.1 cm
Colour:	Dark and light brown; gloss or matte
Issued:	Spring 1956

Model No.	U.S. $	Can. $	U.K. £
H-1530	65.00	130.00	115.00

**German Shepherd Puppy 'Mitzi',
one paw up**

Model No.:	H-1531
Designer:	Tom Masterson
Height:	3", 7.6 cm
Colour:	Black and tan; gloss or matte
Issued:	Spring 1956, fall 1961

Description	U.S. $	Can. $	U.K. £
1. Gloss	65.00	130.00	115.00
2. Matte	60.00	120.00	105.00

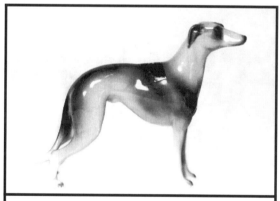

Great Dane 'Hamlet'

Model No.:	H-1503
Designer:	Tom Masterson
Height:	4 ½", 11.9 cm
Colour:	See below
Issued:	Fall 1954 - spring 1957, fall 1961 - 1962, 1966 - spring 1968
Series:	Champion Line

Colourways	U.S. $	Can. $	U.K. £
1. Fawn; gloss/matte	100.00	200.00	175.00
2. Harlequin; matte (1959)		Rare	

Note: The harlequin's spot pattern was incised in the mould. These moulds were sometimes used for the fawn colourway.

Greyhound 'Comet'

Model No.:	H-1003
Designer:	Tom Masterson
Height:	3 ¼", 8.3 cm
Colour:	Light grey, black shading on back and shoulders
Issued:	1954 - spring 1955

Model No.	U.S. $	Can. $	U.K. £
H-1003	55.00	110.00	95.00

Irish Setter
Style One

Model No.:	H-1504
Designer:	Tom Masterson
Height:	5 ¼", 13.3 cm
Colour:	Red; gloss or matte
Issued:	Fall 1956 - spring 1957
Series:	Champion Line

Model No.	U.S. $	Can. $	U.K. £
H-1504	80.00	160.00	140.00

Note: Model H-1504 was also used to make English Setter 'Squire', page 439.

Irish Setter
Style Two

Model No.:	H-1009
Designer:	Tom Masterson
Height:	3 ¾", 9.5 cm
Colour:	Red; gloss or matte
Issued:	Spring 1957, spring 1958, spring 1966

Description	U.S. $	Can. $	U.K. £
1. Monrovia	65.00	130.00	115.00
2. San Dimas	45.00	90.00	80.00

Note: This model is also known as 'Setter'.

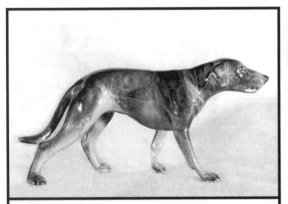

Labrador Retriever

Model No.:	H-1011
Designer:	Tom Masterson
Height:	2 ½", 6.4 cm
Colour:	Charcoal grey; gloss or matte
Issued:	1. Matte — Spring 1958 (with dumb-bell)
	2. Gloss — Spring 1972 (without dumb-bell)

Description	U.S. $	Can. $	U.K. £
1. With dumb-bell	80.00	160.00	140.00
2. Without dumb-bell	65.00	130.00	115.00

Manchester Terrier

Model No.:	H-1007
Designer:	Tom Masterson
Height:	3", 7.6 cm
Colour:	1. Black and tan; matte
	2. Red; gloss
Issued:	Spring 1958, spring 1968, spring 1972

Colourways	U.S. $	Can. $	U.K. £
1. Black/tan	65.00	130.00	115.00
2. Red	55.00	110.00	95.00

Old English Sheepdog 'Mops'

Model No.:	H-1001
Designer:	Tom Masterson
Height:	3 ½", 8.9 cm
Colour:	See below
Issued:	Spring 1958 - spring 1959, spring 1968 - spring 1970, 1972

Colourways	U.S. $	Can. $	U.K. £
1. Black/white	55.00	110.00	95.00
2. Shades of grey	35.00	70.00	60.00

Note: The black and white colourway was also used as Disney's 'Shaggy Dog™'; see page 517.

Pekingese 'Choo Choo'

Model No.:	H-1534
Designer:	Tom Masterson
Height:	2", 5.0 cm
Colour:	Browns; matte
Issued:	Fall 1956 - 1957, fall 1961

Model No.	U.S. $	Can. $	U.K. £
H-1534	35.00	70.00	60.00

Pekingese 'Ming Toy'

Model No.:	H-1533
Designer:	Tom Masterson
Height:	3", 7.6 cm
Colour:	Browns
Issued:	Fall 1956 - fall 1957, fall 1961, 1967 - spring 1968

Description	U.S. $	Can. $	U.K. £
1. Monrovia	50.00	100.00	85.00
2. San Dimas	40.00	80.00	70.00

Pointer 'Gypsy', closed mouth

Model No.:	H-1004
Designer:	Tom Masterson
Height:	2 ½", 6.4 cm
Colour:	1. White, black spots; gloss
	2. White, red spots; gloss
Issued:	1954 - spring 1955

Colourways	U.S. $	Can. $	U.K. £
1. White/black	85.00	170.00	150.00
2. White/red	60.00	120.00	105.00

Note: Model H-1004 may have been released in 1953.

Pointer 'Ranger', running, tongue out

Model No.: H-1015
Designer: Tom Masterson
Height: 2 ½", 6.4 cm
Colour: See below
Issued: 1. Gloss — 1954 - fall 1955
         2. Matte — Fall 1964

Colourways	U.S. $	Can. $	U.K. £
1. Black/tan; matte (1964)	70.00	140.00	120.00
2. White, black spots; gloss	65.00	130.00	115.00
3. White, red spots; gloss	55.00	110.00	95.00

German Pointer

Model No.: H-1010
Designer: Tom Masterson
Height: 3", 7.6 cm
Colour: Brown; matte
Issued: Spring 1958

Model No.	U.S. $	Can. $	U.K. £
H-1010	55.00	110.00	95.00

Pointer

Model No.: H-1010
Designer: Tom Masterson
Height: 3", 7.6 cm
Colour: White with brown spots; matte
Issued: 1968

Model No.	U.S. $	Can. $	U.K. £
H-1010	55.00	110.00	95.00

Note: Model H-1010 was also used to make Vizsla, page 448.

Pomeranian 'Mickey'

Model No.: H-1535
Designer: Tom Masterson
Height: 3 ½", 6.4 cm
Colour: Reddish brown; matte
Issued: Spring 1956 - 1957,
        fall 1961 - 1962,
        1966 - spring 1968

Description	U.S. $	Can. $	U.K. £
1. Monrovia	50.00	100.00	85.00
2. San Dimas	40.00	80.00	70.00

Poodle 'Cecil'
Model No.:   H-1583
Designer: Tom Masterson
Height: 4", 10.1 cm
Colour: 1. Grey; matte
                 2. White; matte
Issued: Fall 1960 - spring 1961,
                 1966 - spring 1968

Colourways	U.S. $	Can. $	U.K. £
1. Grey	65.00	130.00	115.00
2. White	65.00	130.00	115.00

Poodle 'Fifi'
First Version (With crown)
Model No.:   H-1537
Designer: Tom Masterson
Height: 5", 12.7 cm
Colour: 1. Grey; matte
                 2. White; matte
Issued: Fall 1956
Varieties: Also called Poodle, standing

Description	U.S. $	Can. $	U.K. £
With crown		Rare	

Note: See Black Bisque section, page 16.

Poodle 'Fifi'
Second Version (Without crown)
Model No.:   H-1537
Designer: Tom Masterson
Height: 5", 12.7 cm
Colour: 1. Grey; matte
                 2. White; matte
Issued: Spring 1957, fall 1961
Varieties: Also called Poodle, standing

Description	U.S. $	Can. $	U.K. £
Without crown	75.00	150.00	130.00

Note: See Black Bisque section, page 16.

Poodle 'Yvonne'
Model No.:   H-1022
Designer: Tom Masterson
Height: 3", 7.6 cm
Colour: 1. Grey; gloss or matte
                 2. White; gloss or matte
Issued: Fall 1954 - fall 1955,
                 Spring 1959 - spring 1961,
                 spring 1964 - fall 1965

Colourways	U.S. $	Can. $	U.K. £
1. Grey	75.00	150.00	130.00
2. White	75.00	150.00	130.00

Poodle Puppy 'Ralph'

Model No.:	H-1584
Designer:	Tom Masterson
Height:	2", 5.0 cm
Colour:	White; matte
Issued:	Fall 1960 - fall 1961

Model No.	U.S. $	Can. $	U.K. £
H-1584	45.00	90.00	80.00

Poodle 'Rembrandt'

Model No.:	Unknown
Designer:	Tom Masterson
Height:	3", 7.6 cm
Colour:	1. Grey; gloss or matte
	2. White poodle; gloss
Issued:	Fall 1954 - 1955
Varieties:	Also called Poodle, seated

Colourways	U.S. $	Can. $	U.K. £
1. Grey	55.00	110.00	95.00
2. White	55.00	110.00	95.00

Note: The 'Rembrandt' mould was also used for Black Bisque Poodle, seated (16), page 16.

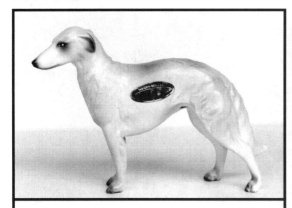

Russian Wolfhound

Model No.:	H-1003
Designer:	Tom Masterson
Height:	3 5/8", 9.2 cm
Colour:	White; matte
Issued:	Spring 1957, 1968

Model No.	U.S. $	Can. $	U.K. £
H-1003	60.00	120.00	105.00

Note: Model H-1003 was also used to make Borzoi, page 422.

Saint Bernard 'Friar'

Model No.:	H-1000
Designer:	Tom Masterson
Height:	2 ½", 6.4 cm
Colour:	Brown and white; matte
Issued:	1958 - spring 1959, 1968, 1972

Model No.	U.S. $	Can. $	U.K. £
H-1000	50.00	100.00	85.00

Schnauzer 'Baron'

Model No.:	H-1548
Designer:	Tom Masterson
Height:	5", 12.7 cm
Colour:	Grey; matte
Issued:	Fall 1957 - spring 1958, fall 1967 - spring 1968

Model No.	U.S. $	Can. $	U.K. £
H-1548	70.00	140.00	120.00

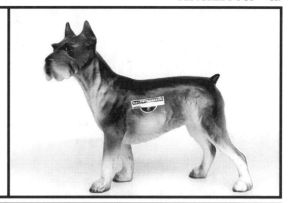

Scottish Terrier 'Mac', adult standing

Model No.:	H-1549
Designer:	Tom Masterson
Height:	5 ½", 14.0 cm
Colour:	Black; matte
Issued:	Fall 1957 - spring 1958, 1966 - spring 1968

Model No.	U.S. $	Can. $	U.K. £
H-1549	65.00	130.00	115.00

Scottish Terrier Puppy 'Robbie', seated

Model No.:	H-1551
Designer:	Tom Masterson
Height:	2 ½", 6.4 cm
Colour:	Black; matte
Issued:	Spring 1957 - spring 1958

Model No.	U.S. $	Can. $	U.K. £
H-1551	50.00	100.00	85.00

Scottish Terrier Puppy 'Bonnie', standing

Model No.:	H-1550
Designer:	Tom Masterson
Height:	2 ½", 6.4 cm
Colour:	Black; matte
Issued:	Spring 1957, spring 1958, fall 1966 - 1967

Model No.	U.S. $	Can. $	U.K. £
H-1550	50.00	100.00	85.00

Sealyham Terrier

Model No.:	H-1006
Designer:	Tom Masterson
Height:	2", 5.0 cm
Colour:	White, red-brown patches; gloss or matte
Issued:	Spring 1958, 1968

Model No.	U.S. $	Can. $	U.K. £
H-1006	50.00	100.00	85.00

Smooth Fox Terrier 'Vicki'

Model No.:	H-1538
Designer:	Tom Masterson
Height:	4 ½", 11.9 cm
Colour:	1. White, black markings, white face
	2. White, black eyes and ears and markings
Issued:	Fall 1956 - spring 1957, 1967

Colourways	U.S. $	Can. $	U.K. £
1. White face	100.00	200.00	175.00
2. White face/black eyes	100.00	200.00	175.00

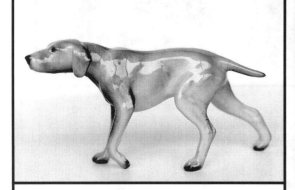

Vizsla

Model No.:	H-1010
Designer:	Tom Masterson
Height:	3", 7.6 cm
Colour:	Tan; gloss
Issued:	1972

Model No.	U.S. $	Can. $	U.K. £
H-1010	65.00	130.00	115.00

Note: Model H-1010 was also used to make the German Pointer, page 444.

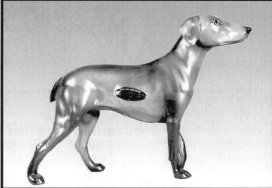

Weimaraner 'Blue Boy'

Model No.:	H-1555
Designer:	Tom Masterson
Height:	5", 12.7 cm
Colour:	Grey; matte
Issued:	Spring 1957 - spring 1959, fall 1967 - spring 1968

Model No.	U.S. $	Can. $	U.K. £
H-1555	75.00	150.00	130.00

PEDIGREE DOGS • 449

Pedigree - Miscellaneous

Photograph not
available
at press time

Bone

Model No.:	H-1526A	
Designer:	Tom Masterson	
Length:	1 ½", 3.8 cm	
Colour:	White; gloss	
Issued:	Spring 1956	

Model No.	U.S. $	Can. $	U.K. £
H-1526A		Rare	

Note: This forms a pair with 'Princess' (H-1526), page 425.

Crown

Model No.:	H-1537A	
Designer:	Tom Masterson	
Height:	¾", 1.9 cm	
Colour:	Gold; gloss	
Issued:	Fall 1956	

Model No.	U.S. $	Can. $	U.K. £
H-1537A		Rare	

Note: See also Poodle 'Fifi' (H-1537), Pedigree Dog section, page 445.

Dachshund Basket

Model No.:	H-1575	
Designer:	Tom Masterson	
Height:	2 ¾", 3.2 cm	
Colour:	Yellow	
Issued:	Fall 1959, spring 1961	

Model No.	U.S. $	Can. $	U.K. £
H-1575	40.00	80.00	70.00

Shoe

Model No.:	H-1509A	
Designer:	Maureen Love	
Height:	1/2", 1.3 cm	
Colour:	Brown; gloss	
Issued:	Spring 1955 - fall 1956, fall 1961	

Model No.	U.S. $	Can. $	U.K. £
H-1509A	25.00	50.00	45.00

Note: This forms a pair with English Bulldog Puppy 'Nobby' (H-1509), page 439.

Boxer 'Duchess' (H-1525)

STONEWARE AND SPECIALTIES LINE

Maureen Love's work inspired the Stoneware line, which was launched in 1988 with three ducks. These were cast in stoneware and were matte, and sgraffito was used to define the feather details. In 1989, more figurines were added to the line. In the fall of 1990, the line was renamed Specialties and all pieces were given a glossy finish. The pieces are almost a miniature Designer's Workshop line, allowing just that little more room for details, like the decals on the frogs' instruments and the colour range on the kudu. At present, the Specialties line accounts for about 10 percent of sales. It would be wonderful if this line could continue to grow and take a greater share of the market.

INDEX TO
STONEWARE AND SPECIALTIES LINE

BIRDS

Bluebirds on Birdhouse
Model No.: 3115
Designer: Edith Carrion
Height: 3", 7.6 cm
Colour: Blue birds, white birdhouse, green roof
Issued: 1993, 1994
Series: Specialties

Model No.	U.S. $	Can. $	U.K.£
3115	17.00	34.00	30.00

Budgies
Model No.: 2030
Designer: Maureen Love
Height: 2 3/8", 8.6 cm
Colour: Blue and green budgerigars on branch, green leaves
Issued: Spring 1991 to the present
Series: Specialties

Model No.	U.S. $	Can. $	U.K.£
2030	12.00	24.00	20.00

Note: See also Budgie (In hoop), page 144.

Canada Goose, head up
Model No.: 2026
Designer: Maureen Love
Height: 1 ¼", 3.1 cm
Colour: Brown-grey body, black neck, black and white head
Issued: 1989
Series: Stoneware

Model No.	U.S. $	Can. $	U.K.£
2026	12.00	24.00	20.00

Canada Goose, head down
Model No.: 2027
Designer: Maureen Love
Height: 1 3/8", 3.5 cm
Colour: Brown-grey body, black neck, black and white head
Issued: 1989
Series: Stoneware

Model No.	U.S. $	Can. $	U.K.£
2027	12.00	24.00	20.00

Canada Geese on Pond

Model No.:	3030
Designer:	Maureen Love
Height:	3 1/8", 7.9 cm
Colour:	Brown-grey geese; black heads, necks and feet; brown rocks; green pond
Issued:	Fall 1991 - fall 1994
Series:	Specialties

Model No.	U.S. $	Can. $	U.K.£
3030	30.00	60.00	50.00

Cardinal, short

Model No.:	2054
Designer:	Maureen Love
Height:	2 ¼", 5.7 cm
Colour:	Red bird on a brown bisque branch
Issued:	1989
Series:	Stoneware

Model No.	U.S. $	Can. $	U.K.£
2054	22.00	44.00	38.00

Cardinal, tall

Model No.:	2054
Designer:	Maureen Love
Height:	3", 7.6 cm
Colour:	Red bird on a grey bisque branch
Issued:	1991 - 1992
Series:	Specialties

Model No.	U.S. $	Can. $	U.K.£
2054	20.00	40.00	35.00

Note: A grey gloss branch is also known.
See also miniature Cardinal (A-3289), page 144.

Cockatoo

Model No.:	897
Designer:	Maureen Love
Height:	3", 7.6 cm
Colour:	White and yellow bird, black bill, brown branch, green leaves
Issued:	1991 - 1993
Series:	Specialties

Model No.	U.S. $	Can. $	U.K.£
897	20.00	40.00	35.00

Note: See also miniature Cockatoo (A-897), page 144.

Doves in Bower

Model No.:	895
Designer:	Maureen Love
Size:	2 1/8" x 3 ½", 5.4 x 8.9 cm
Colour:	1. White doves, green branch
	2. White doves, white branch, black eyes
	3. White doves, white branch, red eyes
Issued:	1992 - 1993
Series:	Specialties

Colourways	U.S. $	Can. $	U.K.£
1. White/green	20.00	40.00	35.00
2. White, black eyes	22.00	44.00	38.00
3. White, red eyes	24.00	48.00	40.00

Note: See also Miniatures Section, page 147.

Eagle
Style One

Model No.:	3077
Designer:	Shi Yi Chen
Size:	2 15/16" x 5 7/8", 7.5 x 14.9 cm
Colour:	Brown, white head, beige rock
Issued:	Fall 1992 - 1993
Series:	Specialties

Model No.	U.S. $	Can. $	U.K.£
3077	18.00	36.00	30.00

Eagle
Style Two

Model No.:	3153
Designer:	Maureen Love
Size:	3 7/8" x 4 ½", 9.8 x 11.9 cm
Colour:	Brown, white head, gold rock
Issued:	1994 to the present
Series:	Specialties

Model No.	U.S. $	Can. $	U.K.£
3153	15.00	30.00	25.00

Egret

Model No.:	2095
Designer:	Maureen Love
Height:	3 ¾", 9.5 cm
Colour:	White, yellow bill, grey rock, green leaves
Issued:	1991
Series:	Specialties

Model No.	U.S. $	Can. $	U.K.£
2095	21.00	42.00	35.00

Hen

Model No.:	3008
Designer:	Maureen Love
Height:	2 1/8", 5.4 cm
Colour:	Red-brown and tan
Issued:	Fall 1990 - spring 1991
Series:	Specialties

Model No.	U.S. $	Can. $	U.K.£
3008	20.00	40.00	35.00

Note: This forms a pair with Rooster (3007), page 459.

Henny Penny

Model No.:	3132
Designer:	Helen Perrin Farnlund
Height:	2 ½", 6.4 cm
Colour:	Brown
Issued:	Fall 1993 - fall 1995
Series:	Specialties

Model No.	U.S. $	Can. $	U.K.£
3132	17.00	34.00	30.00

Hummingbird

Model No.:	3128
Designer:	Edith Carrion
Height:	2", 5.0 cm
Colour:	Green and red bird, white and pink flowers
Issued:	Fall 1993 - spring 1996
Series:	Specialties

Model No.	U.S. $	Can. $	U.K.£
3128	14.00	28.00	24.00

Hummingbird on Flower

Model No.:	3270
Designer:	Robert McGuinness
Height:	3 1/8", 7.9 cm
Colour:	Blue and red bird, white and yellow flowers, green branch
Issued:	Spring 1998 to the present
Series:	Specialties

Model No.	U.S. $	Can. $	U.K.£
3270	15.00	30.00	25.00

Loons on Golden Pond

Model No.:	2006
Designer:	Maureen Love
Size:	1 ½" x 5 1/8", 3.8 x 13.0 cm
Colour:	Black and white loons, grey chick, golden pond
Issued:	Fall 1991 - fall 1993
Series:	See below

Series	U.S. $	Can. $	U.K.£
1. Specialties	28.00	56.00	49.00
2. Stoneware (singly)	13.00	26.00	23.00

Mallard Duck on Pond

Model No.:	3035
Designer:	Maureen Love
Size:	2 ¾" x 3 7/8", 7.0 x 9.8 cm
Colour:	White duck, dark brown breast, light brown wings, green head, green pond
Issued:	Fall 1991 - fall 1992
Series:	Specialties

Model No.	U.S. $	Can. $	U.K.£
3035	18.00	36.00	30.00

Mallard

Model No.:	2036
Designer:	Maureen Love
Height:	1 3/8", 3.5 cm
Colour:	Brown body, beige underbody, green head
Issued:	1989
Series:	Stoneware / Specialties

Model No.	U.S. $	Can. $	U.K.£
2036	14.00	28.00	24.00

Note: This model was reworked to make the miniature Wood Duck (A-3443), page 185.

Owl

Model No.:	2072
Designer:	Maureen Love
Height:	2 3/8", 6.0 cm
Colour:	Brown
Issued:	Fall 1989
Series:	Stoneware

Model No.	U.S. $	Can. $	U.K.£
2072	20.00	40.00	35.00

Parrot

Model No.:	3211
Designer:	Robert McGuinness
Height:	3 ¾", 9.5 cm
Colour:	Green parrot, black wing tips and broom branch, white flowers
Issued:	Fall 1997 to the present
Series:	Specialties

Model No.	U.S. $	Can. $	U.K.£
3211	12.00	24.00	20.00

Pelican

Model No.:	2037
Designer:	Maureen Love
Height:	2", 5.0 cm
Colour:	Light brown
Issued:	1. Specialties —1991
	2. Stoneware —1989

Series	U.S. $	Can. $	U.K.£
1. Specialties	20.00	40.00	35.00
2. Stoneware	18.00	36.00	30.00

Peregrine Falcon

Model No.:	3197
Designer:	Maureen Love
Height:	3 ½", 8.9 cm
Colour:	Dark brown body, white neck and breast, light brown underbody, yellow talons, brown base
Issued:	Spring 1998 to the present
Series:	Specialties

Model No.	U.S. $	Can. $	U.K.£
3197	13.00	26.00	23.00

Pintail Duck on Pond

Model No.:	2005
Designer:	Maureen Love
Height:	1. Specialties — 2 ½", 6.4 cm
	2. Stoneware — 1 7/16", 3.6 cm
Colour:	Dark and light brown, black and white
Issued:	1. Specialties — Fall 1991 - fall 1992
	2. Stoneware — 1989

Series	U.S. $	Can. $	U.K.£
1. Specialties	18.00	36.00	30.00
2. Stoneware	14.00	28.00	24.00

Quail

Model No.:	2038
Designer:	Maureen Love
Height:	1 5/8", 4.1 cm
Colour:	Light brown, black and white
Issued:	1. Specialties — 1991
	2. Stoneware — 1989

Series	U.S. $	Can. $	U.K.£
1. Specialties	18.00	36.00	30.00
2. Stoneware	17.00	34.00	30.00

Robins

Model No.:	3031
Designer:	Maureen Love
Height:	2 5/8", 6.6 cm
Colour:	Dark brown robin with red breast, dark brown chick with light brown breast, brown nest
Issued:	Fall 1991 - fall 1994
Series:	Specialties

Model No.	U.S. $	Can. $	U.K.£
3031	19.00	38.00	33.00

Rooster

Model No.:	3007
Designer:	Maureen Love
Height:	2 5/8", 6.6 cm
Colour:	Yellow, brown and black; gloss
Issued:	Fall 1990, spring 1991, 1993, spring 1994
Series:	Specialties

Model No.	U.S. $	Can. $	U.K.£
3007	19.00	38.00	33.00

Note: This forms a pair with Hen (3008), page 456.

Seagulls

Model No.:	3050
Designer:	Maureen Love
Height:	4 3/8", 11.1 cm
Colour:	White seagulls with grey wings, pale blue base
Issued:	Spring 1992 - spring 1995
Series:	Specialties

Model No.	U.S. $	Can. $	U.K.£
3050	35.00	70.00	60.00

Teal Duck

Model No.:	2004
Designer:	Maureen Love
Height:	1 ¼", 3.1 cm
Colour:	Beige body, brown head, green eye patch
Issued:	1. Specialties — Unknown
	2. Stoneware — 1989

Series	U.S. $	Can. $	U.K.
1. Specialties	18.00	36.00	30.00
2. Stoneware	14.00	28.00	24.00

Note: The first Stoneware models were issued without a ceramic base and later models, with a base.

Teal Duck With Cattails

Model No.:	2004
Designer:	Maureen Love
Height:	1 3/8", 3.5 cm
Colour:	Beige body, brown speckled breast, brown head, green eye patch, brown base, green reeds
Issued:	1. Specialties — Fall 1991 - fall 1993
	2. Stoneware — 1989

Series	U.S. $	Can. $	U.K.£
1. Specialties	18.00	36.00	30.00
2. Stoneware	14.00	28.00	24.00

Toucan

Model No.:	899
Designer:	Maureen Love
Height:	2 1/8", 5.4 cm
Colour:	Black and white bird, yellow bill
Issued:	Spring 1991 - spring 1992
Series:	Specialties

Model No.	U.S. $	Can. $	U.K.£
899	22.00	44.00	38.00

Note: See also miniature Toucan (A-899), page 182.

BUTTERFLIES

Monarch Butterfly

Model No.:	3103		
Designer:	Maureen Love		
Height:	3 15/16″, 10.0 cm		
Colour:	Orange and black butterfly, yellow flower, green stem		
Issued:	Spring 1993 to the present		
Series:	Specialties		

Model No.	U.S. $	Can. $	U.K.£
3103	18.00	36.00	30.00

Swallowtail Butterfly on Flower

Model No.:	3166		
Designer:	Maureen Love		
Height:	2 5/8″, 6.6 cm		
Colour:	Yellow and black butterfly, white flower, green leaves		
Issued:	Spring 1995 to the present		
Series:	Specialties		

Model No.	U.S. $	Can. $	U.K.£
3166	18.00	36.00	30.00

CATS

Cat on Pillow

Model No.:	3108		
Designer:	Edith Carrion		
Height:	2 3/8″, 6.0 cm		
Colour:	White cat, blue pillow		
Issued:	Fall 1993 - fall 1994		
Series:	Specialties		

Model No.	U.S. $	Can. $	U.K.£
3108	15.00	30.00	25.00

Puss in Boots

Model No.:	3236		
Designer:	Helen Perrin Farnlund		
Height:	3 5/8″, 9.2 cm		
Colour:	Grey cat; blue vest, cloak and hat; pink bows; white feathers; black boots		
Issued:	Spring 1997 to the present		
Series:	Specialties		

Model No.	U.S. $	Can. $	U.K.£
3236	15.00	30.00	25.00

Note: See also Puss in Boots (82), page 41.

CATTLE

Cow

Model No.:	3244
Designer:	Maureen Love
Height:	2 ¾", 7.0 cm
Colour:	Red-brown and white
Issued:	Fall 1997 to the present
Series:	Specialties

Model No.	U.S. $	Can. $	U.K.£
3244	27.00	54.00	47.00

Calf

Model No.:	3245
Designer:	Maureen Love
Height:	1 2/3", 4.2 cm
Colour:	Red-brown and white
Issued:	Fall 1997 to the present
Series:	Specialties

Model No.	U.S. $	Can. $	U.K.£
3245	16.00	32.00	28.00

HORSES

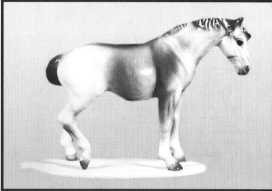

Appaloosa Foal 'Sizzle'

Model No.:	3268	
Designer:	Maureen Love	
Height:	2 3/8", 6.0 cm	
Colour:	Chestnut and white	
Re-issued:	Fall 1998 to the present	
Series:	Specialties	

Model No.	U.S. $	Can. $	U.K.£
3268	10.00	20.00	17.00

Appaloosa Mare 'Kamiah'

Model No.:	3266	
Designer:	Maureen Love	
Height:	2 ½", 6.4 cm	
Colour:	Chestnut and white	
Re-issued:	Fall 1998 to the present	
Series:	Specialties	

Model No.	U.S. $	Can. $	U.K.£
3266	14.00	28.00	25.00

Appaloosa Stallion 'Orion'

Model No.:	3267	
Designer:	Maureen Love	
Height:	3 1/8", 8.0 cm	
Colour:	Sandy-bay and white	
Re-issued:	Fall 1998 to the present	
Series:	Specialties	

Model No.	U.S. $	Can. $	U.K.£
3267	14.00	28.00	25.00

Bucking Bronco

Model No.:	3233
Designer:	Maureen Love
Height:	5", 12.7 cm
Colour:	White horse with black mane and tail; cowboy with blue jeans and shirt, black hat; brown base
Issued:	Spring 1997 to the present
Series:	Specialties

Model No.	U.S. $	Can. $	U.K.£
3233	27.00	54.00	47.00

Cutting Horse and Steer

Cutting Horse

Model No.:	3214
Designer:	Maureen Love
Height:	2 15/16", 7.5 cm
Colour:	Light brown horse with black mane, tail and legs; rider wears blue shirt and jeans, white stetson
Issued:	Fall 1996 to the present
Series:	Specialties

Model No.	U.S. $	Can. $	U.K.£
3214	20.00	40.00	35.00

Steer

Model No.:	3216
Designer:	Maureen Love
Height:	1 ½", 3.8 cm
Colour:	Brown and white
Issued:	Fall 1996 to the present
Series:	Specialties

Model No.	U.S. $	Can. $	U.K.£
3216	10.00	20.00	17.00

Note: Later models of 3216 have pink around the eyes.

Girl and Pony

Model No.:	3170
Designer:	Robert McGuinness
Height:	2 11/16", 6.82 cm
Colour:	1. Chestnut pony, blonde girl
	2. Chestnut pony, brunette girl
Issued:	Fall 1995 to the present
Series:	Specialties

Colourways	U.S. $	Can. $	U.K.£
1. Blonde girl	22.00	44.00	38.00
2. Brunette girl	18.00	36.00	30.00

Note: Earlier colourways show the girl with blonde hair.

Horse, rearing, 'Skywalker'

Model No.:	3284
Designer:	Maureen Love
Height:	4 ½", 11.9 cm
Colour:	Silver dun
Issued:	Fall 1998 to the present
Series:	Specialties

Model No.	U.S. $	Can. $	U.K.£
3284	16.00	30.00	250.0

Indian on Pony

Model No.:	3277
Designer:	Maureen Love
Height:	3 7/8", 9.8 cm
Colour:	Chestnut pinto horse; brown blanket; Indian wears red headband, green and lavender poncho, tan pants
Issued:	Fall 1998 to the present
Series:	Specialties

Model No.	U.S. $	Can. $	U.K.£
3277	20.00	40.00	35.00

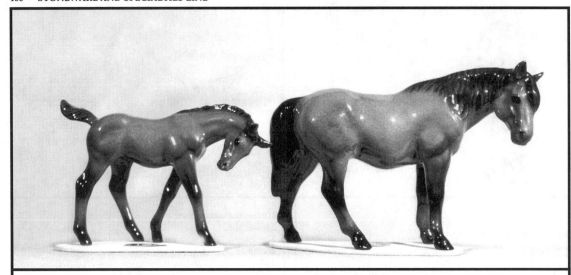

Morgan Foal 'Legacy'

Model No.:	3263
Designer:	Maureen Love
Height:	1 7/8", 4.8 cm
Colour:	Bay
Issued:	Spring 1998 to the present
Series:	Specialties

Model No.	U.S. $	Can. $	U.K.£
3263	10.00	20.00	17.00

Morgan Mare 'Liberty Belle'

Model No.:	3262
Designer:	Maureen Love
Height:	2 5/16", 5.9 cm
Colour:	Bay
Issued:	Spring 1998 to the present
Series:	Specialties

Model No.	U.S. $	Can. $	U.K.£
3262	14.00	28.00	24.00

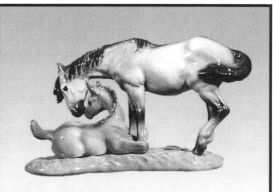

Morgan Stallion 'Shiloh'

Model No.:	3261	
Designer:	Maureen Love	
Height:	3 1/16", 7.8 cm	
Colour:	Dark red bay	
Issued:	Spring 1998 to the present	
Series:	Specialties	

Model No.	U.S. $	Can. $	U.K.£
3261	18.00	36.00	30.00

Mustang and Colt

Model No.:	3175	
Designer:	Maureen Love	
Height:	2 ½", 6.4 cm	
Colour:	Light bay mare, chestnut foal	
Issued:	Fall 1995 to the present	
Series:	Specialties	

Model No.	U.S. $	Can. $	U.K.£
3175	18.00	36.00	30.00

Thoroughbred Stallion 'Mistweaver'

Model No.:	3273	
Designer:	Maureen Love	
Height:	2 ¾", 7.0 cm	
Colour:	Grey-white horse; black mane, tail and legs	
Issued:	Spring 1998 to the present	
Series:	Specialties	

Model No.	U.S. $	Can. $	U.K.£
3273	14.00	28.00	24.00

Thoroughbred Mare 'Quicksilver'

Model No.:	3259
Designer:	Maureen Love
Height:	3 1/8", 7.9 cm
Colour:	White with black mane and tail
Issued:	Spring 1998 to the present
Series:	Specialties

Model No.	U.S. $	Can. $	U.K.£
3259	14.00	28.00	24.00

Thoroughbred Foal 'Raindrop'

Model No.:	3260
Designer:	Maureen Love
Height:	2 ½", 6.4 cm
Colour:	White with black mane and tail
Issued:	Spring 1998 to the present
Series:	Specialties

Model No.	U.S. $	Can. $	U.K.£
3260	10.00	20.00	17.00

HORSES - MISCELLANEOUS

Unicorn

Model No.:	3040
Designer:	Helen Perrin Farnlund
Height:	2 3/8", 6.0 cm
Colour:	White; grey mane and tail; brown horn and feet; green-brown base; blue, white, pink and yellow flowers
Issued:	Fall 1991 to the present
Series:	Specialties

Model No.	U.S. $	Can. $	U.K.£
3040	15.00	30.00	25.00

Wise Man, arm out (3000); Shepherd Boy With Lamb (3025); Baby Jesus (3000); Mary (3000);
Shepherd With Crook (3039); Joseph (3000); Wise Man, standing (3000); Wise Man, kneeling (3000); Manger (3024)

Nativity Set

Robert McGuinness is the designer of the boxed Nativity Set, model number 3000, which was introduced in the fall 1991 and is still being produced. These models belong to the Specialties series.

Name	Colourways	Height	U.S. $	Can. $	U.K. £
Baby Jesus	Brown and white	7/16", 1.1 cm			
Joseph	Brown clothing, black hair	2 3/8", 6.0 cm			
Mary	White clothing, brown hair	1 5/8", 4.1 cm		Complete boxed set	
Wise Man, arm out	White robe, green cape, yellow turban	1 5/8", 4.1 cm	40.00	80.00	70.00
Wise Man, kneeling	Violet cape, gold crown	1 ¾", 4.4 cm			
Wise Man, standing	Green clothes, white beard	2 3/8", 6.03 cm			

Note: For information on the Manger (3024), Shepherd Boy With Lamb (3025) and Shepherd With Crook (3039), see page 471.

Nativity Scene

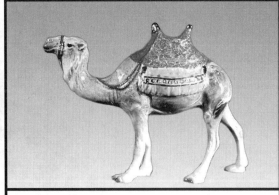

Angel

Model No.:	1. 3023, 2. 3023-1
Designer:	Robert McGuinness
Height:	2", 5.0 cm
Colour:	1. White robe, blue sleeves, gold wings and collar, blond hair
	2. White robe, pink sleeves and collar, white wings, red hair
Issued:	Fall 1991 - fall 1992
Series:	Specialties

Colourways	U.S. $	Can. $	U.K.£
1. Gold wings	24.00	48.00	40.00
2. White wings	16.00	32.00	28.00

Camel

Model No.:	3027
Designer:	Robert McGuinness
Height:	2 ¾", 7.0 cm
Colour:	Buff camel, orange and blue saddle
Issued:	Fall 1991 - fall 1992
Series:	Specialties

Model No.	U.S. $	Can. $	U.K.£
3027	40.00	80.00	70.00

Donkey

Model No.:	3026
Designer:	Robert McGuinness
Height:	1 9/16", 4.0 cm
Colour:	Grey donkey, purple blanket
Issued:	Fall 1991 - fall 1992
Series:	Specialties

Model No.	U.S. $	Can. $	U.K.£
3026	20.00	40.00	35.00

Ewe

Model No.:	3075
Designer:	Robert McGuinness
Height:	1", 2.5 cm
Colour:	White
Issued:	Fall 1992
Series:	Specialties

Model No.	U.S. $	Can. $	U.K.£
3075	15.00	30.00	25.00

Lamb

Model No.:	3076	
Designer:	Robert McGuinness	
Height:	5/8", 1.6 cm	
Colour:	White	
Issued:	Fall 1992	
Series:	Specialties	

Model No.	U.S. $	Can. $	U.K.£
3076	13.00	26.00	23.00

For illustration of
the Manger (3024),
see page 469

Manger

Model No.:	3024	
Designer:	Robert McGuinness	
Height:	3 11/16", 9.4 cm	
Colour:	Light and dark brown	
Issued:	Fall 1991 to the present	
Series:	Specialties	

Model No.	U.S. $	Can. $	U.K.£
3024	10.00	20.00	17.00

For illustration of
Shepherd Boy With Lamb,
see page 469

Shepherd Boy With Lamb

Model No.:	3025	
Designer:	Robert McGuinness	
Height:	1 1/8", 2.8 cm	
Colour:	Brown clothing, white lamb	
Issued:	Fall 1991, fall 1992	
Series:	Specialties	

Model No.	U.S. $	Can. $	U.K.£
3025	14.00	28.00	24.00

For illustration of
Shepherd With Crook,
see page 469

Shepherd With Crook

Model No.:	3039	
Designer:	Robert McGuinness	
Height:	1 ½", 3.8 cm	
Colour:	Brown and white clothing, brown hair	
Issued:	Fall 1991, fall 1992	
Series:	Specialties	

Model No.	U.S. $	Can. $	U.K.£
3039	15.00	30.00	25.00

AMPHIBIANS

Dancing Frogs
Model No.: 3052
Designer: Nell Bortells
Height: 3 ½", 8.9 cm
Colour:
1. Green frog, pink skirt, brown-green frog, green lily pad
2. Green frog, pink skirt, brown-green frog, white ceramic base
Issued: Spring 1992 to the present
Series: Specialties

Colourways	U.S. $	Can. $	U.K.£
1. Green lily pad	15.00	30.00	25.00
2. White base	15.00	30.00	25.00

Note: Earlier models came on green lily pads.

Frog Groom
Model No.: 3114
Designer: Helen Perrin Farnlund
Height: 2 3/8", 6.0 cm
Colour: Green frog, white shirt, black tie and tails, cream base
Issued: Spring 1993 - spring 1996
Series: Specialties

Model No.	U.S. $	Can. $	U.K.£
3114	15.00	30.00	25.00

Note: The forms a pair with Mouse Bride (3113), page 479.

Frog Prince
Model No.: 2055
Designer: Maureen Love
Height: 2 1/8", 5.4 cm
Colour: Green frog, red crown, brown base
Issued: 1989
Series: Stoneware

Model No.	U.S. $	Can. $	U.K.£
2055	21.00	42.00	35.00

Note: Model 2055 was also used to make the Tree Frog (without crown), page 474.

Froggie Mountain Breakdown
Frog Bluegrass Band

Fiddle Player (3181), Banjo Player (3180), Bass Player (3182), Guitar Player (3179), Dulcimer Player (3183)

These models are all current, with Mandolin Player having been introduced in the fall of 1998 and the rest of the band, in the fall of 1995.

Designer: Helen Perrin Farnlund
Colour: Green frogs playing brown instruments
Issued: Fall 1995 to the present, model 3288 - fall 1998 to the present
Series: Specialties

Name	Model No.	Height	U.S. $	Can. $	U.K. £
Banjo Player	3180	2 5/16", 5.9 cm	15.00	30.00	25.00
Bass Player	3182	2 15/16", 7.5 cm	15.00	30.00	25.00
Dulcimer Player	3183	2", 5.0 cm	15.00	30.00	25.00
Fiddle Player	3181	2 1/8", 5.4 cm	15.00	30.00	25.00
Guitar Player	3179	2 5/16", 5.9 cm	15.00	30.00	25.00
Mandolin Player	3288	1 7/8", 4.8 cm	15.00	30.00	25.00

Note: The Mandolin Player (3288) is not illustrated.

Iguana
Model No.:   3061
Designer: Maureen Love
Height: 2 ¼", 5.7 cm
Colour: Green iguana on black rock
Issued: Spring 1992 - spring 1995
Series: Specialties

Model No.	U.S. $	Can. $	U.K.£
3061	25.00	50.00	45.00

Toadally Brass

Tuba Player (3252), Trumpet Player (3254), Trombone Player (3251),
French Horn Player (3253), Flute Player (3257), Clarinet Player (3258)

Designer: Helen Perrin Farnlund
Colour: Green frogs wearing purple jackets and playing gold instruments
Issued: Fall 1997 to the present
Series: Specialties

Name	Model No.	Height	U.S. $	Can.$	U.K. £
Clarinet Player	3258	1 3/8", 3.5 cm	15.00	30.00	25.00
Flute Player	3257	1 5/16", 3.3 cm	15.00	30.00	25.00
French Horn Player	3253	1 1/8", 2.8 cm	15.00	30.00	25.00
Trombone Player	3251	1 ¼", 3.1 cm	15.00	30.00	25.00
Trumpet Player	3254	1 ¼", 3.1 cm	15.00	30.00	25.00
Tuba Player	3252	1 ¾", 4.4 cm	15.00	30.00	25.00

Tree Frog
Model No.:   2055
Designer: Maureen Love
Height: 1 7/8", 4.8 cm
Colour: Green gloss frog, grey bisque base
Issued: Fall 1990 - spring 1991
Series: Specialties

Model No.	U.S. $	Can. $	U.K.£
2055	20.00	40.00	35.00

Note: Model 2055 was also used to make Frog Prince
(with crown), page 472.

SEA CREATURES

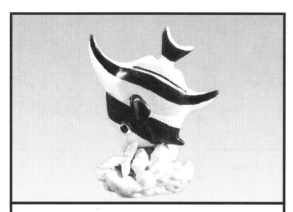

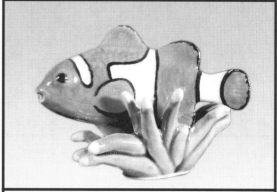

Angel Fish

Model No.:	2034
Designer:	Laurilyn Burson
Height:	2 7/16", 6.2 cm
Colour:	Yellow, black and white fish
Issued:	1. Specialties – Fall 1990 - spring 1991
	2. Stoneware – 1989

Series	U.S. $	Can. $	U.K.£
1. Specialties	20.00	40.00	35.00
2. Stoneware	18.00	36.00	30.00

Clown Fish

Model No.:	2031
Designer:	Laurilyn Burson
Height:	1 7/16", 3.6 cm
Colour:	Orange, black and white fish
Issued:	1. Specialties – Fall 1990 - spring 1991
	2. Stoneware – 1989

Series	U.S. $	Can. $	U.K.£
1. Specialties	20.00	40.00	35.00
2. Stoneware	18.00	36.00	30.00

Coin Fish

Model No.:	2088
Designer:	Helen Perrin Farnlund
Height:	2", 5.0 cm
Colour:	Blue fish, black markings; yellow fish, dark brown markings; grey-green rock
Issued:	Fall 1990 - spring 1995
Series:	Specialties

Model No.	U.S. $	Can. $	U.K.£
2088	15.00	30.00	25.00

Note: See also Miniatures section, page 301.

Dolphin

Model No.:	3189
Designer:	Maureen Love
Height:	2 ¼", 5.7 cm
Colour:	Dark grey
Issued:	Fall 1995 to the present
Series:	Specialties

Model No.	U.S. $	Can. $	U.K.£
3189	10.00	20.00	17.00

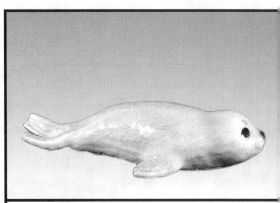

Goldfish

Model No.:	426
Designer:	Helen Perrin Farnlund
Height:	1 5/8", 4.1 cm
Colour:	Orange goldfish, green base
Issued:	Fall 1990 to the present
Series:	Specialties

Model No.	U.S. $	Can. $	U.K.£
426	20.00	40.00	35.00

Note: Model 426 was previously released as miniature 'Fantail Fish' (A-426); see page 301.

Harp Seal

Model No.:	3195
Designer:	Robert McGuinness
Size:	½" x 2 5/8", 1.3 x 6.6 cm
Colour:	1. Iridescent white
	2. White
Issued:	1996
Series:	Specialties

Colourways	U.S. $	Can. $	U.K.£
1. Iridescent	13.00	26.00	23.00
2. White	11.00	22.00	19.00

Sea Horse

Model No.:	2089
Designer:	Helen Perrin Farnlund
Height:	2 ½", 6.4 cm
Colour:	1. Blue
	2. Orange
Issued:	Fall 1990 - spring 1991
Series:	Specialties

Colourways	U.S. $	Can. $	U.K.£
1. Blue	20.00	40.00	35.00
2. Orange	20.00	40.00	35.00

Sea Turtle

Model No.:	3256
Designer:	Maureen Love
Size:	1 1/8" x 2 ¾", 2.8 x 7.0 cm
Colour:	Brown
Issued:	Fall 1997 to the present
Series:	Specialties

Model No.	U.S. $	Can. $	U.K.£
3256	10.00	20.00	17.00

WILD ANIMALS

Chimpanzees
Model No.: 3148
Designer: Robert McGuinness
Height: 2", 5.0 cm
Colour: Brown
Issued: Spring 1994 - spring 1996
Series: Specialties

Model No.	U.S. $	Can. $	U.K.£
3148	18.00	36.00	30.00

Elephant Baby
Model No.: 3269
Designer: Maureen Love
Height: 1 ½", 3.8 cm
Colour: Grey
Issued: Spring 1998 to the present
Series: Specialties

Model No.	U.S. $	Can. $	U.K.£
3269	10.00	20.00	17.00

Elephant Mama
Model No.: 2053
Designer: Maureen Love
Height: 2 ¾", 7.0 cm
Colour: Shades of grey-brown
Issued: 1. Specialties — Unknown to the present
2. Stoneware — Spring 1989

Series	U.S. $	Can. $	U.K.£
1. Specialties	15.00	30.00	25.00
2. Stoneware	20.00	40.00	35.00

Giraffe
Model No.: 3036
Designer: Maureen Love
Height: 3 ¼", 8.3 cm
Colour: Cream with brown spots
Issued: Fall 1991 to the present
Series: Specialties

Model No.	U.S. $	Can. $	U.K.£
3036	20.00	40.00	35.00

Gorilla

Model No.:	3015
Designer:	Maureen Love
Height:	2 7/16", 2.4 cm
Colour:	Black, yellow eyes
Issued:	Spring 1991 - fall 1993
Series:	Specialties

Model No.	U.S. $	Can. $	U.K.£
3015	15.00	30.00	25.00

Kudu

Model No.:	2098
Designer:	Maureen Love
Height:	4 ¼", 10.8 cm
Colour:	Brown
Issued:	Spring 1991 - spring 1992
Series:	Specialties

Model No.	U.S. $	Can. $	U.K.£
2098	45.00	90.00	80.00

Lion, seated

Model No.:	2093
Designer:	Maureen Love
Height:	2 1/8", 5.4 cm
Colour:	Golden brown
Issued:	Fall 1990 - spring 1993
Series:	Specialties

Model No.	U.S. $	Can. $	U.K.£
2093	18.00	36.00	30.00

Lion, walking

Model No.:	2067
Designer:	Maureen Love
Height:	2 1/8", 5.4 cm
Colour:	Golden brown
Issued:	1989
Series:	Stoneware

Model No.	U.S. $	Can. $	U.K.£
2067	20.00	40.00	35.00

Mouse Band

Cat and Fiddle (3062), Singing Mouse (3059), Bongo Mouse (3057), Concertina Mouse (3058)

Designer: Helen Perrin Farnlund
Issued: Cat — Spring 1992 - fall 1993
             Mice — Spring 1992 - spring 1993
Series: Specialties

Name	Model No.	Colour	Height	U.S. $	Can.$	U.K. £
Bongo Mouse	3057	Grey, green jacket	1 7/8", 4.8 cm	23.00	46.00	40.00
Cat and Fiddle	3062	Grey, blue pants, pink tie	2 7/8", 7.3 cm	18.00	36.00	30.00
Concertina Mouse	3058	Grey, purple jacket	1 7/8", 4.8 cm	23.00	46.00	40.00
Singing Mouse	3059	Grey, blue jacket, white tie	2 ¼", 5.7 cm	23.00	46.00	40.00

Mouse Bride
Model No.:   3113
Designer: Helen Perrin Farnlund
Height: 2 1/8", 5.4 cm
Colour: Grey mouse; white veil and shoes, flower
              on veil and in bouquet; cream base
Issued: Spring 1993 - spring 1996
Series: Specialties

Model No.	U.S. $	Can. $	U.K.£
3113	16.00	32.00	28.00

Note: This forms a pair with Frog Groom (3114), page 472.

Pronghorn

Model No.:	2097
Designer:	Maureen Love
Height:	3 ¼", 8.3 cm
Colour:	Tan, black horns and nose
Issued:	Fall 1991 - fall 1992
Series:	Specialties

Model No.	U.S. $	Can. $	U.K.£
2097	35.00	70.00	60.00

Rabbit Bride and Rabbit Groom

Model No.:	1. Bride — 3107
	2. Groom — 3106
Designer:	Edith Carrion
Height:	2 3/8", 6.0 cm
Colour:	1. Bride — White rabbit, blue daisy chain
	2. Groom — White rabbit, black vest and bow tie
Issued:	Fall 1994 - spring 1995
Series:	Specialties

Description	U.S. $	Can. $	U.K.£
1. Rabbit Bride	12.00	24.00	20.00
2. Rabbit Groom	12.00	24.00	20.00

Rhino

Model No.:	3009
Designer:	Maureen Love
Size:	2" x 3 5/8", 5.0 x 9.2 cm
Colour:	Grey
Issued:	1991 - 1992
Series:	Specialties

Model No.	U.S. $	Can. $	U.K.£
3009	25.00	50.00	45.00

Skunk and Cockapoo

Model No.:	1. Cockapoo — 2065
	2. Skunk — 2073
Designer:	Maureen Love
Height:	1. Cockapoo — 1 ¾", 4.4 cm
	2. Skunk — 2 1/8", 5.4 cm
Colour:	1. Cockapoo — Tan
	2. Skunk — Black and white
Issued:	Fall 1989
Series:	Stoneware

Description	U.S. $	Can. $	U.K.£
1. Cockapoo	15.00	30.00	25.00
2. Skunk	15.00	30.00	25.00
3. Skunk/Cockapoo/base	30.00	60.00	50.00

Note: Skunk and Cockapoo were available separately or together on a tan base.

Tiger

Model No.:	3006
Designer:	Maureen Love
Height:	1 ½", 3.8 cm
Colour:	Brown, dark brown stripes
Issued:	Fall 1991 - spring 1994
Series:	Specialties

Model No.	U.S. $	Can. $	U.K.£
3006	20.00	40.00	35.00

Tiger (Miniature)

Model No.:	A-2029
Designer:	Shi Yi Chen
Height:	1 ½", 3.8 cm
Colour:	Tan and brown
Issued:	1989
Series:	Specialties

Model No.	U.S. $	Can. $	U.K.£
3006	20.00	40.00	35.00

Note: See also Miniature Section, page 379.

Triceratops Baby

Model No.:	3152
Designer:	Maureen Love
Height:	1 1/16", 2.7 cm
Colour:	Light green-brown, blue toes and horns
Issued:	1994
Series:	Specialties

Model No.	U.S. $	Can. $	U.K.£
3152	12.00	24.00	20.00

Triceratops Mama

Model No.:	3151
Designer:	Maureen Love
Height:	2 3/8", 6.0 cm
Colour:	Light green-brown, blue toes and horns
Issued:	1994 - spring 1995
Series:	Specialties

Model No.	U.S. $	Can. $	U.K.£
3151	18.00	36.00	30.00

Wolf

Model No.:	3041
Designer:	Maureen Love
Height:	2", 5.1 cm
Colour:	Light grey
Issued:	Fall 1991 to the present
Series:	Specialties

Model No.	U.S. $	Can. $	U.K.£
3041	.00	.00	.00

Zebra

Model No.:	2069
Designer:	Maureen Love
Height:	2", 5.1 cm
Colour:	White, black stripes
Issued:	Fall 1989
Series:	Specialties

Model No.	U.S. $	Can. $	U.K.£
2069	30.00	60.00	50.00

MISCELLANEOUS

Apple and Worm
Model No.: 3105
Designer: Edith Carrion
Height: 2", 5.0 cm
Colour: Green and brown
Issued: 1993, 1994
Series: Specialties

Model No.	U.S. $	Can. $	U.K.£
3105	17.00	34.00	30.00

Bat
Model No.: 3143
Designer: Robert McGuinness
Height: 3 ½", 8.9 cm
Colour: Grey
Issued: 1994
Series: Specialties

Model No.	U.S. $	Can. $	U.K.£
3143	18.00	36.00	30.00

Bookworm
Model No.: 3158
Designer: Edith Carrion
Height: 1 7/8", 4.8 cm
Colour: Green worm, white and blue hat,
white and brown book
Issued: Fall 1994 to the present
Series: Specialties

Model No.	U.S. $	Can. $	U.K.£
3158	10.00	20.00	17.00

Boy Pixie on Mushrooms
Model No.: 3219
Designer: Helen Perrin Farnlund
Height: 2 5/8", 6.6 cm
Colour: Blue clothes and wings, brown hair,
cream mushrooms
Issued: Fall 1996 to the present
Series: Specialties

Model No.	U.S. $	Can. $	U.K.£
3219	15.00	30.00	25.00

Boy With Puppy

Model No.:	3111
Designer:	Robert McGuinness
Height:	3 ¼", 8.3 cm
Colour:	Blond boy wearing blue overalls, white shirt and brown hat; brown puppy
Issued:	Spring 1993 - spring 1994
Series:	Specialties

Model No.	U.S. $	Can. $	U.K.£
3111	20.00	40.00	35.00

Daydreaming Fairy

Model No.:	3212
Designer:	Robert McGuinness
Height:	2 ¾", 7.0 cm
Colour:	White dress and wings, brown hair, green base
Issued:	Fall 1996 to the present
Series:	Specialties

Model No.	U.S. $	Can. $	U.K.£
3212	17.00	34.00	30.00

Fairy Feeding Bunny

Model No.:	3226
Designer:	Robert McGuinness
Height:	3 ½", 8.9 cm
Colour:	White dress, wings and rabbit; brown hair and tree stump
Issued:	Fall 1996 to the present
Series:	Specialties

Model No.	U.S. $	Can. $	U.K.£
3226	18.00	36.00	30.00

Flowers

Model No.:	3165
Designer:	Robert McGuinness
Height:	2 1/8", 5.4 cm
Colour:	1. Pink flower, green leaves
	2. White flower, green leaves
Issued:	Spring 1995 - spring 1996
Series:	Specialties

Colourways	U.S. $	Can. $	U.K.£
1. Pink flower	16.00	32.00	28.00
2. White flower	14.00	28.00	24.00

Flute Player (Fairy)

Model No.:	3222		
Designer:	Robert McGuinness		
Height:	2 ¾", 7.0 cm		
Colour:	1. Amber dress and wings		
	2. White dress and wings		
Issued:	Fall 1996 to the present		
Series:	Specialties		

Colourways	U.S. $	Can. $	U.K.£
1. Amber dress	18.00	36.00	30.00
2. White dress	18.00	36.00	30.00

Girl With Cat

Model No.:	3112
Designer:	Robert McGuinness
Height:	2 3/8", 6.0 cm
Colour:	Brown-haired girl, blue dress and socks, black shoes, grey cat
Issued:	Spring 1993 - spring 1994
Series:	Specialties

Model No.	U.S. $	Can. $	U.K.£
3112	20.00	40.00	35.00

Girl Pixie on Lily Pad

Model No.:	3217
Designer:	Helen Perrin Farnlund
Height:	1 ½", 3.8 cm
Colour:	Pink dress, blonde hair, green lily pad, yellow flower
Issued:	Fall 1996 to the present
Series:	Specialties

Model No.	U.S. $	Can. $	U.K.£
3217	15.00	30.00	25.00

Mermaid on Piling and Mermaid on Rock

Model No.:	1. Mermaid on Piling — 2092
	2. Mermaid on Rock — 2090
Designer:	Helen Perrin Farnlund
Height:	1. 2 5/8", 6.6 cm
	2. 2 1/8", 5.4 cm
Colour:	Red hair, green tail
Issued:	1. Fall 1990 - fall 1991
	2. Fall 1990 - spring 1995
Series:	Specialties

Description	U.S. $	Can. $	U.K.£
1. Mermaid on piling	23.00	46.00	40.00
2. Mermaid on rock	17.00	34.00	30.00

HAGEN - RENAKER
SPECIALTIES

Fall 1991 advertising pamphlet

WALT DISNEY PRODUCTIONS

Hagen-Renaker, according to Walt Disney, "made the finest three-dimensional reproductions of the drawings that he ever saw." This care and detail has made these pieces very collectable.

Disneyland opened on July 17, 1955, and Hagen-Renaker was one of two companies authorized to manufacture and market Walt Disney designs in the United States. The other firm's contract expired on December 31, 1955, leaving Hagen-Renaker as the exclusive licensee. A circus tent was temporarily set up at Disneyland while the attractions were being completed, and so, in addition to Disney characters, a set of circus-related ceramics was designed and released.

The first series of Disney models was sculpted by Helen Perrin Farnlund, Nell Bortells, Don Winton and Martha Armstrong. The smaller pieces were sold attached to a card printed with a description of the piece and larger models, such as Donald Duck, had a name sticker. The Disney line was distributed nationally from fall 1955 through spring 1960. During and after that time, pieces may have been ordered to sell exclusively at Disneyland; therefore, production information is probably not accurate as no wholesale price sheets were available. Colours are true to the original character.

Many models (birds, dogs, chipmunks, etc.) were re-issued in the miniature line with revised colour and decorations. Other models (early zebras, lions, head-up and head-down ponies) were directly inspired by characters in *Dumbo*. The 1961 dogs were expected to be released as characters from *101 Dalmations*, but the contract with Disney expired before that could be done. The second Disney series was designed by Russell Schroeder of Walt Disney Productions in 1982 and sold exclusively through Disneyland and Walt Disney World.

INDEX TO WALT DISNEY CHARACTERS

Lady and the Tramp

Name	Model No.	Page No.
Am	5010	497
Bull	5080	497
Dachsie	5011	498
Fluffy	5005	498
Jock	5007	498
Lady	5001	498
Lady Bank	5071	499
Pedro	5006	499
Peg	5079	499
Ruffles	5003	499
Scamp	5004	500
Scooter	5002	500
Si	5009	500
Tramp	5008	500
Trusty	5013	501

Mickey Mouse And Friends

Name	Model No.	Page No.
Chip With Acorn	5034	501
Dale	5035	501
Donald Duck and Nephews		502
Donald	5021	502
Huey	5030	502
Louie	5031	502
Dewey	5032	502
Goofy	5033	503
Mickey Mouse Bandleader	5029	503
Pluto	5019	503
Uncle Scrooge McDuck	5022	504

Peter Pan

Name	Model No.	Page No.
John	5063	504
Mermaid		
kneeling	5068	504
reclining	5069	505
Michael	5062	505
Michael's Teddy Bear	5062A	505
Nana	5061	505
Peter Pan	5067	506
Tinker Bell		
flying	5060	506
kneeling	5064	506
shelf Sitter	5065	506
Wendy	5066	507

Pinocchio

Name	Model No.	Page No.
Figaro	5053	507
Bank	5059	507
Cookie Jar	5051	508
Jiminy Cricket	5018	508
Bank	5018	508

Sleeping Beauty

Name	Model No.	Page No.
Bluebird	5099	509
Cardinal	5098	509
Fauna	5089	509
Flora	5091	510
King Hubert	5093	510
King Stefan	5096	510
Maleficent	5092	510
Merryweather	5090	511
Owl	5097	511
Prince Phillip	5102	511
Princess Aurora	Unk.	511
Queen	5100	512
Rabbit	5094	512
Samson the Horse	5103	512
Squirrel	5096	512

Snow White and the Seven Dwarfs

Name	Model No.	Page No.
Bashful		
Style One	5038	513
Style Two	5088	515
Doc		
Style One	5043	513
Style Two	5084	515
Dopey		
Style One	5016	513
Style Two	5082	515
Grumpy		
Style One	5040	513
Style Two	5087	515
Happy		
Style One	5038	513
Style Two	5085	515
Sleepy		
Style One	5036	513
Style Two	5083	515
Sneezy		
Style One	5039	513
Style Two	5086	515
Snow White		
Style One	5044	513
Style Two	5081	515

Disney — Miscellaneous

Name	Model No.	Page No.
Disney Sign	5104	517
Shaggy Dog	H-1001	517
Practical Pig		
Bank	5049	517
Cookie Jar	5050	517

ALICE IN WONDERLAND

Alice™

Model No.:	5047
Designer:	Nell Bortells
Height:	1 13/16", 4.6 cm
Colour:	Blue dress, white apron, blond hair
Issued:	Fall 1956 - spring 1957
Series:	Alice in Wonderland

Model No.	U.S. $	Can. $	U.K. £
5047	250.00	500.00	435.00

Note: Alice™ is a shelf sitter.

Caterpillar™

Model No.:	5057
Designer:	Nell Bortells
Height:	1 5/8", 4.1 cm
Colour:	Green, purple shoes
Issued:	Fall 1956
Series:	Alice in Wonderland

Model No.	U.S. $	Can. $	U.K. £
5057	275.00	550.00	480.00

Note: For technical details on the toadstool, see page 394.

Mad Hatter ™

Model No.:	5045
Designer:	Nell Bortells
Height:	1 1/8", 2.9 cm
Colour:	Grey hat with a dark green band, light green coat, dark green vest and shoes, purple bow tie, grey pants, yellow teapot with a grey lid
Issued:	Fall 1956
Series:	Alice in Wonderland

Model No.	U.S. $	Can. $	U.K. £
5045	300.00	600.00	525.00

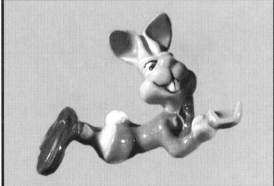

March Hare™

Model No.:	5046
Designer:	Nell Bortells
Height:	1 ½", 3.8 cm
Colour:	Tan rabbit; orange jacket; pink teacup, nose and inner ears; brown shoes
Issued:	Fall 1956
Series:	Alice in Wonderland

Model No.	U.S. $	Can. $	U.K. £
5046	300.00	600.00	525.00

BAMBI

Bambi™
Style One

Model No.:	5055
Designer:	Don Winton
Height:	3 ½", 8.9 cm
Colour:	Light brown
Issued:	Fall 1956 - spring 1957
Series:	Bambi

Model No.	U.S. $	Can. $	U.K. £
5055	300.00	600.00	525.00

Bambi ™
Style Two

Model No.:	5028
Designer:	Helen Perrin Farnlund
Height:	1 5/8", 4.1 cm
Colour:	Pale caramel fawn
Issued:	1957 - spring 1960
Series:	Bambi

Model No.	U.S. $	Can. $	U.K. £
5028	150.00	300.00	260.00

Note: Model 5028 was also used to make Faline™.

Bambi™ With Butterfly

Model No.:	5025
Designer:	Helen Perrin Farnlund
Height:	1 5/8", 4.1 cm
Colour:	1. Pale caramel fawn
	2. Pale caramel fawn, yellow butterfly
Issued:	Fall 1956 - spring 1960
Series:	Bambi

Description	U.S. $	Can. $	U.K. £
1. Without butterfly	130.00	260.00	225.00
2. With butterfly	150.00	300.00	260.00

Faline™

Model No.:	5028
Designer:	Helen Perrin Farnlund
Height:	1 5/8", 4.1 cm
Colour:	Light grey-brown
Issued:	Fall 1956
Series:	Bambi

Model No.	U.S. $	Can. $	U.K. £
5028	150.00	300.00	260.00

Note: Model 5028 was also used to make Bambi™.
See also Fawn, facing right (A-875), page 333.

Flower™
Style One
Model No.: 5023
Designer: Helen Perrin Farnlund
Height: 1 1/6", 3.0 cm
Colour: Black, white stripe, grey chest
Issued: Fall 1956 - spring 1960
Series: Bambi

Model No.	U.S. $	Can. $	U.K. £
5023	65.00	130.00	115.00

Note: There is a hole in the right paw for small flowers.

Flower™
Style Two
Model No.: 5054
Designer: Don Winton
Height: 2 ¼", 5.7 cm
Colour: Black; white stripes; blue iris; blue, pink and yellow flowers
Issued: Fall 1956 - spring 1957
Series: Bambi

Model No.	U.S. $	Can. $	U.K. £
5054	200.00	400.00	350.00

Thumper™
Model No.: 5020
Designer: Helen Perrin Farnlund
Height: 1 5/16", 3.3 cm
Colour: Light brown, beige cheeks and belly, white nose
Issued: Fall 1956 - spring 1960
Series: Bambi

Model No.	U.S. $	Can. $	U.K. £
5020	65.00	130.00	115.00

Note: See also Rabbit Brother (A-858), page 368.

Thumper™ Bank
Model No.: 5070
Designer: Don Winton
Height: 5 13/16", 14.8 cm
Colour: Grey with white belly
Issued: Fall 1956
Series: Bambi

Model No.	U.S. $	Can. $	U.K. £
5070	350.00	700.00	610.00

Note: Banks had removable labels.

CINDERELLA

Cinderella™

Model No.:	5048
Designer:	Helen Perrin Farnlund
Height:	2 5/8", 6.6 cm
Colour:	Blond hair, burgundy bodice, tan skirt, white apron and duster, wire broom handle, yellow bristles
Issued:	Fall 1956 - spring 1957
Series:	Cinderella

Model No.	U.S. $	Can. $	U.K. £
5048	275.00	550.00	480.00

Gus™

Model No.:	5042
Designer:	Helen Perrin Farnlund
Height:	1 ¼", 3.2 cm
Colour:	Light tan, green hat, yellow tie, brown shoes, wire tail, faux pearl
Issued:	Fall 1956 - spring 1957
Series:	Cinderella

Model No.	U.S. $	Can. $	U.K. £
5042	175.00	350.00	300.00

Note: The length of the tail and the number of faux pearls vary.

Jaq™

Model No.:	5041
Designer:	Helen Perrin Farnlund
Height:	1 5/8", 4.1 cm
Colour:	Light tan, purple shirt and hat, orange jacket, brown shoes, faux pearl
Issued:	Fall 1956 - spring 1957
Series:	Cinderella

Model No.	U.S. $	Can. $	U.K. £
5041	175.00	350.00	300.00

DUMBO

Dumbo™, flying

Model No.:	5015
Designer:	Helen Perrin Farnlund
Height:	1 3/8", 3.4 cm
Colour:	Grey, pink inner ears, yellow hat
Issued:	Fall 1956 - spring 1957
Series:	Dumbo

Model No.	U.S. $	Can. $	U.K. £
5015	150.00	300.00	260.00

Note: Dumbo™ holds a parakeet feather in his trunk.

Dumbo™, seated

Model No.:	5056
Designer:	Don Winton
Height:	3 ¾", 9.5 cm
Colour:	Grey, pink inner ears, yellow hat
Issued:	Fall 1956
Series:	Dumbo

Model No.	U.S. $	Can. $	U.K. £
5056	300.00	600.00	525.00

Dumbo™ Bank

Model No.:	5058
Designer:	Don Winton
Height:	5 ¾", 14.6 cm
Colour:	Grey, pink inner ears, pale yellow hat, white collar with red trim
Issued:	Fall 1956
Series:	Dumbo

Model No.	U.S. $	Can. $	U.K. £
5058	300.00	600.00	525.00

Dumbo™ Cookie Jar

Model No.:	5052
Designer:	Don Winton
Height:	10", 25.4 cm
Colour:	Grey, pink inner ears, blue hat
Issued:	Fall 1956
Series:	Dumbo

Model No.	U.S. $	Can. $	U.K. £
5052		Rare	

Timothy™ Mouse

Model No.:	5014
Designer:	Helen Perrin Farnlund
Height:	1 3/16", 3.0 cm
Colour:	1. Brown mouse; grey jacket and hat; yellow epaulets, buttons and tassle
	2. Brown mouse; red jacket and hat; yellow epaulets, buttons and tassle
Issued:	Fall 1956 - spring 1957
Series:	Dumbo

Colourways	U.S. $	Can. $	U.K. £
1. Grey jacket	100.00	200.00	175.00
2. Red jacket	150.00	300.00	260.00

FANTASIA

Bacchus™, pink toga

Model No.:	5078
Designer:	Helen Perrin Farnlund
Height:	1 11/16", 4.3 cm
Colour:	Pink toga, lavender robe, gold goblet
Issued:	Fall 1957
Series:	Fantasia

Model No.	U.S. $	Can. $	U.K. £
5078	225.00	450.00	390.00

Note: The model illustrated is bisque.

Bacchus™, white toga

Model No.:	Unknown
Designer:	Russell Schroeder
Height:	2 ¾", 7.0 cm
Colour:	Beige, white toga, maroon cape
Issued:	1982
Series:	Fantasia

Description	U.S. $	Can. $	U.K. £
Bacchus	175.00	350.00	300.00

Broom™

Model No.:	Unknown
Designer:	Russell Schroeder
Height:	2 5/8", 6.6 cm
Colour:	Beige and brown
Issued:	1982
Series:	Fantasia

Description	U.S. $	Can. $	U.K. £
Broom	180.00	360.00	315.00

Hop Low™

Model No.:	Unknown
Designer:	Russell Schroeder
Height:	¾", 1.9 cm
Colour:	1. Beige stem, maroon top
	2. Beige stem, purple top
Issued:	1982
Series:	Fantasia

Colourways	U.S. $	Can. $	U.K. £
1. Maroon	40.00	80.00	70.00
2. Purple	40.00	80.00	70.00

Fauns and Columns

Designer:	Helen Perrin Farnlund
Colour:	Faun — Pale tan, brown hair
	Column — Green
Issued:	Fall 1957
Series:	Fantasia

Faun™, seated, left leg up

Model No.:	5072
Height:	1 1/8", 2.9 cm

Faun™, seated, right leg up

Model No.:	5073
Height:	1 1/8", 2.9 cm

Faun™, seated

Model No.:	5074
Height:	1 1/8", 2.9 cm

Column

Model No.:	5074A
Height:	1 3/8", 3.5 cm

Description	U.S. $	Can. $	U.K. £
1. Faun, left leg up	175.00	350.00	300.00
2. Faun, right leg up	175.00	350.00	300.00
3. Faun, seated	175.00	350.00	300.00
4. Column	65.00	130.00	115.00
5. Faun and column	200.00	400.00	350.00

Note: An illustration of model 5072 was not available at press time.

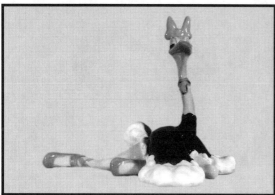

Madama Upanova™

Model No.:	Unknown
Designer:	Russell Schroeder
Height:	3 ¼", 8.3 cm
Colour:	Pale pink neck and legs, red bow and shoes, black body, white plumes
Issued:	1982
Series:	Fantasia

Description	U.S. $	Can. $	U.K. £
Madama Upanova	200.00	400.00	350.00

Mickey™ as the Sorcerer's Apprentice™

Model No.:	Unknown
Designer:	Russell Schroeder
Height:	2 5/8", 6.6 cm
Colour:	Red kimono, blue hat
Issued:	1982
Series:	Fantasia

Description	U.S. $	Can. $	U.K. £
Mickey	180.00	360.00	315.00

Pegasus™ Baby, standing

Model No.:	5077
Designer:	Helen Perrin Farnlund
Height:	1 5/8", 4.1 cm
Colour:	1. Pale pink with blue wings
	2. Yellow with blue wings
Issued:	Fall 1957 - spring 1958
Series:	Fantasia

Colourways	U.S. $	Can. $	U.K. £
1. Pink	175.00	350.00	300.00
2. Yellow	175.00	350.00	300.00

Note: See also Unicorn Baby (A-956), page 293.

Pegasus™ Baby, seated

Model No.:	Unknown
Designer:	Russell Schroeder
Height:	1 7/8", 4.8 cm
Colour:	See below
Issued:	1982
Series:	Fantasia

Colourways	U.S. $	Can. $	U.K. £
1. Black	125.00	250.00	220.00
2. Blue	125.00	250.00	220.00
3. Pink	125.00	250.00	220.00

Unicorn™

Model No.:	5075
Designer:	Helen Perrin Farnlund
Height:	2 ¾", 7.0 cm
Colour:	Light blue; white mane, tail and dapples; gold horn and details
Issued:	Fall 1957 - spring 1958
Series:	Fantasia

Model No.	U.S. $	Can. $	U.K. £
5075	200.00	400.00	350.00

Unicorn™ Baby

Model No.:	5056
Designer:	Helen Perrin Farnlund
Height:	1 7/8", 4.8 cm
Colour:	Light blue; white mane, tail and dapples; gold horn and details
Issued:	Fall 1957 - spring 1958
Series:	Fantasia

Model No.	U.S. $	Can. $	U.K. £
5056	175.00	350.00	300.00

LADY AND THE TRAMP

Am™

Model No.:	5010
Designer:	Don Winton
Height:	1 11/16", 4.3 cm
Colour:	Ivory, dark brown points, grey face, pink inner ears
Issued:	Fall 1955 - fall 1959
Series:	Lady and the Tramp

Model No.	U.S. $	Can. $	U.K. £
5010	90.00	180.00	155.00

Note: This forms a pair with Si™, (5009), page 500.
See also Miniature Section, page 215.

Bull™

Model No.:	5080
Designer:	Don Winton
Height:	1 ¼", 3.1 cm
Colour:	Brown, beige muzzle and feet
Issued:	Fall 1957 - fall 1959
Series:	Lady and the Tramp

Model No.	U.S. $	Can. $	U.K. £
5080	150.00	300.00	260.00

Note: See also Bulldog, Style One (A-855), page 224.

Dachsie™
Model No.:   5011
Designer: Don Winton
Height: 1 1/16", 2.7 cm
Colour: Dark brown, black ears
              and nose, pink mouth
Issued: Fall 1955 - fall 1959
Series: Lady and the Tramp

Model No.	U.S. $	Can. $	U.K. £
5011	75.00	150.00	130.00

Note: See also Dachshund (A-74), page 230.

Fluffy™
Model No.:   5005
Designer: Don Winton
Height: 15/16", 2.4 cm
Colour: Caramel, brown ears, beige
              muzzle and chest
Issued: Fall 1955 - fall 1959
Series: Lady and the Tramp

Model No.	U.S. $	Can. $	U.K. £
5005	45.00	90.00	80.00

Note: Facial expressions may vary.
See also Cocker Spaniel Puppy (A-91), page 228.

Jock™
Model No.:   5007
Designer: Don Winton
Height: 1 ½", 3.8 cm
Colour: Charcoal grey, pale grey eyebrows
              and mustache, pink collar
Issued: Fall 1955 - fall 1959
Series: Lady and the Tramp

Model No.	U.S. $	Can. $	U.K. £
5007	50.00	100.00	85.00

Note: See also Scottish Terrier (A-075/856), page 241.

Lady™
Model No.:   5001
Designer: Don Winton
Height: 1 ¾", 4.4 cm
Colour: Caramel, brown ears, beige
              muzzle and chest
Issued: Fall 1955 - fall 1959
Series: Lady and the Tramp

Model No.	U.S. $	Can. $	U.K. £
5001	50.00	100.00	85.00

Note: See also Cocker Spaniel, Mama (A-90), page 228.

Lady™ Bank

Model No.:	5071	
Designer:	Don Winton	
Height:	5 ½", 14.0 cm	
Colour:	Buff, blue collar	
Issued:	Fall 1956	
Series:	Lady and the Tramp	

Model No.	U.S. $	Can. $	U.K. £
5071	350.00	700.00	610.00

Note: The collar may be either light or dark blue.

Pedro™

Model No.:	5006
Designer:	Don Winton
Height:	1 5/16", 3.3 cm
Colour:	Brown; beige muzzle, chest and belly; black hair
Issued:	Fall 1955 - fall 1959
Series:	Lady and the Tramp

Model No.	U.S. $	Can. $	U.K. £
5006	85.00	170.00	150.00

Note: See also Chihuahua (A-078), page 224.

Peg™

Model No.:	5079
Designer:	Don Winton
Height:	1 5/8", 4.1 cm
Colour:	1. Lemon, yellow ears, purple eye shadow
	2. Tan, yellow ears, purple eye shadow
Issued:	Fall 1957 - fall 1959
Series:	Lady and the Tramp

Colourways	U.S. $	Can. $	U.K. £
1. Lemon	140.00	280.00	245.00
2. Tan	140.00	280.00	245.00

Note: See also Pekinese (A-076), page 237.

Ruffles™

Model No.:	5003
Designer:	Don Winton
Height:	5/8", 1.6 cm
Colour:	Caramel, brown ears, beige muzzle and chest
Issued:	Fall 1955 - fall 1959
Series:	Lady and the Tramp

Model No.	U.S. $	Can. $	U.K. £
5003	35.00	70.00	60.00

Note: See also Cocker Spaniel Puppy (A-92), page 228.

Scamp™

Model No.:	5004
Designer:	Don Winton
Height:	15/16", 2.4 cm
Colour:	Taupe; beige muzzle, chest and belly
Issued:	Fall 1955 - fall 1959
Series:	Lady and the Tramp

Model No.	U.S. $	Can. $	U.K. £
5004	40.00	80.00	70.00

Note: See also Terrier Puppy (A-94), page 244.

Scooter™

Model No.:	5002
Designer:	Don Winton
Height:	1", 2.5 cm
Colour:	Caramel, brown ears, beige muzzle and chest
Issued:	Fall 1955 - fall 1959
Series:	Lady and the Tramp

Model No.	U.S. $	Can. $	U.K. £
5002	45.00	90.00	80.00

Note: See also Cocker Spaniel Puppy (A-93), page 228.

Si™

Model No.:	5009
Designer:	Don Winton
Height:	1 ¾", 4.4 cm
Colour:	Ivory; grey face; dark brown points, tail and legs; pink inner ears
Issued:	Fall 1955 - fall 1959
Series:	Lady and the Tramp

Model No.	U.S. $	Can. $	U.K. £
5009	90.00	180.00	155.00

Note: This forms a pair with Am™, (5010), page 497.
See also Miniature Section, page 215.

Tramp™

Model No.:	5008
Designer:	Don Winton
Height:	2 ¼", 5.7 cm
Colour:	Taupe; beige muzzle, chest and belly
Issued:	Fall 1955 - fall 1959
Series:	Lady and the Tramp

Model No.	U.S. $	Can. $	U.K. £
5008	140.00	280.00	245.00

Note: See also Terrier (A-079/93), page 243.

Trusty™
Model No.:   5013
Designer: Don Winton
Height: 1 15/16", 4.9 cm
Colour: Dark brown, tan muzzle,
               black collar, yellow tag
Issued: Fall 1955 - fall 1959
Series: Lady and the Tramp

Model No.	U.S. $	Can. $	U.K. £
5013	80.00	160.00	140.00

Note: See also Bloodhound, seated (A-77/854), page 221.

MICKEY MOUSE AND FRIENDS

Chip™ With Acorn
Model No.:   5034
Designer: Helen Perrin Farnlund
Height: 1 ¼", 3.1 cm
Colour: Dark brown, beige face and chest,
               green and orange acorn
Issued: Fall 1956
Series: Mickey Mouse and Friends

Model No.	U.S. $	Can. $	U.K. £
5034	85.00	170.00	150.00

Note: See also Chipmunk, holding acorn (A-81),
          page 329.

Dale™
Model No.:   5035
Designer: Helen Perrin Farnlund
Height: 1 ¼", 3.1 cm
Colour: Dark brown, beige face and chest
Issued: Fall 1956
Series: Mickey Mouse and Friends

Model No.	U.S. $	Can. $	U.K. £
5035	65.00	130.00	115.00

Note: The model illustrated has its right arm missing.
          See also Chipmunk, arms open (A-82), page 329.

Donald Duck And Nephews

| Huey, pitcher | Dewey, batter | Donald | Louie, catcher |

Dewey™, batter

Model No.:	5032
Designer:	Don Winton
Height:	1 1/16", 2.7 cm
Colour:	Dark green shirt and hat
Issued:	Fall 1956
Series:	Mickey Mouse and Friends

Model No.	U.S. $	Can. $	U.K. £
5032	100.00	200.00	175.00

Donald™

Model No.:	5021
Designer:	Don Winton
Height:	1 5/8", 4.1 cm
Colour:	Blue sailor suit
Issued:	Fall 1956
Series:	Mickey Mouse and Friends

Model No.	U.S. $	Can. $	U.K. £
5021	140.00	280.00	245.00

Huey™, pitcher

Model No.:	5030
Designer:	Don Winton
Height:	1", 2.5 cm
Colour:	Light blue shirt and hat
Issued:	Fall 1956
Series:	Mickey Mouse and Friends

Model No.	U.S. $	Can. $	U.K. £
5030	100.00	200.00	175.00

Louie™, catcher

Model No.:	5031
Designer:	Don Winton
Height:	1 1/16", 2.7 cm
Colour:	Lavender shirt and hat
Issued:	Fall 1956
Series:	Mickey Mouse and Firends

Model No.	U.S. $	Can. $	U.K. £
5031	100.00	200.00	175.00

Goofy™

Model No.:	5033
Designer:	Don Winton
Height:	2 3/16", 5.5 cm
Colour:	1. Green shirt and hat, brown vest, blue pants, dark brown shoes
	2. White shirt, blue hat and pants, black vest and shoes
Issued:	Fall 1956
Series:	Mickey Mouse and Friends

Colourways	U.S. $	Can. $	U.K. £
1. Green shirt	150.00	300.00	260.00
2. White shirt	150.00	300.00	260.00

Mickey Mouse™ Bandleader

Model No.:	5029
Designer:	Don Winton
Height:	1 13/16", 4.6 cm
Colour:	1. Red suit and hat
	2. White suit, beige and white hat
Issued:	Fall 1956
Series:	Mickey Mouse and Friends

Colourways	U.S. $	Can. $	U.K. £
1. Red	115.00	230.00	200.00
2. White	180.00	360.00	315.00

Note: The model illustrated has the end of the baton missing.

Pluto™

Model No.:	5019
Designer:	Don Winton
Height:	1 5/8", 4.1 cm
Colour:	Caramel, black ears, purple collar
Issued:	Fall 1956
Series:	Mickey Mouse and Friends

Model No.	U.S. $	Can. $	U.K. £
5019	150.00	300.00	260.00

Note: The model illustrated has its tail missing. The tail, when intact, should attach to the right hind leg. The original issue price was 90 cents.

Uncle Scrooge McDuck™
Model No.: 5022
Designer: Don Winton
Height: 1 5/8", 4.1 cm
Colour: White; lavender coat and spats; black hat, collar, cuffs and belt; wire cane; paper dollar bill under cane
Issued: Fall 1956
Series: Mickey Mouse and Friends

Model No.	U.S. $	Can. $	U.K. £
5022	175.00	350.00	300.00

Note: The price is for a mint figure with the dollar bill.

PETER PAN

John™
Model No.: 5063
Designer: Don Winton
Height: 2 1/8", 5.4 cm
Colour: White nightshirt, black hat, grey shoes and umbrella
Issued: Spring 1957 - spring 1960
Series: Peter Pan

Model No.	U.S. $	Can. $	U.K. £
5063	275.00	550.00	480.00

Mermaid™, kneeling
Model No.: 5068
Designer: Don Winton
Height: 2 1/16", 5.2 cm
Colour: 1. Blond hair, black bra
2. Red hair, black bra
Issued: Spring 1957 - spring 1960
Series: Peter Pan

Colourways	U.S. $	Can. $	U.K. £
1. Blond hair	150.00	300.00	260.00
2. Red hair	175.00	350.00	300.00

Mermaid™, reclining

Model No.:	5069
Designer:	Don Winton
Size:	1 ¼" x 3 ¼", 3.1 x 8.3 cm
Colour:	1. Blonde hair, black bra
	2. Red hair, black bra
Issued:	Spring 1957 - spring 1960
Series:	Peter Pan

Colourways	U.S. $	Can. $	U.K. £
1. Blonde hair	150.00	300.00	260.00
2. Red hair	175.00	350.00	300.00

Note: The colourway of blonde hair and blue bra is also known.

Michael™

Model No.:	5062
Designer:	Don Winton
Height:	1 1/16", 2.7 cm
Colour:	Pink
Issued:	Spring 1957 - spring 1960
Series:	Peter Pan

Model No.	U.S. $	Can. $	U.K. £
5062	150.00	300.00	260.00

Michael's Teddy Bear™

Model No.:	5062A
Designer:	Don Winton
Height:	9/16", 1.4 cm
Colour:	Dark brown; beige ears, muzzle and pads
Issued:	Spring 1957 - spring 1960
Series:	Peter Pan

Model No.	U.S. $	Can. $	U.K. £
5062A	60.00	120.00	105.00

Note: See also Little Brother Teddy (A-467), page 325.

Nana™

Model No.:	5061
Designer:	Don Winton
Height:	1 ½", 3.8 cm
Colour:	Brown and white Saint Bernard, blue bonnet
Issued:	Spring 1957 - spring 1960
Series:	Peter Pan

Model No.	U.S. $	Can. $	U.K. £
5061	135.00	270.00	235.00

Peter Pan™

Model No.:	5067
Designer:	Don Winton
Height:	1 ¾", 4.4 cm
Colour:	Dark green tunic and hat, light green pants, brown hair and shoes
Issued:	Spring 1957 - spring 1960
Series:	Peter Pan

Model No.	U.S. $	Can. $	U.K. £
5067	125.00	250.00	220.00

Tinker Bell™, flying

Model No.:	5060
Designer:	Don Winton
Height:	2 ½", 6.4 cm
Colour:	Light green dress, white wings
Issued:	Spring 1957 - spring 1960
Series:	Peter Pan

Model No.	U.S. $	Can. $	U.K. £
5060	400.00	800.00	700.00

Note: This model has an attached wire for placement. Earlier models of Tinker Bell™ had rouged cheeks.

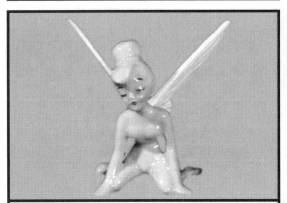

Tinker Bell™, kneeling

Model No.:	5064
Designer:	Don Winton
Height:	1 ¾", 4.4 cm
Colour:	Light green dress, white wings
Issued:	Spring 1957 - spring 1960
Series:	Peter Pan

Model No.	U.S. $	Can. $	U.K. £
5064	200.00	400.00	350.00

Tinker Bell™, shelf sitter

Model No.:	5065
Designer:	Don Winton
Height:	1 7/16", 3.6 cm
Colour:	Light green dress, white wings
Issued:	Spring 1957 - spring 1960
Series:	Peter Pan

Model No.	U.S. $	Can. $	U.K. £
5065	400.00	800.00	700.00

Note: Earlier models of Tinker Bell™ had rouged cheeks.

Note: Earlier models of Tinker Bell™ had rouged cheeks.

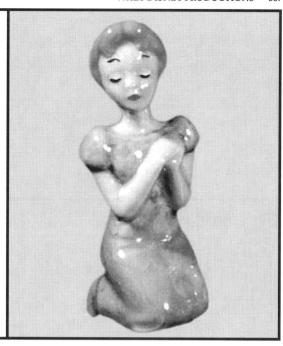

Wendy™
Model No.: 5066
Designer: Don Winton
Height: 2", 5.0 cm
Colour: Green nightgown
Issued: Spring 1957 - spring 1960
Series: Peter Pan

Model No.	U.S. $	Can. $	U.K. £
5066	175.00	350.00	300.00

PINOCCHIO

Figaro™
Model No.: 5053
Designer: Helen Perrin Farnlund
Height: 2 ¼", 5.7 cm
Colour: Black; tan face, chest and feet
Issued: Fall 1956
Series: Pinocchio

Model No.	U.S. $	Can. $	U.K. £
5053	150.00	300.00	260.00

Figaro™ Bank
Model No.: 5059
Designer: Don Winton
Height: 5 ½", 14.0 cm
Colour: Black and white, coin slot in the mouth
Issued: Fall 1956
Series: Pinocchio

Model No.	U.S. $	Can. $	U.K. £
5059	300.00	600.00	525.00

Photograph
not available
at press time

Figaro™ Cookie Jar
Model No.: 5051
Designer: Don Winton
Height: Unknown
Colour: Unknown
Issued: Fall 1956
Series: Pinocchio

Model No.	U.S. $	Can. $	U.K. £
5051		Rare	

Jiminy Cricket™
Model No.: 5018
Designer: Helen Perrin Farnlund
Height: 3 ½", 8.9 cm
Colour: Tan face and pants, grey hat with black band, grey vest and spats, black coat and shoes, red necktie
Issued: Fall 1956
Series: Pinocchio

Model No.	U.S. $	Can. $	U.K. £
5018	300.00	600.00	525.00

BANKS

In the fall 1967, after the expiration of the Disney license, Hagen-Ranaker Inc., issued the following banks in an all-white colourway:

Dumbo™ (5058) issued as Elephant (775) — catalogue value $125.00 U.S.F.

Figaro™ (5059) issued as Cat (774) — catalogue value $125.00 U.S.F.

Practical Pig™ (5049) issued as Pig (773) — catalogue value $125.00 U.S.F.

SLEEPING BEAUTY

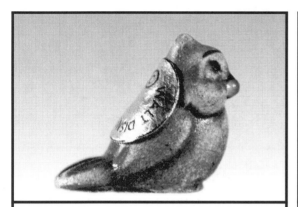

Bluebird™

Model No.:	5099
Designer:	Martha Armstrong
Height:	7/16″, 1.1 cm
Colour:	Blue
Issued:	Spring 1959 - 1960
Series:	Sleeping Beauty

Model No.	U.S. $	Can. $	U.K. £
5099	50.00	100.00	85.00

Cardinal™

Model No.:	5098
Designer:	Martha Armstrong
Height:	½″, 1.3 cm
Colour:	Red
Issued:	Spring 1959 - 1960
Series:	Sleeping Beauty

Model No.	U.S. $	Can. $	U.K. £
5098	50.00	100.00	85.00

Fauna™

Model No.:	5089
Designer:	Martha Armstrong
Height:	2 1/4″, 5.7 cm
Colour:	Orange dress, brown cape and hat
Issued:	Spring 1959 - 1960
Series:	Sleeping Beauty

Model No.	U.S. $	Can. $	U.K. £
5089	170.00	340.00	300.00

Flora™

Model No.:	5091
Designer:	Martha Armstrong
Height:	2 3/16", 5.5 cm
Colour:	Pink dress, maroon cape and hat
Issued:	Spring 1959 - 1960
Series:	Sleeping Beauty

Model No.	U.S. $	Can. $	U.K. £
5091	170.00	340.00	300.00

King Hubert™

Model No.:	5093
Designer:	Martha Armstrong
Height:	2 1/16", 5.2 cm
Colour:	Tan tunic and pants, brown coat trimmed with black, red hair
Issued:	Spring 1959 - 1960
Series:	Sleeping Beauty

Model No.	U.S. $	Can. $	U.K. £
5093	250.00	500.00	435.00

King Stefan™

Model No.:	5096
Designer:	Martha Armstrong
Height:	2 13/16", 7.1 cm
Colour:	Brown suit; black robe, hair and beard
Issued:	Spring 1959 - 1960
Series:	Sleeping Beauty

Model No.	U.S. $	Can. $	U.K. £
5096	250.00	500.00	435.00

Note: The model illustrated is unfinished.

Maleficent™

Model No.:	5092
Designer:	Martha Armstrong
Height:	2 ½", 6.4 cm
Colour:	Black robe, raven-topped walking stick
Issued:	Spring 1959 - 1960
Series:	Sleeping Beauty

Model No.	U.S. $	Can. $	U.K. £
5092	800.00	1,600.00	1,400.00

Merryweather™

Model No.:	5090
Designer:	Martha Armstrong
Height:	1 ¾", 4.4 cm
Colour:	Light blue dress, dark blue cape and hat
Issued:	Spring 1959 - 1960
Series:	Sleeping Beauty

Model No.	U.S. $	Can. $	U.K. £
5090	170.00	340.00	300.00

Owl™

Model No.:	5097
Designer:	Martha Armstrong
Height:	7/8", 2.2 cm
Colour:	Brown, beige breast and eye patches, black eyes and brows
Issued:	Spring 1959 - 1960
Series:	Sleeping Beauty

Model No.	U.S. $	Can. $	U.K. £
5097	100.00	200.00	175.00

Photograph
not available
at press time

Prince Phillip™

Model No.:	5102
Designer:	Martha Armstrong
Height:	2 11/16", 6.8 cm
Colour:	Light blue tunic, brown pants, black shirt and boots, blond hair
Issued:	Spring 1959 - 1960
Series:	Sleeping Beauty

Model No.	U.S. $	Can. $	U.K. £
5102	200.00	400.00	350.00

Princess Aurora™

Model No.:	Unknown
Designer:	Martha Armstrong
Height:	Unknown
Colour:	Grey skirt, black bodice, blond hair
Issued:	Spring 1959 - 1960
Series:	Sleeping Beauty

Description	U.S. $	Can. $	U.K. £
Princess Aurora	200.00	400.00	350.00

Queen™

Model No.:	5100		
Designer:	Martha Armstrong		
Height:	2 7/16″, 6.2 cm		
Colour:	Light pink dress and veil, blue cape		
Issued:	Spring 1959 - 1960		
Series:	Sleeping Beauty		

Model No.	U.S. $	Can. $	U.K. £
5100	200.00	400.00	350.00

Rabbit™

Model No.:	5094		
Designer:	Martha Armstrong		
Height:	2 1/8″, 5.4 cm		
Colour:	Light brown body, beige underbelly, pink inner ears and nose		
Issued:	Spring 1959 - 1960		
Series:	Sleeping Beauty		

Model No.	U.S. $	Can. $	U.K. £
5094	50.00	100.00	85.00

Samson the Horse™

Model No.:	5103		
Designer:	Martha Armstrong		
Height:	2 ¾″, 7.0 cm		
Colour:	White; black mane, tail and tack; brown saddlecloth		
Issued:	Spring 1959 - 1960		
Series:	Sleeping Beauty		

Model No.	U.S. $	Can. $	U.K. £
5103	800.00	1,600.00	1,400.00

Squirrel™

Model No.:	5096		
Designer:	Martha Armstrong		
Height:	1 1/16″, 2.7 cm		
Colour:	Dark brown, white stripes		
Issued:	Spring 1959 - 1960		
Series:	Sleeping Beauty		

Model No.	U.S. $	Can. $	U.K. £
5096	50.00	100.00	85.00

SNOW WHITE AND THE SEVEN DWARFS

Bashful™
Style One
Model No.: 5038
Designer: Nell Bortells
Height: 3 3/8", 8.6 cm
Colour: Brown coat, grey hat,; black pants
Issued: Fall 1956 - spring 1957
Series: Snow White and the Seven Dwarfs

Model No.	U.S. $	Can. $	U.K. £
5038	175.00	350.00	300.00

Doc™
Style One
Model No.: 5043
Designer: Nell Bortells
Height: 3 5/8", 9.2 cm
Colour: Blue pants, brown coat and shoes, green hat
Issued: Fall 1956 - spring 1957
Series: Snow White and the Seven Dwarfs

Model No.	U.S. $	Can. $	U.K. £
5043	175.00	350.00	300.00

Dopey™
Style One
Model No.: 5016
Designer: Nell Bortells
Height: 3 1/8", 7.9 cm
Colour: Green coat, purple hat, brown shoes
Issued: Fall 1956 - spring 1957
Series: Snow White and the Seven Dwarfs

Model No.	U.S. $	Can. $	U.K. £
5016	175.00	350.00	300.00

Grumpy™
Style One
Model No.: 5040
Designer: Nell Bortells
Height: 3 1/6", 8.0 cm
Colour: Blue pants, grey coat with patches, brown shoes
Issued: Fall 1956 - spring 1957
Series: Snow White and the Seven Dwarfs

Model No.	U.S. $	Can. $	U.K. £
5040	175.00	350.00	300.00

Happy™
Style One

Model No.:	5037
Designer:	Nell Bortells
Height:	3 ¼", 8.3 cm
Colour:	Grey pants, brown coat, yellow hat
Issued:	Fall 1956 - spring 1957
Series:	Snow White and the Seven Dwarfs

Model No.	U.S. $	Can. $	U.K. £
5037	175.00	350.00	300.00

Sleepy™
Style One

Model No.:	5036
Designer:	Nell Bortells
Height:	3 3/8", 8.8 cm
Colour:	Brown pants, purple coat, green hat
Issued:	Fall 1956 - spring 1957
Series:	Snow White and the Seven Dwarfs

Model No.	U.S. $	Can. $	U.K. £
5036	175.00	350.00	300.00

Sneezy™
Style One

Model No.:	5039
Designer:	Nell Bortells
Height:	3 ¼", 8.3 cm
Colour:	Brown coat, shoes and hat; green pants
Issued:	Fall 1956 - spring 1957
Series:	Snow White and the Seven Dwarfs

Model No.	U.S. $	Can. $	U.K. £
5039	175.00	350.00	300.00

Snow White™
Style One

Model No.:	5044
Designer:	Nell Bortells
Height:	5 ¾", 14.6 cm
Colour:	Blue bodice, yellow skirt, black hair, pink bow
Issued:	Fall 1956, spring 1957
Series:	Snow White and the Seven Dwarfs

Model No.	U.S. $	Can. $	U.K. £
5044	275.00	550.00	480.00

Note: Some models have a bird on the outstretched hand.

Snow White and the Seven Dwarfs™
Style Two, Colourway One

Designer:	Martha Armstrong	
Issued:	Spring 1958	
Colourways:	Bashful™	Red coat, lilac pants, grey-green hat
	Doc™	Red coat, brown hat
	Dopey™	Light brown coat, purple hat
	Grumpy™	Brown jacket, grey pants, red hat
	Happy™	Red jacket, brown pants, yellow hat
	Sleepy™	Purple coat, red pants, brown hat
	Sneezy™	Red coat and hat, brown pants
	Snow White™	Blue bodice, yellow skirt, white and red puffed sleeves, pink bow in hair

Name	Model No.	Height	U.S. $	Can. $	U.K. £
Bashful™	5088	1 1/8", 2.8 cm	60.00	120.00	105.00
Doc™	5084	1 3/16", 3.0 cm	60.00	120.00	105.00
Dopey™	5082	1 3/16", 3.0 cm	60.00	120.00	105.00
Grumpy™	5087	1 1/8", 2.8 cm	60.00	120.00	105.00
Happy™	5085	1 1/8", 2.8 cm	60.00	120.00	105.00
Sleepy™	5083	3/8", 0.9 cm	60.00	120.00	105.00
Sneezy™	5086	1 1/16", 2.7 cm	60.00	120.00	105.00
Snow White™	5081	2 ¼", 5.7 cm	115.00	230.00	200.00

Note: The earlier models can be identified by their vibrant decoration.

Snow White and the Seven Dwarfs™
Style Two, Colourway Two

Designer: Martha Armstrong
Issued: Unknown
Colourways: Bashful™   Brown coat, grey hair
                Doc™   Pale green jacket, brown pants and hat
                Dopey™   Green coat, purple hat
                Grumpy™   Unknown
                Happy™   Pale blue jacket, deep blue pants and hat
                Sleepy™   Dark brown coat, yellow pants and hat
                Sneezy™   Red-brown coat and hat, green pants
                Snow White™   Blue bodice and puffed sleeves, yellow skirt, blue bow in hair

Name	Model No.	Height	U.S. $	Can. $	U.K. £
Bashful™	5088	1 1/8", 2.8 cm	50.00	100.00	85.00
Doc™	5084	1 3/16", 3.0 cm	50.00	100.00	85.00
Dopey™	5082	1 3/16", 3.0 cm	50.00	100.00	85.00
Grumpy™	5087	1 1/8", 2.8 cm	50.00	100.00	85.00
Happy™	5085	1 1/8", 2.8 cm	50.00	100.00	85.00
Sleepy™	5083	3/8", 0.9 cm	50.00	100.00	85.00
Sneezy™	5086	1 1/16", 2.7 cm	50.00	100.00	85.00
Snow White™	5081	2 ¼", 5.7 cm	105.00	210.00	185.00

Note: The illustrated model of Sneezy™ has a broken foot.

DISNEY - MISCELLANEOUS

Photograph not
available
at press time

Disney™ Sign

Model No.:	5104
Designer:	Unknown
Height:	Unknown
Colour:	Unknown
Issued:	Spring 1959

Model No.	U.S. $	Can. $	U.K. £
5104	.00	.00	.00

Note: This may have been made only for Disneyland.

Shaggy Dog™

Model No.:	H-1001
Designer:	Tom Masterson
Height:	3 3/8", 8.6 cm
Colour:	Black and white
Issued:	Fall 1959

Model No.	U.S. $	Can. $	U.K. £
H-1001	55.00	110.00	95.00

Note: This pedigree model was issued to complement Disney's *The Shaggy Dog.* See also Old English Sheepdog 'Mops' (H-1001), page 443.

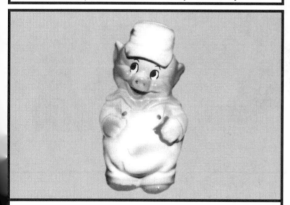

Practical Pig™ Bank

Model No.:	5049
Designer:	Don Winton
Height:	7", 17.8 cm
Colour:	Pink pig, blue overalls
Issued:	Fall 1956

Model No.	U.S. $	Can. $	U.K. £
5049	350.00	700.00	610.00

Practical Pig™ Cookie Jar

Model No.:	5050
Designer:	Don Winton
Height:	12 ¼", 31.1 cm
Colour:	Pink pig, yellow shirt, blue overalls and hat
Issued:	Fall 1956

Model No.	U.S. $	Can. $	U.K. £
5050		Rare	

Characters from the Zany Zoo
The Cat (K-11), The Baboon (K-14), The Lion (K-10)

ZANY ZOO

Moss Renaker wrote and illustrated poems that were published in *Successful Farming* magazine and in a book, *Zany Zoo*, published by Meredith Publishing Company. The Zany Zoo animals were sculpted by Nell Bortells and Tom Masterson after illustrations based on these poems.

Moss Renaker also used the same three-dimensional illustrations of her poems in some of her Walker-Renaker pottery (see Walker-Renaker page, 563).

The Zany Zoo series was available during the spring of 1960 and consisted of twelve pieces, each of which was accompanied by a studio card printed with the poem describing the piece. They were decorated in bright matte colours. Fourteen pieces were listed in the mould book as the K-series, but the lynx and a dog were never released. The K-9 dog was re-issued from San Marcos as model B-88 from fall 1984 to spring 1985.

INDEX TO
ZANY ZOO

Baboon, The

Model No.:	K-14
Designer:	Tom Masterson
Height:	3 ½", 8.9 cm
Colour:	Brown, white mane, green-brown nose
Issued:	Spring 1960

Model No.	U.S. $	Can. $	U.K. £
K-14		Rare	

Note: A blue colourway is also known.

Bear, The

Model No.:	K-3
Designer:	Tom Masterson
Height:	3 ½", 8.9 cm
Colour:	Brown and white
Issued:	Spring 1960

Model No.	U.S. $	Can. $	U.K. £
K-3		Rare	

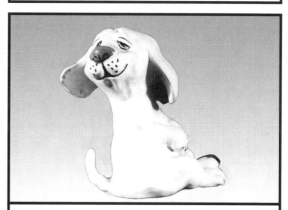

Cat, The

Model No.:	K-11
Designer:	Nell Bortells
Height:	3 ¾", 9.5 cm
Colour:	Yellow with purple stripes
Issued:	Spring 1960

Model No.	U.S. $	Can. $	U.K. £
K-11		Rare	

Dog, The

Model No.:	K-9/B-88
Designer:	Nell Bortells
Height:	3", 7.6 cm
Colour:	White, brown nose
Issued:	Spring 1960
Re-issued:	Fall 1984 - spring 1985

Model No.	U.S. $	Can. $	U.K. £
K-9/B-88		Rare	

Note: Model K-9 was released as a miniature (88),
Curbstone Setter 'Mutt' (88), seated, page 432.

Duck, The

Model No.:	K-4
Designer:	Tom Masterson
Height:	2 ½", 6.4 cm
Colour:	1. White, brown and orange
	2. Yellow
Issued:	Spring 1960

Colourways	U.S. $	Can. $	U.K. £
1. White		Rare	
2. Yellow		Rare	

Frog, The

Model No.:	K-4
Designer:	Tom Masterson
Height:	2 1/8", 5.4 cm
Colour:	Green
Issued:	Spring 1960

Model No.	U.S. $	Can. $	U.K. £
K-4		Rare	

Note: The model illustrated is white and believed to be a second.

Lion, The

Model No.:	K-10
Designer:	Nell Bortells
Height:	3", 7.6 cm
Colour:	Yellow
Issued:	Spring 1960

Model No.	U.S. $	Can. $	U.K. £
K-10		Rare	

Mouse, The

Model No.:	K-2
Designer:	Tom Masterson
Height:	2 ¼", 5.7 cm
Colour:	Purple with white belly
Issued:	Spring 1960

Model No.	U.S. $	Can. $	U.K. £
K-2		Rare	

Ostrich, The

Model No.:	K-6
Designer:	Tom Masterson
Height:	3 9/16", 9.0 cm
Colour:	Lavender and white
Issued:	Spring 1960

Model No.	U.S. $	Can. $	U.K. £
K-6		Rare	

Skunk, The

Model No.:	K-13
Designer:	Tom Masterson
Height:	2 7/8", 7.3 cm
Colour:	Black and white
Issued:	Spring 1960

Model No.	U.S. $	Can. $	U.K. £
K-13		Rare	

Walrus With Monocle

Model No.:	K-1
Designer:	Tom Masterson
Height:	3 1/8", 7.9 cm
Colour:	Grey
Issued:	Spring 1960

Model No.	U.S. $	Can. $	U.K. £
K-1		Rare	

Yak, The

Model No.:	K-5
Designer:	Nell Bortells
Height:	1 7/8", 4.8 cm
Colour:	Purple, white horns
Issued:	Spring 1960

Model No.	U.S. $	Can. $	U.K. £
K-5		Rare	

Note: The model illustrated is bisque.

Note: The model illustrated has broken horns.

THE WILDCAT.

No wonder that the wild cat's wild
And all upset and vexed and riled!
His feline soul is filled with passion
Because his tail's too brief for lashin'.

KEIKIS AND PIXIES

Hagen-Renaker Pedigree Series
Great Dane 'Hamlet' in fawn colourway showing
the incised pattern used to decorate the dog as a
'Harlequin' Great Dane, see page 441.

KEIKIS (Hawaiian Children)

As with the Pixies, the Keikis were originally produced by Millesan Drews and then licensed to Hagen-Renaker. These may have been test-marketed at Knott's Berry Farm in 1955/1956 but were never put into production. They are considered rare.

By 1958, Millesan Drews had licensed the Keikis to National Potteries (Napcoware) of Cleveland, Ohio, and they were produced in Japan.

Napcoware model of
Boy, crouching

Description	Height	Colourway
Girl, lying, resting on arm	1 5/8", 4.12 cm	Bisque skin tone, white and yellow leis
Girl, standing, arms open	3 7/8", 9.84 cm	Bisque skin tone, blue and white leis
Girl, standing, hands to hair	3 7/8", 9.84 cm	Bisque skin tone, yellow and white leis
Boy, crouching	2 5/8", 6.6 cm	Bisque skin tone, red trunks, green and white leis
Girl, lying, looking up	1 2/3", 4.23 cm	Bisque skin tone; green, white and yellow leis
Girl, seated, hand on knee	3 5/8", 9.20 cm	Bisque skin tone, green leis

PIXIES

In 1955, Hagen-Renaker produced Millesan Drews' Pixies. Until this time, she had been forming these pixies by hand, but when their popularity became great, Hagen-Renaker was licensed to continue production of the Pixies.

As the Pixies were moulded in two separate parts, many combinations are possible. Shoes and buttons are gold; the face is bisque, with the rest of the model having a gloss finish.

Possible combinations:

Bottom:	Top:
Sitting, knees straight	Hands out (for crawling)
Sitting, knees slightly bent	Both hands holding hat
Sitting, knees more bent	Hands forward (to rest on knees)
Reclining on hip	Hands next to body (to rest on ground)
Knees on ground	One hand up, waving
Standing, one leg up	
Standing, knees flexed	

Colourway combinations:

Pixie's Coat	Pixie's Pants
1. Autum brown	1. Dark green
2. Forest green	2. Purple
3. Golden moss	3. Red-brown
4. Thimbleberry pink	4. Yellow with brown flecks

Height:

1. Crawling — 2 ¾", 7.0 cm	3. Standing — 6", 15.0 cm
2. Seated — 4", 10.1 cm	

Description	U.S. $	Can. $	U.K. £
Pixie	50.00	100.00	90.00

TRAYS AND WALL PLAQUES

We have no further information on the following items that were listed on the order form. We would appreciate hearing from any collector who could supply the size, the colour or an illustration.

1959 Plaques

Buck
Butterfly, side view left
Butterfly, side view right
Crab
Doe
Fawn
Horse, rearing left
Horse, rearing right
Horses, pair

1960 Plaques

Bottles
Siamese Cats
Toucan, facing left
Toucan, facing right

1959 Wooden Plaques

Hen
Horse, facing right
King
Queen
Rooster

1960 Trays

Butterfly
Horses

CERAMIC PLAQUES

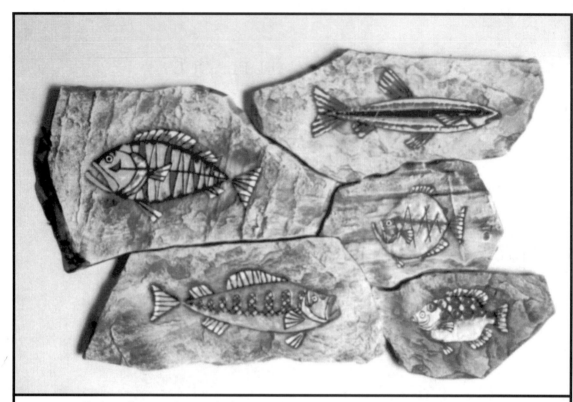

Clockwise from top: Snapper (F-1), Barracuda (F-9), Pompano (F-7), Perch (F-5), Corbina (F-6)

The designs for these plaques were incised into forms cast from Arizona flagstone. The designs were then painted in vibrant enamel-like colours.

Model No.:   See below
Designer: See below
Length: Various
Colour: Blues, reds, and greens
Issued: Spring 1959

Name	Designer	Model No.	U.S. $	Can. $	U.K. £
1. Barracuda	Unknown	F-9			
2. Buck (not illustrated)	Unknown	—			
3. Butterfly, left (not illustrated)	Unknown	F-8			
4. Butterfly, right (not illustrated)	Unknown	F-3			
5. Corbina	Unknown	F-6			
6. Crab (not illustrated	Unknown	—		All plaques are	
7. Doe (not illustrated)	Maureen Love	—		are considered rare	
8. Horse, rearing left (not illustrated)	Maureen Love	F-11			
9. Horse, rearing right (not illustrated)	Maureen Love	F-12			
10. Horses, pair (not illustrated)	Maureen Love	F-2			
11. Perch	Unknown	F-5			
12. Pompano	Unknown	F-7			
13. Snapper	Unknown	F-1			

CERAMIC TRAYS

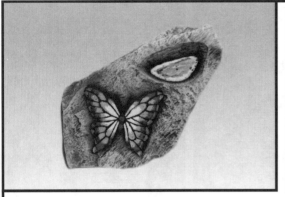

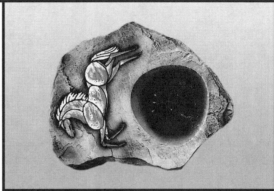

Butterfly Tray (F-27)　　　　　　　　　　　Horse Tray (F-26)

Model No.:　1. Butterfly tray — F-27
　　　　　　2. Horse tray — F-26
Designer:　Maureen Love
Issued:　Spring 1959 - spring 1960

Description	Length	Colour	U.S. $	Can. $	U.K. £
1. Butterfly	12", 30.5 cm	Blue, white, yellow and black		Rare	
2. Horse	18", 45.7 cm	Blue and black			

CERAMIC WALL CLOCK

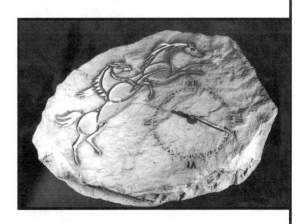

Horse, rearing
Model No.:　Unknown
Designer:　Maureen Love
Length:　12", 30.5 cm
Colour:　Yellow
Issued:　Spring 1959

Description	U.S. $	Can. $	U.K. £
Wall clock		Rare	

WOODEN PLAQUES

Jack

Geisha Girl

Geisha Girl With Fan

Horse, trotting

The design for these plaques, which were issued in 1959, was assembled as for a stained glass window, in mutiple sections.

Name	Size	Colourways	U.S. $	Can. $	U.K. £
1. Geisha	12" x 18", 30.4 x 45.7 cm	Red			
2. Geisha with fan	12" x 18", 30.4 x 45.7 cm	Yellow			
3. Jack	12" x 18", 30.4 x 45.7 cm	Red, green, brown, blue and yellow		Rare	
4. Horse, trotting	12" x 18", 30.4 x 45.7 cm	Blue, black			

NEW RELEASES FOR 1999

Nativity Angel (3023)
Re-released fall 1999
Lavender shawl, brown hair

SPECIALTIES

Mother Goose

Model No.: 3293
Designer: Helen Perrin Farnlund
Height: 3 5/8", 9.2 cm
Colour: White goose, yellow straw hat with red ribbon, red boots, yellow carpet bag; gloss
Issued: Spring 1999

Model No.	U.S. $	Can. $	U.K. £
3293	22.00	44.00	37.00

Racehorse With Jockey

Model No.: 3297
Designer: Maureen Love
Height: 4 ½", 7.6 cm
Colour: Dark bay horse; jockey's silks are salmon and white; gloss
Issued: Spring 1999

Model No.	U.S. $	Can. $	U.K. £
3297	24.00	48.00	40.00

Sandpiper

Model No.: 3280
Designer: Maureen Love
Height: 3", 7.6 cm
Colour: Brown; gloss
Issued: Spring 1999

Model No.	U.S. $	Can. $	U.K. £
3280	18.00	35.00	30.00

Saxophone Player (Toadally Brass)

Model No.: 3291
Designer: Maureen Love
Height: 1 ½", 2.5 cm
Colour: Green toad, purple jacket, gold saxophone; gloss
Issued: Spring 1999

Model No.	U.S. $	Can. $	U.K. £
3291	17.00	35.00	30.00

MINIATURE ANIMALS

Scaredy-cat

Model No.:	A-3301
Designer:	Kathleen Ellis
Height:	2 3/8", 6.0 cm
Colour:	Dark grey; gloss
Issued:	Spring 1999

Model No.	U.S. $	Can. $	U.K. £
A-3301	4.00	8.00	7.00

Pitbull

Model No.:	A-3292
Designer:	Robert McGuinness
Height:	2", 5.1 cm
Colour:	Grey; gloss
Issued:	Spring 1999

Model No.	U.S. $	Can. $	U.K. £
A-3292	6.00	12.00	10.00

Cairn Terrier

Model No.:	A-3290
Designer:	Robert McGuinness
Height:	1 ¼", 3.2 cm
Colour:	Tan; gloss
Issued:	Spring 1999

Model No.	U.S. $	Can. $	U.K. £
A-3290	4.50	9.00	7.50

Kangaroo and Joey

Model No.:	A-3299
Designer:	Robert McGuinness
Height:	2 ¼", 5.7 cm
Colour:	Brown; gloss
Issued:	Spring 1999

Model No.	U.S. $	Can. $	U.K. £
A-3299	7.00	14.00	12.00

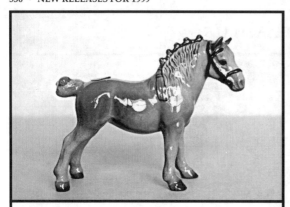

Belgian Horse
Model No.:   A-3296
Designer: Maureen Love
Height: 2 3/8", 5.9 cm
Colour: Chestnut; gloss
Issued: Spring 1999

Model No.	U.S. $	Can. $	U.K. £
A-3296	8.50	17.00	14.00

Colt, standing
Model No.:   A-3294
Designer: Maureen Love
Height: 2", 5.1 cm
Colour: Black pinto; gloss
Issued: Spring 1999

Model No.	U.S. $	Can. $	U.K. £
A-3294	8.00	16.00	13.50

Colt, lying
Model No.:   A-3295
Designer: Maureen Love
Height: 1 5/8", 2.8 cm
Colour: Black pinto; gloss
Issued: Spring 1999

Model No.	U.S. $	Can. $	U.K. £
A-3295	8.00	16.00	13.50

OTHER COMPANIES

Designer's Workshop Line
Molly (B-570), see page 109

ARCADIA CERAMICS

Hagen-Renaker purchased Arcadia Ceramics, in partnership with John Bennett, around 1955 to produce a line of novelty salt and pepper shakers. These bowls were released from Arcadia Ceramics.

Ice Cream Bowls 'Cantaloupe shape'

Model No.:	Unknown
Designer:	Unknown
Size:	2 1/6" x 4 1/8", 5.2 x 10.5 cm
Colour:	Orange, light brown; gloss
Issued:	Unknown

Description	U.S. $	Can. $	U.K.£
Ice cream bowl	.	Rare	

BREYER MOLDING COMPANY

The Breyer Molding Company, a division of Reeves International, has leased many mould rights for production in plastic. Breyer's "classic" Arabian, mustang, quarter horse families; several Thoroughbreds; and all pre-1997 "stablemates" were all originally sculpted by Maureen Love.

In the late 1950s, Breyer released an Arabian mare and foal patterned after the 9" 'Zara' and 'Zilla'. Legal action was filed by Hagen-Renaker, damages were paid and Breyer replaced these horses with another Arab mare and foal set in 1960. The early plastic horses are now called the 'Old Mould Proud Arabian Mare and Foal'.

Ten years later, Hagen-Renaker and Breyer reached a new legal agreement and the old moulds were released as 'Proud Arabian Mare' and 'Proud Arabian Foal'. Please refer to page 191 of Nancy A. Young's *Breyer Molds and Models: Horses, Riders and Animals (1950 to 1995)* (Schiffer, 1997) regarding these events.

FREEMAN-McFARLIN

McFarlin Potteries was established in El Monte in 1927. In 1951, Maynard Anthony Freeman entered into partnership and the pottery's name was changed to Freeman-McFarlin. Freeman designed many pieces and marked them with an incised 'Anthony' in the base. When Kay Finch closed shop in 1963, Freeman-McFarlin bought many moulds and added them to its line. The Freeman-McFarlin line included animal figurines, pedestals, bowls, candlesticks, vases, ashtrays, etc. The pottery made some marvelously dramatic large-scale figures. The 'Eagle' (model 872) has a wing span of 17".

Hagen-Renaker, Inc. purchased the Freeman-McFarlin pottery factory in San Marcos, California, in 1980 and the existing Freeman-McFarlin line was supplemented by new and re-released Hagen-Renaker designs. By the time this factory had closed in 1986, only a handful of original Freeman designs were on the order form.

At the time that Hagen-Renaker took over, Freeman-McFarlin was producing large pieces decorated in solid colours: gloss white, gold or wood-tone. This is why several Hagen-Renaker designs appear in gold or white.

The following is a selection of Freeman-McFarlin moulds produced under the Hagen-Renaker label.

INDEX TO FREEMAN-McFARLIN

BIRDS

Mr. Bird

Model No.:	825
Designer:	Unknown
Size:	4″ x 5″, 10.1 x 12.7 cm
Colour:	See below
Issued:	Unknown - 1981

Colourways	U.S. $	Can. $	U.K. £
1. Gold	8.00	16.00	14.00
2. White	8.00	16.00	14.00

Mrs. Bird

Model No.:	826
Designer:	Unknown
Size:	3 ¾″ x 3 ½″, 9.5 x 8.9 cm
Colour:	See below
Issued:	Unknown - 1981

Colourways	U.S. $	Can. $	U.K. £
1. Gold	8.00	16.00	14.00
2. White	8.00	16.00	14.00

Loving Doves

Model No.:	134
Designer:	Unknown
Size:	7″ x 13 ½″, 17.8 x 34.3 cm
Colour:	See below
Issued:	Unknown - 1986

Colourways	U.S. $	Can. $	U.K. £
1. Gold	50.00	100.00	85.00
2. White	50.00	100.00	85.00

Duck, flying

Model No.:	960
Designer:	Unknown
Size:	11 ½″ x 12 ½″, 29.2 x 31.7 cm
Colour:	See below
Issued:	Unknown - 1981

Colourways	U.S. $	Can. $	U.K. £
1. Gold	40.00	80.00	70.00
2. White	40.00	80.00	70.00

Duck, landing

Model No.:	961
Designer:	Unknown
Size:	12 ½″ x 7 ¾″, 31.7 x 19.7 cm
Colour:	See below
Issued:	Unknown - 1981

Colourways	U.S. $	Can. $	U.K. £
1. Gold	40.00	80.00	70.00
2. White	40.00	80.00	70.00

Mr. Duck

Model No.:	126
Designer:	Unknown
Size:	7 ¾″ x 4 ½″, 19.7 x 11.9 cm
Colour:	See below
Issued:	Unknown - 1981

Colourways	U.S. $	Can. $	U.K. £
1. Gold	5.00	10.00	8.00
2. White	5.00	10.00	8.00

Mrs. Duck

Model No.:	125
Designer:	Unknown
Size:	4 ¾″ x 5 ¼″, 12.1 x 13.3 cm
Colour:	1. Gold
	2. White
Issued:	Unknown - 1981

Colourways	U.S. $	Can. $	U.K. £
1. Gold	5.00	10.00	8.00
2. White	5.00	10.00	8.00

Eagle

Model No.:	872
Designer:	Unknown
Size:	7 ¾″ x 17″, 19.7 x 43.2 cm
Colour:	See below
Issued:	Unknown - 1981

Colourways	U.S. $	Can. $	U.K. £
1. Gold	50.00	100.00	85.00
2. White	50.00	100.00	85.00

Mr. Egret

Model No.:	873
Designer:	Unknown
Size:	12 ½″ x 15″, 31.7 x 38.1 cm
Colour:	See below
Issued:	Unknown - 1981

Colourways	U.S. $	Can. $	U.K. £
1. Gold	50.00	100.00	85.00
2. White	50.00	100.00	85.00

Mrs. Egret

Model No.:	874
Designer:	Unknown
Size:	11″ x 9 ¼″, 27.9 x 23.5 cm
Colour:	See below
Issued:	Unknown - 1981

Colourways	U.S. $	Can. $	U.K. £
1. Gold	50.00	100.00	85.00
2. White	50.00	100.00	85.00

Goose

Model No.:	62
Designer:	Unknown
Size:	9″ x 6 ¾″, 22.9 x 17.2 cm
Colour:	See below
Issued:	Unknown - 1981

Colourways	U.S. $	Can. $	U.K. £
1. Gold	25.00	50.00	43.00
2. White	25.00	50.00	43.00

Barn Owl, flying

Model No.:	096
Designer:	Unknown
Size:	12″ x 18″, 30.5 x 45.7 cm
Colour:	See below
Issued:	Unknown - 1981

Colourways	U.S. $	Can. $	U.K. £
1. Gold	60.00	125.00	100.00
2. White	60.00	125.00	100.00

Barn Owl, perched

Model No.:	095
Designer:	Unknown
Size:	9″ x 7″, 22.9 x 17.8 cm
Colour:	See below
Issued:	Unknown - 1981

Colourways	U.S. $	Can. $	U.K. £
1. Gold	30.00	60.00	50.00
2. White	30.00	60.00	50.00

Owl Baby 'Hoot'

Model No.:	094
Designer:	Unknown
Size:	5″ x 5″, 12.7 x 12.7 cm
Colour:	See below
Issued:	Unknown - 1983

Colourways	U.S. $	Can. $	U.K. £
1. Gold	5.00	10.00	8.00
2. White	5.00	10.00	8.00

Owl Baby 'Toot'

Model No.:	093
Designer:	Unknown
Size:	5″ x 5″, 12.7 x 12.7 cm
Colour:	See below
Issued:	Unknown - 1983

Colourways	U.S. $	Can. $	U.K. £
1. Gold	5.00	10.00	8.00
2. White	5.00	10.00	8.00

Owl Mama

Model No.:	092
Designer:	Unknown
Size:	16 ¾″ x 6″, 42.5 x 15.0 cm
Colour:	See below
Issued:	Unknown - 1981

Colourways	U.S. $	Can. $	U.K. £
1. Gold	15.00	30.00	25.00
2. White	15.00	30.00	25.00

Pelican

Model No.:	29
Designer:	Unknown
Size:	9 ½" x 7 ½", 24.0 x 19.1 cm
Colour:	See below
Issued:	Unknown - 1982

Colourways	U.S. $	Can. $	U.K. £
1. Gold	30.00	40.00	50.00
2. White	30.00	40.00	50.00

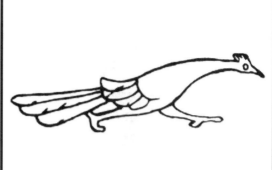

Roadrunner

Model No.:	166
Designer:	Unknown
Size:	5" x 18", 12.7 x 45.7 cm
Colour:	See below
Issued:	Unknown - 1983

Colourways	U.S. $	Can. $	U.K. £
1. Gold	15.00	30.00	25.00
2. White	15.00	30.00	25.00

Bantam Rooster

Model No.:	687
Designer:	Maureen Love
Size:	7 ½" x 11", 19.1 x 27.9 cm
Colour:	See below
Issued:	Unknown - 1981

Colourways	U.S. $	Can. $	U.K. £
1. Gold		Rare	
2. White		Rare	

Note: See page 29 for the original Hagen-Renaker release.

Seagull, flying

Model No.:	875
Designer:	Unknown
Sizet:	10 ½" x 16", 26.7 x 40.6 cm
Colour:	See below
Issued:	Unknown - 1981

Colourways	U.S. $	Can. $	U.K. £
1. Gold	40.00	80.00	70.00
2. White	40.00	80.00	70.00

Seagull, perched

Model No.:	876
Designer:	Unknown
Size:	8 ¾″ x 6 ½″, 22.2 x 16.5 cm
Colour:	See below
Issued:	Unknown - 1981

Colourways	U.S. $	Can. $	U.K. £
1. Gold	20.00	40.00	35.00
2. White	20.00	40.00	35.00

Swan

Model No.:	881
Designer:	Unknown
Size:	9 ½″ x 13″, 24.0 x 33.0 cm
Colour:	See below
Issued:	Unknown - 1981

Colourways	U.S. $	Can. $	U.K. £
1. Gold	40.00	80.00	70.00
2. White	40.00	80.00	70.00

CATS

Cat, lying

Model No.:	177
Designer:	Unknown
Size:	4 ½″ x 11 ½″, 11.9 x 29.2 cm
Colour:	See below
Issued:	Unknown - 1981

Colourways	U.S. $	Can. $	U.K. £
1. Gold	15.00	30.00	25.00
2. White	15.00	30.00	25.00

Cat, washing

Model No.:	178
Designer:	Unknown
Size:	15 ½″ x 9″, 39.4 x 22.9 cm
Colour:	See below
Issued:	Unknown - 1981

Colourways	U.S. $	Can. $	U.K. £
1. Gold	15.00	30.00	25.00
2. White	15.00	30.00	25.00

Kitten, lying on back

Model No.:	864
Designer:	Unknown
Size:	4″ x 9″, 10.1 x 22.9 cm
Colour:	See below
Issued:	Unknown - 1981

Colourways	U.S. $	Can. $	U.K. £
1. Gold	15.00	30.00	25.00
2. White	15.00	30.00	25.00

Kitten, seated

Model No.:	865
Designer:	Unknown
Size:	6 ½″ x 7 ½″, 16.5 x 19.1 cm
Colour:	See below
Issued:	Unknown - 1981

Colourways	U.S. $	Can. $	U.K. £
1. Gold	10.00	20.00	17.00
2. White	10.00	20.00	17.00

Kitten With Ball

Model No.:	858
Designer:	Unknown
Size:	7 ½″ x 7 ½″, 19.1 x 19.1 cm
Colour:	See below
Issued:	Unknown - 1983

Colourways	U.S. $	Can. $	U.K. £
1. Gold	15.00	30.00	25.00
2. White	15.00	30.00	25.00

Kitty

Model No.:	133
Designer:	Unknown
Size:	4″ x 3 ½″, 10.1 x 8.9 cm
Colour:	See below
Issued:	Unknown - 1986

Colourways	U.S. $	Can. $	U.K. £
1. Gold	30.00	60.00	50.00
2. White	30.00	60.00	50.00

Note: See Designer's Workshop Kitten (133), page 52.

Loving Cats

Model No.:	132
Designer:	Unknown
Size:	10 ½" x 12", 26.7 x 30.5 cm
Colour:	See below
Issued:	Unknown - 1986

Colourways	U.S. $	Can. $	U.K. £
1. Gold	50.00	100.00	85.00
2. White	50.00	100.00	85.00

Note: See also Designer's Workshop, Loving Cats, page 52.

Persian Cat

Model No.:	22
Designer:	Don Winton
Size:	12 ¼" x 11 ¾", 31.1 x 29.8 cm
Colour:	See below
Issued:	1981

Colourways	U.S. $	Can. $	U.K. £
1. Gold	60.00	125.00	100.00
2. White	60.00	125.00	100.00

Note: See also Designer's Workshop, Persian Cat, 'Silver', page 40.

Siamese Kitten, pouncing

Model No.:	Unknown
Designer:	Unknown
Height:	2 ½", 6.4 cm
Colour:	Beige and dark brown
Issued:	c.1950

Description	U.S. $	Can. $	U.K. £
Siamese kitten, pouncing	15.00	30.00	25.00

Siamese Kitten, sleeping

Model No.:	Unknown
Designer:	Unknown
Height:	1 ½", 3.81 cm
Colour:	Beige and dark brown
Issued:	c.1950

Description	U.S. $	Can. $	U.K. £
Siamese kitten, sleeping	15.00	30.00	25.00

DOGS

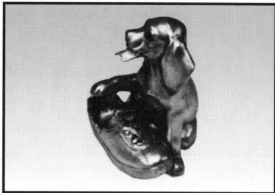

Cocker Spaniel

Model No.:	846
Designer:	Kay Finch
Size:	8″ x 6 ½″, 20.3 x 16.5 cm
Colour:	See below
Issued:	Unknown - 1981

Colourways	U.S. $	Can. $	U.K. £
1. Gold	20.00	40.00	35.00
2. White	20.00	40.00	35.00

Dog With Shoe

Model No.:	859
Designer:	Unknown
Size:	7″ x 7″, 17.8 x 17.8 cm
Colour:	See below
Issued:	Unknown - 1981

Colourways	U.S. $	Can. $	U.K. £
1. Gold	20.00	40.00	35.00
2. White	20.00	40.00	35.00

FARM ANIMALS

Pig, lying

Model No.:	436
Designer:	Unknown
Size:	7″ x 3″, 17.8 x 7.6 cm
Colour:	See below
Issued:	Unknown - 1981

Colourways	U.S. $	Can. $	U.K. £
1. Gold	8.00	16.00	14.00
2. White	8.00	16.00	14.00

Pig, seated

Model No.:	435
Designer:	Unknown
Size:	6″ x 4″, 15.0 x 10.1 cm
Colour:	See below
Issued:	Unknown - 1981

Colourways	U.S. $	Can. $	U.K. £
1. Gold	8.00	16.00	14.00
2. White	8.00	16.00	14.00

Pig, sitting up

Model No.:	437
Designer:	Unknown
Size:	5 ¾" x 5", 14.6 x 12.7 cm
Colour:	See below
Issued:	Unknown - 1981

Colourways	U.S. $	Can. $	U.K. £
1. Gold	8.00	16.00	14.00
2. White	8.00	16.00	14.00

Photo FM6ii

HORSES

Donkey, seated

Model No.:	838
Designer:	Unknown
Size:	7" x 7", 17.8 x 17.8 cm
Colour:	See below
Issued:	Unknown - 1981

Colourways	U.S. $	Can. $	U.K. £
1. Gold	20.00	40.00	35.00
2. White	20.00	40.00	35.00

Mare and Foal (On base)

Model No.:	121
Designer:	Unknown
Height:	Unknown
Colour:	White
Issued:	c. 1979

Model No.	U.S. $	Can. $	U.K. £
121	30.00	60.00	50.00

Pegasus Baby, lying

Model No.:	119
Designer:	Unknown
Size:	6" x 9", 15.0 x 22.9 cm
Colour:	See below
Issued:	Unknown - 1984

Colourways	U.S. $	Can. $	U.K. £
1. Gold	35.00	70.00	60.00
2. White	35.00	70.00	60.00

Pegasus, standing

Model No.:	120			
Designer:	Unknown			
Size:	9″ x 8″, 22.9 x 20.3 cm			
Colour:	See below			
Issued:	Unknown - 1984			

Colourways	U.S. $	Can. $	U.K. £
1. Gold	35.00	70.00	60.00
2. White	35.00	70.00	60.00

Unicorn, lying

Model No.:	139			
Designer:	Unknown			
Size:	7″ x 9″, 17.8 x 22.9 cm			
Colour:	See below			
Issued:	Unknown - 1983			

Colourways	U.S. $	Can. $	U.K. £
1. Gold	35.00	70.00	60.00
2. White	35.00	70.00	60.00

Unicorn, standing

Model No.:	140			
Designer:	Unknown			
Size:	9″ x 9″, 22.9 x 22.9 cm			
Colour:	See below			
Issued:	Unknown - 1983			

Colourways	U.S. $	Can. $	U.K. £
1. Gold	35.00	70.00	60.00
2. White	35.00	70.00	60.00

Unicorn's Head

Model No.:	60			
Designer:	Maureen Love			
Size:	8 ½″ x 6 ¾″, 21.6 x 17.2 cm			
Colour:	See below			
Issued:	1981, 1982			

Colourways	U.S. $	Can. $	U.K. £
1. Gold		Rare	
2. White		Rare	

SEA CREATURES

WILD ANIMALS

Dolphins

Model No.:	878		
Designer:	Unknown		
Height:	Unknown		
Colour:	White		
Issued:	c.1979		

Model No.	U.S. $	Can. $	U.K. £
878	30.00	60.00	50.00

Elephant, seated

Model No.:	147		
Designer:	Unknown		
Size:	4 ½″ x 5 ¾″, 11.9 x 14.6 cm		
Colour:	See below		
Issued:	Unknown - 1986		

Colourways	U.S. $	Can. $	U.K. £
1. Gold	15.00	30.00	25.00
2. Grey	15.00	30.00	25.00
3. White	15.00	30.00	25.00

Elephant, standing

Model No.:	146		
Designer:	Unknown		
Size:	5″ x 7 ½″, 12.7 x 19.1 cm		
Colour:	See below		
Issued:	Unknown - 1986		

Colourways	U.S. $	Can. $	U.K. £
1. Gold	15.00	30.00	25.00
2. Grey	15.00	30.00	25.00
3. White	15.00	30.00	25.00

Fawn, lying

Model No.:	862		
Designer:	Unknown		
Size:	5 ½″ x 9″, 14.0 x 22.9 cm		
Colour:	See below		
Issued:	Unknown - 1981		

Colourways	U.S. $	Can. $	U.K. £
1. Gold	30.00	60.00	50.00
2. White	30.00	60.00	50.00

Fawn, standing

Model No.:	861
Designer:	Unknown
Size:	9 ½″ x 8″, 24.0 x 20.3 cm
Colour:	See below
Issued:	Unknown - 1981

Colourways	U.S. $	Can. $	U.K. £
1. Gold	30.00	60.00	50.00
2. White	30.00	60.00	50.00

Mr. Fox

Model No.:	144
Designer:	Unknown
Size:	9 ¾″ x 6 ¾″, 24.7 x 17.2 cm
Colour:	See below
Issued:	Unknown - 1986

Colourways	U.S. $	Can. $	U.K. £
1. Brown	35.00	70.00	60.00
2. Gold	35.00	70.00	60.00
3. White	35.00	70.00	60.00

Mrs. Fox

Model No.:	145
Designer:	Unknown
Size:	9″ x 6″, 22.9 x 15.0 cm
Colour:	See below
Issued:	Unknown - 1986

Colourways	U.S. $	Can. $	U.K. £
1. Brown	35.00	70.00	60.00
2. Gold	35.00	70.00	60.00
3. White	35.00	70.00	60.00

Giraffe

Model No.:	904
Designer:	Unknown
Size:	21″ x 13″, 53.34 x 33.0 cm
Colour:	See below
Issued:	Unknown - 1981

Colourways	U.S. $	Can. $	U.K. £
1. Gold	35.00	70.00	60.00
2. White	35.00	70.00	60.00

Grizzly Bear

Model No.:	738
Designer:	Maureen Love
Size:	7 ¾″ x 6 ½″, 19.7 x 16.5 cm
Colour:	See below
Issued:	1981

Colourways	U.S. $	Can. $	U.K. £
1. Gold	125.00	250.00	210.00
2. White	125.00	250.00	210.00

Note: See also Grizzly Bear (B-738), page 95.

Mountain Sheep

Model No.:	726
Designer:	Tom Masterson
Size:	7 ½″ x 5 ¼″, 19.1 x 13.3 cm
Colour:	See below
Issued:	1981

Colourways	U.S. $	Can. $	U.K. £
1. Gold	175.00	350.00	300.00
2. White	175.00	350.00	300.00

Note: See also Bighorn Sheep on Base (B-726), page 61.

Mr. Mouse

Model No.:	142
Designer:	Unknown
Size:	5 ½″ x 5 ½″, 14.0 x 14.0 cm
Colour:	See below
Issued:	Unknown - 1985

Colourways	U.S. $	Can. $	U.K. £
1. Gold	10.00	20.00	17.00
2. White	10.00	20.00	17.00

Mrs. Mouse

Model No.:	143
Designer:	Unknown
Size:	5 ½″ x 5 ½″, 14.0 x 14.0 cm
Colour:	See below
Issued:	Unknown - 1985

Colourways	U.S. $	Can. $	U.K. £
1. Gold	10.00	20.00	17.00
2. White	10.00	20.00	17.00

Mr. Rabbit

Model No.:	114
Designer:	Unknown
Size:	10 ½″ x 6 ½″, 26.7 x 16.5 cm
Colour:	See below
Issued:	Unknown - 1981

Colourways	U.S. $	Can. $	U.K. £
1. Gold	10.00	20.00	17.00
2. White	10.00	20.00	17.00

Mrs. Rabbit

Model No.:	115
Designer:	Unknown
Size:	6 ½″ x 8″, 16.5 x 20.3 cm
Colour:	See below
Issued:	Unknown - 1981

Colourways	U.S. $	Can. $	U.K. £
1. Gold	8.00	16.00	14.00
2. White	8.00	16.00	14.00

Ram's Head

Model No.:	61
Designer:	Maureen Love
Size:	7 ¼″ x 7 ¼″, 18.4 x 18.4 cm
Colour:	See below
Issued:	1981, 1982

Colourways	U.S. $	Can. $	U.K. £
1. Gold		Rare	
2. White		Rare	

Stag

Model No.:	879
Designer:	Unknown
Height:	Unknown
Colour:	White
Issued:	c.1979

Model No.	U.S. $	Can. $	U.K. £
879	30.00	60.00	50.00

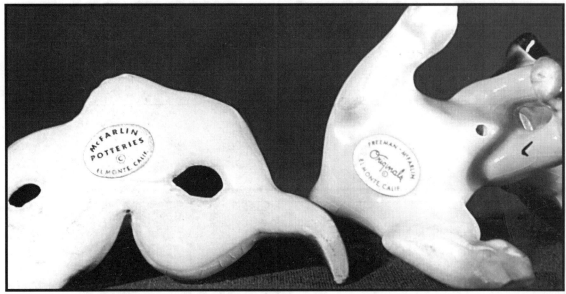

Base of Siamese Kitten, sleeping; Base Siamese Kitten, pouncing (see page 550)

LOZA ELECTRICA

Loza Electrica was a ceramics company owned by Jim Renaker, son of John and Maxine; his wife, Freya; and his son, Eric. The factory was founded in 1992 in Mexico and closed in 1998. Loza Electrica produced ceramic figurines, including horses in a 6″ size and in a 3″ size; many species of animals, averaging 3″ in size; and figurines licensed for sale in theme parks. Loza has also done special-order colours on horse figurines.

Loza used white, untinted slip and pieces are marked with a paper label, "Hecho in Mexico," or with an incised "Loza Electrica." Jose Garcia sculpted Loza's pieces, as he had for Renaker-Brazel. Some early Loza pieces were painted in acrylics on bisque and were not glazed. These differ from the Auerspurse colours used by Hagen-Renaker in the early 1960s.

INDEX TO LOZA ELECTRICA

Designer's Workshop Line
Fighting Cock (B-687), see page 29

Alligator

Model No.:	Unknown
Designer:	Jose Garcia
Size:	7/8″ x 4″, 2.2 x 10.1 cm
Colour:	Brown
Issued:	c.1997

Description	U.S. $	Can. $	U.K. £
Alligator	8.00	16.00	14.00

Arabian Stallion

Model No.:	Unknown
Designer:	Jose Garcia
Height:	3 ½″, 8.9 cm
Colour:	White
Issued:	c.1997

Description	U.S. $	Can. $	U.K. £
Arabian stallion	10.00	20.00	17.00

Dressage Horse

Model No.:	Unknown
Designer:	Jose Garcia
Height:	6″, 15.0 cm
Colour:	Bay
Issued:	c.1997

Description	U.S. $	Can. $	U.K. £
Dressage horse	20.00	40.00	35.00

Lioness

Model No.:	Unknown
Designer:	Jose Garcia
Height:	1 5/8″, 4.1 cm
Colour:	Golden brown
Issued:	c.1997

Description	U.S. $	Can. $	U.K. £
Lioness	5.00	10.00	7.00

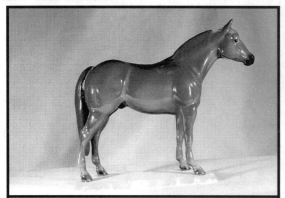

Quarter Horse Stallion, on base

Model No.:	Unknown
Designer:	Jose Garcia
Height:	6", 15.0 cm
Colour:	Chestnut horse on beige base
Issued:	c.1997

Description	U.S. $	Can. $	U.K. £
Quarter horse	20.00	40.00	35.00

Tyrannosaurus Rex

Model No.:	Unknown
Designer:	Jose Garcia
Height:	2 5/6", 7.2 cm
Colour:	Green
Issued:	c.1997

Description	U.S. $	Can. $	U.K. £
Tyrannosaurus rex	5.00	10.00	7.00

MAUREEN LOVE ORIGINALS

For a short time in the late 1960s, Hagen-Renaker distributed Maureen Love Originals, which were pieces moulded and finished by Maureen herself. The list from fall 1969 included the following: wild stallion, Arabian horse, baby burro, burro, lying colt, Indian on pony, male and female quail, roadrunner, mallard, mourning dove, sandpiper, sanderling, sparrow, hummingbird, mouse. Sizes are not available, but they varied between 2 ½" and 10". Most pieces were on bases and generally the pieces were signed and dated. Birds had wire legs. Maureen used a heavy stoneware body with a matte finish, and often the surface was deliberately roughened.

Maureen Love Originals were also available for a period of time through a gift store, The Third Bird, in Encinitas, California.

INDEX TO MAUREEN LOVE ORIGINALS

Maureen Love Originals flyer, circa fall 1969

Black-bellied Plover
Designer: Maureen Love
Height: 7", 17.8 cm
Colour: Black bird with grey markings
Issued: c.fall 1969

Description	U.S. $	Can. $	U.K. £
Black-bellied plover		Rare	

Hooded Oriole
Designer: Maureen Love
Height: 6", 15.2 cm
Colour: Yellow bird with black face and breast,
              black wings and tail feathers, white
              wing tips
Issued: Fall 1969

Description	U.S. $	Can. $	U.K. £
Hooded oriole		Rare	

Horny Toad
Designer: Maureen Love
Height: 2 ¾", 7.0 cm
Colour: Brown
Issued: c.fall 1969

Description	U.S. $	Can. $	U.K. £
Horny toad		Rare	

Colt, lying
Designer: Maureen Love
Height: 3", 7.6 cm
Colour: Brown with black highlights
Issued: c.fall 1969

Description	U.S. $	Can. $	U.K. £
Colt, lying		Rare	

Mouse
Designer: Maureen Love
Height: 3 ¼″, 8.3 cm
Colour: Light brown and white
Issued: c.fall 1969

Description	U.S. $	Can. $	U.K. £
Mouse		Rare	

MADE WITH LOVE

In the last few years, in conjunction with Laurilyn Burson, who was a Hagen-Renaker mouldmaker, Maureen Love has designed a Wild Horse and a Clydesdale under the Made with Love label. Laurilyn does the casting and decoration and the models are signed and numbered by Maureen. Extremely limited runs of each have been produced, in both matte and gloss.

Clydesdale
Designer: Maureen Love
Height: 5 ¾″, 14.6 cm
Colour: Brown, black mane and tail,
             white stockings and nose, blue
             and white ribbons in mane
Issued: 1998

Description	U.S. $	Can. $	U.K. £
Clydesdale	150.00	300.00	500.00

THE POUR HORSE POTTERY
and LUCAS STUDIO

The horses of Maureen Love were the inspiration for this pottery begun by Joan Berkwitz in 1995. All horses released to date have been designed by Kristina Lucas, who also designed the miniature guinea pig (A-3221) for Hagen-Renaker. Great attention to sculpting and painting have made these horses very desirable.

In addition, Kristina Lucas, in a separate endeavour, Lucas Studio, sculpts unique pieces by reshaping clay bodies. By doing this, she is able to create forms that would have been technically difficult to cast from a mould, for instance, crossed legs.

LUCAS STUDIO

Norwegian Fjord Stallion 'Knut'
Designer: Kristina Lucas
Height: 6", 15.0 cm
Colour: Brown dun; gloss
Issued: 1998

Description	U.S. $	Can. $	U.K. £
Norwegian fjord stallion	400.00	800.00	700.00

THE POUR HORSE POTTERY

Head of 'Suspiro'
Andalusian Stallion
Designer: Kristina Lucas
Height: 2", 5.0 cm
Colour: Chestnut; gloss
Issued: 1998

Description	U.S. $	Can. $	U.K. £
'Suspiro'	180.00	350.00	300.00

Note: This model was selected to illustrate detail. The Pour Horse Pottery produces whole-body models.

RENAKER-BRAZEL
BEACHSTONE

Beachstone was the ceramics line produced by Renaker-Brazel, the pottery company formed by Mary Renaker, daughter of John and Maxine, and her husband, Eric Brazel. This company was in business from 1974 to about 1990. Beads were the first items produced and some pieces are marked with a "BSB" sticker for "Beachstone Beads." Later, figurines were made and the line was called "Storybook Figurines." Collectors generally refer to all items produced by Renaker-Brazel as "Beachstone."

Mary Renaker's special delight is Mother Goose, carousel figures, Steiff toys, and designs by the illustrator Eulalie. Some early Hagen-Renaker moulds were re-released as ornaments, notably the 1949 teddy bear baby and the 1950 Rabbit, running, ears apart. Renaker-Brazel used coloured slip for many pieces, and so they may often be confused with Hagen-Renaker. Renaker-Brazel did two things that Hagen-Renaker never did:

1. Renaker-Brazel created ornaments by inserting a hanger wire into the piece; and

2. Renaker-Brazel pieces are not dry-footed. "Dry-footing" is wiping the glaze off the bottom of the piece before firing; thus, Renaker-Brazel pieces are glossy on the bottom.

Jose Garcia designed many of Beachstone's pieces, as he did for Loza Electrica. Values range from $10 to $25, depending on the complexity of the piece.

INDEX TO BEACHSTONE

Designer's Workshop Line
Arabian Stallion 'Amir' showing tri-eye with eyeliner, see page 69

Black Forest Carousel Bear

Model No.:	C-424
Designer:	Unknown
Height:	2 3/8", 6.0 cm
Colour:	Brown bear, blue and black saddle, yellow saddlecloth, light brown base
Issued:	c.1988
Series:	Carousel Animals

Model No.	U.S. $	Can. $	U.K. £
C-424	30.00	60.00	50.00

Bears in Bed

Model No.:	C-3320
Designer:	Unknown
Height:	1 5/8", 4.1 cm
Colour:	Brown bears and bed, white pillows and sheets, orange and blue cover
Issued:	c.1988

Model No.	U.S. $	Can. $	U.K. £
C-3320	20.00	40.00	35.00

Carousel Horse

Model No.:	C-420
Designer:	Unknown
Height:	4", 10.1 cm
Colour:	1. Palomino
	2. White
Issued:	c.1988
Series:	Carousel Animals

Model No.	U.S. $	Can. $	U.K. £
C-420	20.00	40.00	35.00

Cow That Jumped Over the Moon, The

Model No.:	C-3391
Designer:	Unknown
Height:	3 ½", 8.9 cm
Colour:	Black and white holstein cow, yellow moon rockers
Issued:	c.1988

Model No.	U.S. $	Can. $	U.K. £
C-3391	15.00	30.00	26.00

Cubs in Cradle

Model No.:	C-3230
Designer:	Unknown
Height:	1 1/8", 2.8 cm
Colour:	Brown cubs and cradle, white pillows and sheets, purple and lavender cover
Issued:	c.1988

Model No.	U.S. $	Can. $	U.K. £
C-3230	15.00	30.00	26.00

Donkey

Model No.:	C-3349
Designer:	Unknown
Height:	2 9/16", 6.5 cm
Colour:	Light grey; black mane, tail and hooves; blue saddle; pink reins
Issued:	1949
Series:	Ornaments

Model No.	U.S. $	Can. $	U.K. £
C-3349	8.00	16.00	14.00

Dragon, tail down

Model No.:	C-3010
Designer:	Unknown
Height:	3", 7.6 cm
Colour:	1. Green
	2. Purple, salmon belly, yellow teeth
Issued:	c.1985

Model No.	U.S. $	Can. $	U.K. £
C-3010	10.00	20.00	17.00

Dragon, tail up

Model No.:	C-3012
Designer:	Unknown
Height:	4", 10.1 cm
Colour:	1. Green
	2. Purple, light salmon belly
Issued:	c.1985

Model No.	U.S. $	Can. $	U.K. £
C-3012	20.00	40.00	35.00

Polar Bear

Model No.: Unknown
Designer: Unknown
Height: 2 3/8", 6.0 cm
Colour: White
Issued: 1988

Description	U.S. $	Can. $	U.K. £
Polar Bear	10.00	20.00	17.00

Polar Cub

Model No.: C-548
Designer: Unknown
Height: 1 ¾", 4.4 cm
Colour: White
Issued: c.1988

Model No.	U.S. $	Can. $	U.K. £
C-548	8.00	16.00	14.00

Sailor Elephant

Model No.: C-3349
Designer: Unknown
Height: 2 9/16", 6.5 cm
Colour: Light grey elephant, blue sailor suit, white hat
Issued: c.1988
Series: Ornaments

Model No.	U.S. $	Can. $	U.K. £
C-3349	8.00	16.00	14.00

Swan Queen

Model No.: C-3207
Designer: Unknown
Height: 3 ½", 8.9 cm
Colour: White swan, gold crown
Issued: c.1988

Model No.	U.S. $	Can. $	U.K. £
C-3207	15.00	30.00	26.00

STORYBOOK ORNAMENTS
Order form for Renaker-Brazel, Spring 1988

Description	Stock No.	Desription	Stock No.
Baby Green Dragon	C-3012G	Little Boy Kitten	C-604
Black Forest Carousel Bear	C-424	Little Girl Bear	C-3481
Blue Bird	C-1400	Little Girl Kitten — Pink	C-608P
Blue Hummingbird	C-584	Little Girl Kitten — White	C-608
Brer Rabbit	C-544	Ma Duck	C-542A
Bunnies in a Wheel Barrow	C-534	Mary's Lamb on Pull Toy	C-3342P
Canada Goose	C-3307	Mary's Little Lamb	C-3342
Carousel Ostrich	C-422	Miss Mousie	C-715
Cat and the Fiddle	C-510	Mom Cat with Cake	C-850
Cow	C-3390	Mom Cat with Pie	C-852
Cow on Pull Toy	C-3390P	Mom Cat with Storybook	C-853
Dove	C-1410	Mother Goose	C-612
Duck	C-542	Mother Goose on Pull Toy	C-612P
Ducklings in a Wheel Barrow	C-532	Mrs. Pig	C-3346
Dutch Bunny	C-3350	Teddy Bear, original — Caramel colour	C-3260
Elephant on Pull Toy	C-3349P	Teddy Bear, original — Creme colour	C-3260
Elephant with Crown	C-3349C	Owl	C-620
Fox on the Town	C-650	Pa Duck	C-542H
Frog Prince	C-710	Penguin with Gift	C-3200
Froggy went A Courtin	C-710	Peter Rabbit	C-560
Frolicking Lamb	C-520	Pig to Market	C-640
Frolicking Lamb on Pull Toy	C-520P	Puss in Boots	C-616
Fuzzy Bear	C-3001	Rocking Horse — Palomino	C-3370P
Giraffe	C-3380	Rocking Horse — White	C-3370W
Giraffe on Pull Toy	C-3380P	Sister Fuzzy Bear	C-3271
Green Dragon	C-3010G	Snow Goose	C-3207
Green Hummingbird	C-3000	Standing Palomino Carousel Horse	C-320P
Indian Pony	C-360	Standing White Carousel Horse	C-320W
Jumping White Carousel Horse	C-420W	Swan	C-500
Kittens Who Lost Their Mittens	C-618	Unicorn	C-2003
Kitty	C-3395	White Bunny	C-3351
Little Boy Blue Bear	C-3281	White Rabbit	C-544W

Mother Goose Magnets

Description	Stock No.	Description	Stock No.
Green Dragon	M-110G	Purple Dragon	M-110P
Persian Cat	M-98	The Cow/Jumped Over the Moon	M-91

Mother Goose Pins

Description	Stock No.	Description	Stock No.
Green Dragon	P-110G	Purple Dragon	P-110P
Persian Cat	P-98	The Cow Jumped Over the Moon	P-91

ROSELANE

Roselane was never made by Hagen-Renaker but was a separate company whose wares were distributed by Hagen-Renaker from 1965 to 1967. Occasionally Hagen-Renaker stickers appeared on these pieces.

Roselane was founded in 1938, sold in 1973 and closed in 1977. Its specialty was Sparklers, a line of animal figurines with rhinestone or plastic eyes. Roselane can usually be identified by an in-mould mark on the base.

The two pieces illustrated below were distributed by Hagen-Renaker. The bear is 3 ½″ (8.9 cm) and the lemur, 2″ (5.0cm); both are brown (matte).

Bear (3 ½″) and Lemur (2″)

SHIRMAR

Shirmar was a southern California ceramics company that, for a short time, produced five Hagen-Renaker moulds in plaster for the hobby painting market:

Arab Family (9")
Amir
Zara
Zilla
Modern Horse
Girl and Foal

Walker-Renaker
1952 - 1959

Walker-Renaker was formed in 1952 by Joseph Walker, John Renaker and Moss Renaker, John's mother, who was the major designer. She created the Holy Cow, which was so successful, according to Jim Renaker, that at one time 40 people were employed to produce that one piece of which over 100,000 pieces were made.

Several Walker-Renaker pieces were originally Hagen-Renaker pieces (for example Holy Cow and Calf), but the slip colour and decoration is distinctly different from the Hagen-Renaker pieces.

Walker-Renaker models were produced in porcelain bisque in either pink, blue or purple tinted slip and then decorated with flowers, bows and gold. The pieces were stamped "Walker-Renaker" or "WR." Operations closed in 1959.

Many, many copies of Walker-Renaker have been made and can be identified by the less intricate decoration.

INDEX TO
WALKER-RENAKER

A bevy of Hagen-Renaker Butches
Miniature Cocker Spaniel Puppy, running (A-029/340), see page 229;
Miniature 'Butch', large 'Butch' and matching 'Dot', see page 428;
accompanied by a large 'Butch' Studio Card

Boy on Pedestal

Model No.:	Unknown		
Designer:	Susi Singer		
Height:	4 3/8", 11.1 cm		
Colour:	Pink flesh-tone, robes and roses; gold accordion; grey base		
Issued:	c.1955		

Description	U.S. $	Can. $	U.K. £
Boy	25.00	50.00	45.00

Girl on Pedestal

Model No.:	Unknown		
Designer:	Susi Singer		
Height:	4 ½", 11.9 cm		
Colour:	Pink flesh-tone, robes and roses; yellow broom; grey base		
Issued:	c.1955		

Description	U.S. $	Can. $	U.K. £
Girl	25.00	50.00	45.00

Crabby Cat

Model No.:	Unknown		
Designer:	Unknown		
Height:	2 ¾", 7.0 cm		
Colour:	Pink cat, blue hat and bow, gold highlights		
Issued:	c.1955		

Description	U.S. $	Can. $	U.K. £
Crabby cat	20.00	40.00	35.00

Goose That Laid the Golden Egg, The

Model No.:	Unknown		
Designer:	Unknown		
Height:	4", 10.1 cm		
Colour:	Pink bisque goose; blue bonnet and ribbon; golden egg; blue, pink and yellow flowers		
Issued:	c.1955		

Description	U.S. $	Can. $	U.K. £
Goose / Golden egg	20.00	40.00	35.00

Happy Cat

Model No.:	Unknown
Designer:	Unknown
Height:	2 5/6", 7.2 cm
Colour:	Pink, blue and yellow flowers; gold decoration
Issued:	c.1955

Description	U.S. $	Can. $	U.K. £
Happy cat	20.00	40.00	35.00

Holy Calf

Model No.:	Unknown
Designer:	Helen Perrin Farnlund
Height:	1 ¼", 3.1 cm
Colour:	Pink bisque calf, gold halo and hooves, blue and yellow flowers
Issued:	c.1955

Description	U.S. $	Can. $	U.K. £
Holy calf	10.00	20.00	17.00

Note: Hagen-Renaker mould A-60 (Calf, lying), page 263, was used to make Holy Calf.

Holy Cow

Model No.:	Unknown
Designer:	Helen Perrin Farnlund
Height:	2 5/8", 6.6 cm
Colour:	Purple bisque cow; gold halo, hooves and tail end; yellow bow and flowers
Issued:	c.1955

Description	U.S. $	Can. $	U.K. £
Holy cow	20.00	40.00	35.00

Note: Hagen-Renaker mould A-61 (Cow), page 263, was used to make Holy Cow.

Longhorn

Model No.:	Unknown
Designer:	Unknown
Height:	2", 5.0 cm
Colour:	Pink bisque longhorn, gold horns and hooves, blue bow, blue and pink flowers
Issued:	c.1955

Description	U.S. $	Can. $	U.K. £
Longhorn	20.00	40.00	35.00

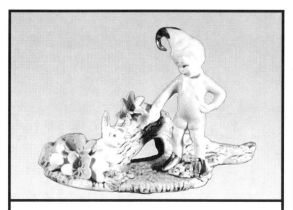

Pixie (Boy With Rabbit)

Model No.:	Unknown
Designer:	Helen Perrin Farnlund
Height:	3", 7.6 cm
Colour:	Boy wears green outfit, yellow and gold hat, gold shoes; pale blue rabbit; beige base with blue, pink and yellow flowers
Issued:	c.1955

Description	U.S. $	Can. $	U.K. £
Pixie (Boy with rabbit)	25.00	50.00	45.00

Note: This piece incorporates 'Driftwood', page 389, and 'Classic Whispering Rabbit', page 363.

Pixie (Girl With Rabbit)

Model No.:	Unknown
Designer:	Helen Perrin Farnlund
Height:	1 ½", 3.81 cm
Colour:	Girl wears green outfit, yellow and gold hat; blue rabbit; beige base with blue, pink and yellow flowers
Issued:	c.1955

Description	U.S. $	Can. $	U.K. £
Pixie (Girl with rabbit)	25.00	50.00	45.00

Note: This piece incorporates 'Driftwood', page 389; 'Classic Whispering Rabbit', page 363; and a Pixie from the Hagen-Renaker mould book.

Puppy

Model No.:	Unknown
Designer:	Helen Perrin Farnlund
Height:	7/8", 2.2 cm
Colour:	Pink bisque puppy with gold collar
Issued:	c.1955

Description	U.S. $	Can. $	U.K. £
Puppy	10.00	20.00	17.00

Note: This model was used by Hagen-Renaker to make Boston Terrier (A-224), see page 222.

Rooster and Hen

Rooster

Model No.:	Unknown
Designer:	Unknown
Height:	3 1/8", 7.93 cm
Colour:	Blue bisque with pink and gold decoration
Issued:	c.1955

Description	U.S. $	Can. $	U.K. £
Rooster	20.00	40.00	35.00

Hen

Model No.:	Unknown
Designer:	Unknown
Height:	2 ½", 6.4 cm
Colour:	Blue bisque with pink and gold decoration
Issued:	c.1955

Description	U.S. $	Can. $	U.K. £
Hen	20.00	40.00	35.00

Note: The Rooster's rose is attached by a wire.

INDEX TO HAGEN-RENAKER

BIRDS

BUTTERFLIES AND MOTHS

CATS

DOGS

HORSES

LITTLE HORRIBLES

SEA CREATURES

TABLEWARE AND DECORATIVE WARE

WALT DISNEY CHARACTERS

WILD ANIMALS

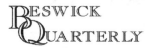